"As a psychotherapist and trainer, I am so excited that this book exists! Lucie Fielding has created a wonderful resource for trans communities in a way that is grounded in context and the many dimensions of experience that might affect trans sex and sexualities. What a refreshingly thoughtful yet humble take on topics that are so often misunderstood, neglected, or oversimplified! Fielding does an excellent job of providing an overview of interesting and relevant concepts related to trans sexualities, and pieces by invited contributors did an excellent job of bridging theory and practice. Well written and thoughtfully laid out for the reader, as well as grounded in social justice and intersectional frameworks, I recommend this book to anyone who wants to deepen their understanding and practice in a more nuanced, complex way when working with concerns related to trans experiences and sexuality."

— *Sand Chang, PhD, author of* A Clinician's Guide to
Gender-Affirming Care

"This is an essential guidebook for *every* medical provider, therapist, social worker, teacher, and helping professional, whether their work focuses on sexuality and gender or not. For those whose work centers these topics, this book is an invaluable resource they'll return to again and again. For those for whom these topics have been peripheral, it will provide a foundational bedrock on which to build a practice where *all* dimensions of a client or patient's identity and body are fully welcomed and supported. Written by an author with rare insight, garnered through transitioning while training as a sex therapist, it speaks to providers in language that demonstrates, as well as explains, how to be present with trans and non-binary clients. Ongoing training in sexuality and gender is necessary for ethical practice. This book will be a vital part of promoting comprehensive literacy in these areas for years to come."

— *Emily Nagoski, PhD, author of* Come As You Are:
The Surprising Science that Will Transform Your Sex Life

"*Trans Sex: Clinical Approaches to Trans Sexualities and Erotic Embodiments* is the book I want every clinician, educator and medical health provider who works with trans and/or nonbinary people to read. Lucie Fielding has created an essential resource that was long overdue in the field of sex therapy and that will be essential reading for many providers outside of our field as well. As well as sharing her own knowledge and wisdom, the author has included activities and practical applications by an incredible range of practitioners. This book is a treasure trove of information and I urge you to read it."

"Too much of the literature on gender transness falls off the balance beam, either ignoring trans sexuality or sexually objectifying trans people. Lucie Fielding's *Trans Sex* hits a sweet spot. It offers psychotherapists, medical care providers, sex educators and other professionals a compassionate and deeply grounded guide to working with trans folx and our sexualities. It is simultaneously erudite and approachable, practical and theoretical, permission-granting and boundary-setting, and encourages the kind of respectful, ethical curiosity about our lives on which successful therapies depend."

TRANS SEX

Despite the increasing visibility of trans and non-binary folx in media, political representation, and popular culture, their sexual lives and erotic embodiments are woefully under-attended-to in both scholarship and clinical practice. The aim of this book is to equip providers with both conceptual frameworks and concrete tools for better engaging their trans, non-binary, and gender expansive clients in pleasure-centered discussions of sexual health.

Challenging the dominant images of trans sexualities that appear in the existing literature, such as an emphasis on avoiding gender dysphoria, the preservation of sexual function, or on sexual losses that may arise as a result of transition pathways, *Trans Sex* offers a pleasure-positive approach to working with trans clients. Providing concrete clinical practices and practical activities that utilize social justice, intersectional trans feminism, and radical queer theory as key conceptual frameworks, this groundbreaking text is designed to be accessible to a wide range of providers. This book draws on Fielding's experiences as both a trans client/patient and as a therapist to shift and expand the conversation and includes contributions from other trans and non-binary providers working at the intersection of gender-affirmative care and sexuality.

Trans Sex seeks to move trans sexualities from the margins of gender-affirmative clinical practice, to center pleasure, and to spark creativity and empathic attunement within the client–provider relationship. Whether they be mental health or medical providers, trainees, or seasoned practitioners in gender-affirmative work or sexualities, readers will be able harness creative strategies to enhance their practice and become more imaginative providers.

Lucie Fielding (she/they) is a sexuality educator and resident in counseling in Charlottesville, Virginia. They have an MA in Counseling Psychology from Pacifica Graduate Institute as well as a PhD in French from Northwestern University. Their background in literature attunes them to ways narrative and image impact our embodied sexualities.

TRANS SEX

Clinical Approaches to Trans Sexualities and Erotic Embodiments

Lucie Fielding

Routledge
Taylor & Francis Group

NEW YORK AND LONDON

First published 2021
by Routledge
52 Vanderbilt Avenue, New York, NY 10017

and by Routledge
2 Park Square, Milton Park, Abingdon, Oxon, OX14 4RN

Routledge is an imprint of the Taylor & Francis Group, an informa business

Library of Congress Cataloging-in-Publication Data
Names: Fielding, Lucie, author.
Title: Trans sex: clinical approaches to trans sexualities and erotic
embodiments/ Lucie Fielding.
Description: New York: Routledge, 2021. | Includes bibliographical
references and index. | Summary: "The aim of this book is to equip
providers with both conceptual frameworks and concrete tools for better
engaging their trans, non-binary, and gender expansive clients in
pleasure-centered discussions of sexual health. Whether they be mental
health or medical providers, trainees, or seasoned practitioners in
gender-affirmative work or sexualities, readers will be able harness
creative strategies to enhance their practice and become better
providers" — Provided by publisher.
Identifiers: LCCN 2020049280 (print) | LCCN 2020049281 (ebook) |
ISBN 9780367331757 (hardback) | ISBN 9780367331764 (paperback) |
ISBN 9780429318290 (ebook)
Subjects: LCSH: Sexual health. | Transgender people — Health and hygiene.
Classification: LCC RA788.F53 2021 (print) | LCC RA788 (ebook) |
DDC 613.9/50867 — dc23
LC record available at https://lccn.loc.gov/2020049280
LC ebook record available at https://lccn.loc.gov/2020049281

ISBN: 978-0-367-33175-7 (hbk)
ISBN: 978-0-367-33176-4 (pbk)
ISBN: 978-0-429-31829-0 (ebk)

Typeset in Minion
by Newgen Publishing UK

To those who came before—those who threw bricks, advocated and agitated, struggled, dreamed, and fucked.

To the leatherdykes, all the QTs, and the communities that have always given me life and hope.

And to my clients, past, present, and future.

CONTENTS

ABOUT THE CONTRIBUTORS

Jaxx Alutalica MA, LMFT, CST (they/them) is a trans, indigiqueer, AASECT certified sex therapist residing in San Francisco, CA. They are a national queer kink educator and a connoisseur of pleasure's many expressions. Their approach to sexuality centers the dynamic experience of the body and becoming wholly present in desire while deepening understanding of the hows and whys behind intimacy and pleasure. In their practice, they work predominantly with transgender and gender non-conforming individuals and their partners to develop affirming sexuality and expansive expressions of self. Jaxx is currently completing their PhD in Human Sexuality where their research interests focus on the intersection of BDSM and transgender embodiment. They are most curious about how the decadence of deviant sexuality intersects with other subversive identities to create unapologetic self-expression.

Aredvi Azad [*Eh-red-vee Ah-zah-d*] (they/them) is a certified sex and relationship coach, and an educator, writer, and speaker who has been producing educational media on gender and sexuality, kink and BDSM, and intersectional approaches to relationship building for the past decade. An Irani-American immigrant, Aredvi is a queer and trans/gendefluid relationship nerd. Their work focuses on identifying patterns of bonding in adults who have experienced childhood emotional and sexual trauma, including generational and oppressive trauma of racism, sexism, classism, and other systems of inequality. As a scientist-turned-sex-educator, Aredvi is a self-proclaimed sexual liberationist working towards a sexually imaginative and expansive world. Aredvi is a co-partner and Director of Education and

Programs at The HEAL Project, on a mission to prevent and end childhood sexual abuse through healing the wounds of sexual oppression and embracing sexual liberation.

Websites: aredviazad.com and heal2end.org

Heather Edwards, PT, CSC (she/they) is a pelvic physical therapist, an AASECT certified sexuality counselor, and a crotch art enthusiast. After her Masters in Physical Therapy, she received a dual certificate in Sexuality Counseling and Sexuality Education from the University of Michigan School of Social Work. She teaches transgender pelvic health and sex counseling (from a queer & kinky lens) to medical professionals through Pelvic Guru (www.pelvicguru.com) as well as through her own teaching platform (www. heatheredwardscreations.com). She has authored and illustrated *Coloring Books for the Crotch Enthusiast*, a three-book series highlighting curiosity and the non-binary nature of crotches. She is the founder of the edgy, inclusive, and informative adult sex ed event, Vino & Vulvas.

Website: www.heatheredwardscreations.com; Instagram: @heatheredwards creations

Fitz (they/them) is a white, queer, non-binary clinical social worker, sex and gender therapist, and educator in Ann Arbor/Ypsilanti, MI. They received their Masters in Social Work from the University of Michigan in 2013 and became an AASECT-Certified Sex Therapist in 2019. Fitz approaches their work from a multicultural feminist lens, centers anti-oppression interventions, and aims to provide an affirming environment for members of sexual minority communities to explore sexual health and functioning concerns. In addition to clinical work, Fitz is passionate about collaborating with like-minded colleagues to develop continuing education workshops for healthcare professionals with the hope of increasing access to affirming care for marginalized populations. Fitz is the owner of Odyssey Sexual Health, PLLC and partners with Integrative Empowerment Group, PLLC to provide therapy and educational services. [Legal name at time of print: S. M. Fitzgerald, LMSW, CST]

Website: https://odysseysexualhealth.com

Laura A. Jacobs, LCSW-R (she/he/they/none) is a trans and genderqueer psychotherapist, speaker, author, and activist specializing in trans and gender nonbinary, LGBTQIA+, as well as gender and sexual diversity issues more broadly. They recently concluded their four-year term as the first transgender and genderqueer Chair of the Board of Directors for the Callen-Lorde

Community Health Center; they are currently a Board Member-At-Large and serve on numerous committees for Callen-Lorde, as well as committees for the World Professional Association for Transgender Health and elsewhere. Laura is a prolific speaker in the media, at conferences, medical schools, and other organizations, having been featured in the New York Times, NPR, MSNBC, NBCNewsOnline, SiriusXM, CBSNews, Mic.com and more. Laura founded the Gender Dysphoria Affirmative Working Group and has authored or coauthored numerous books, chapters, and articles including *"You're in the Wrong Bathroom!" And 20 Other Myths and Misconceptions About Transgender and Gender Nonconforming People* published by Beacon Press, 2017. They are a member of the Kink Clinical Guidelines Workgroup and serve on several editorial boards. Laura was presented the 2019 Standard of Excellence Award by the American Association of Sexuality Educators, Counselors, and Therapists.

Website: https://www.LauraAJacobs.com

Harmony Lee (he/they), MS, is honored to be Your Gay Dance Teacher! After receiving their degree in Environmental Health Sciences from the UCLA Fielding School of Public Health in 2013, they applied their leadership as a Public Health officer in the US Navy. In 2019, they left the military to teach self-healing through movement, and they have been dancing for joy ever since. They believe movement is medicine and play is nourishment. With their unique fusion of somatic psychotherapy, spiritual healing, and playfulness, their online movement classes provide students with a safe, respectful space for self-expression and healing.

Website: https://yourgaydanceteacher.com; Instagram: @yourgaydance teacher

Sadie Lune (she/her) is an interdisciplinary artist, sex worker, BDSM coach, public speaker, and parent. She has won awards for her short films and performances; appeared in feature films and queer porn; shown her cervix internationally; and exhibited explicit, whore-positive work at squats, the Venice Biennale, and SFMOMA. Sadie does consulting work for film sets, theatrical productions, artists, and academics on feminist porn, sex work, and BDSM. She also writes, presents workshops, and speaks publicly on topics of sexuality, gender, intimacy, fertility, shame, feminism, kink, queer parenthood, and sex worker rights. Sadie is white American genderqueer femme who lives in Berlin with her child and baby.

Website: https://www.sadielune.com; Instagram: @sadie_lune; Twitter: @sadielune

Tuck Malloy (they/them) is a queer, non-binary sex educator with a background in global gender studies, sexual assault and domestic violence advocacy, the sex toy industry, and youth education. In the past four years, they have created online classes, workshops and interactive activities that support their students to understand and dismantle sexual, body, and relational shame. They believe that investigating sensual, sexual and relational dynamics in our own bodies is an essential part of destabilizing structural and interpersonal oppression. They support individuals and groups in a collective endeavor to create more fulfilling, self-actualized communities and people.

https://tuckmalloyeducation.com; Instagram: @queerbrainslut

Rae McDaniel, MEd, LCPC, CST (they/them) is a Gender and Certified Sex Therapist who works with folks feeling anxious and lost about a transition they're experiencing in sex, gender, sexual identity, or relationships. Rae also provides consultation & training for professionals and organizations wishing to uplevel their knowledge and expertise in these areas. Rae is the founder of Practical Audacity, a therapy and healing collective in Chicago, Illinois. They hold a Master of Education in Community Counseling from DePaul University in Chicago and are a Licensed Clinical Professional Counselor in Illinois. Rae graduated from the University of Michigan's Sexual Health Certificate Program with specializations in Sex Therapy and Sexuality Education and is a Certified Sex Therapist through the American Association of Sexuality Educators, Counselors, and Therapists.

Website: https://practicalaudacity.com; Instagram: @practicalaudacity

Bianca Palmisano, MSN, RN (they/them) is a registered nurse, sexual health expert, and the owner of Intimate Health Consulting. They specialize in training healthcare providers around issues of sexual health, as well as LGBTQ, sex worker, and sexual assault survivor competency. Bianca graduated from the Johns Hopkins Masters of Nursing program in Spring 2020 and now works as a public health nurse in the DC community. They are also a member of the DC Trainers Network, a two-time presenter for the Philadelphia Transgender Wellness Conference and the Woodhull Sexual Freedom Summit, and a planning committee member for DC's Transgender Day of Remembrance. Bianca is the primary author of "Safer Sex for Trans Bodies," an outreach and education guide for the trans community sponsored by Whitman Walker Health and the Human Rights Campaign. They have been a guest lecturer on transgender health at George Washington University, Johns Hopkins University, and the University of Chicago. In addition to their interests in sexual health, Bianca is committed to anti-racism and harm reduction advocacy work in the DC community and at the national level.

Website: https://intimatehealthconsulting.com; Facebook: @intimatehealth consulting

Jamee Pineda, LAc, MAcOM, MPA (He/Him; siya) is a hilot binabaylan, acupuncturist, and Chinese medicine practitioner. His practice is informed by his identity as a queer, trans, non-binary, Tagalog person living in the US. With the combination of his lived experience and his training, Jamee's goal is to help individuals and communities live their fullest lives by offering a decolonizing approach to medicine rooted in traditional and ancestral practices.

Website: https://linktr.ee/jameepinedahealingarts

Frances Reed, LMT (They/Them) is non-binary, transgender, queer, and a trauma-informed, body-affirming, sex-positive licensed massage therapist in Washington, D.C. They founded Freed Bodyworks Holistic Wellness Center as a place where queer and trans clients are centered in massage, energy work, yoga, and mental health services. In addition to seeing clients and running Freed Bodyworks, they teach cultural competency for trans-affirming care as well as classes for transmasculine people about caring for their bodies while chest binding.

Websites: www.freedbodyworks.com & www.healthybinding.com

Ignacio G Hutía Xeiti Rivera, MA [Ig-Nah-See-Oh Gee Who-tee-ah She-eye-tee Ree-ve-Rah] (They/Them) is a cultural sociologist with expertise in sexual trauma and healing for marginalized populations. Ignacio is a Queer, Trans/Yamoká-hu/Two-Spirit, Black-Boricua, and Taíno activist. They are an internationally known gender non-conforming speaker, educator, writer, and performer with over 20 years of experience on multiple fronts, including economic justice, anti-racist and anti-violence work, as well as mujerista, LGBTQI and sex positive movements. Ignacio is also the founder and curator of Poly Patao Productions, which began 20 years ago and centers the sexual liberation of LGBTQI people of color. Ignacio's work is influenced by their lived experience of homelessness, poverty, and sexual trauma and is focused on providing educational opportunities that are especially geared toward the sexual liberation of queer women, transgender, genderqueer, gender expansive, and queer people of color. As the founder and director of *The HEAL Project*, Ignacio is on a mission to prevent and end childhood sexual abuse through healing the wounds of sexual oppression and embracing sexual liberation.

Website: https://www.igrivera.com; Instagram: @blkbrownred

Hannah Schoonover, PT, DPT (they/them) earned their Doctorate of Physical Therapy in 2014 from Ithaca College. Their primary professional focus is in pelvic health, with a particular passion for treating gender-expansive folx. They promote a safe and inclusive environment for all bodies and aim to incorporate collaborative care whenever possible. Hannah's work is grounded in holistic medicine, with emphasis on wellness and the mind/body connection to improve their patients' quality of life.

Website: https://www.bodyconnecthw.com; Instagram: @bodyconnectdc

ACKNOWLEDGEMENTS

*T*rans Sex is my first book, and it is said that you never forget your first. If I am able to look back on the process of writing this book with such fondness and joy, it is because of the steady hands who have helped guide me through the process. I am grateful to Clare Ashworth for having first seen promise in this project and for having been such a staunch advocate in its first stages. Heather Evans has been an extraordinary editor and for her steadying hand, counsel, fierce advocacy, and responsiveness I will be eternally grateful. The rest of the editorial, marketing, and production staff at Routledge was a pleasure to work with and I'd like to highlight the particular contributions of Ellie Duncan, Kris Šiošytė, and Mary Dalton, I would also like to thank the anonymous reviewers of the book proposal, who provided invaluable commentary and suggestions.

In Chapter 3 you will be treated to images taken from a set of plates covering sexual and reproductive anatomy, *Tabulae Anatomicae Sex* (1538) by sixteenth-century Flemish anatomist Andreas Vesalius (see Figure 3.3). Permission to use, reproduce, and slightly modify these images was generously granted by a holder of a nineteenth-century reproduction of *Tabulae Anatomicae Sex*, the Wellcome Collection in London, England. Few libraries hold *Tabulae Anatomicae Sex* so a fair amount of sleuthing was required to track down a copy. I am grateful to my dear friend, Stephanie Stillo, Curator of the Lessing J. Rosenwald Graphic Arts Collection in the Rare Book and Special Collection Division at the Library of Congress, for performing said sleuthing.

The cover of this book features a film still that was generously provided by AORTA films, a studio that produces films that opulently and sultrily revel in queer and trans identities and erotic embodiments. I wish to thank AORTA's Creative Director, Mahx Capacity, and Communications Manager, Papi Femme, as well as the performers featured in the still, Ze Royale and Indigo, for permitting use of it as the book's cover image. It is still so rare to see trans bodies being celebrated in joyful eroticism and genderfuckery on screen, and AORTA's lush, experimental, imaginative films break that oppressive mold in such stratospherically hot ways. It was a pleasure and delight working with you, Mahx! Thank you!

A great many thanks should be extended to Genna Fierson, who provided fabulous research assistance as I drafted Chapter 1.

The book you are reading is about trans erotic embodiments. My own erotic embodiment has been nurtured along the way by an aerial silks practice I shall talk about in greater depth in Chapter 4. I am deeply appreciative to Stephanie Zilora Neilson, Ellen Taylor, Nicole Brackett, and Erica Barga for teaching me to fly and helping me find sensuality within my own skin.

Until the COVID-19 pandemic had me sheltering in place, much of the writing of this book took place in cafes in Charlottesville, Virginia and Washington, DC. I highlight in particular The Pie Chest in Charlottesville, which has been my first stop each day I've spent at my office since July 2017. I am so grateful to the baristas who kept me caffeinated while steeped in yummy queer energy and, of course, co-owners Tina Morrison and Rachel Pennington.

I have developed as a therapist under the kind and watchful eyes of two fabulous clinical supervisors, Christy Pagels (Virginia LPC licensure) and Samantha Manewitz (AASECT sex therapy certification). I am thankful to have the wise counsel of these two therapists and colleagues.

This book was incubated in several classrooms and conference spaces over the last few years, and I would be terribly remiss if I did not thank the participants of workshops offered at CatalystCon (2017), AASECT (2018, 2019), and Preaching to the Choir: An International LGBTQ Psychology Conference (2020). I am also honored to have been invited onto the following podcasts: Sluts and Scholars, Speaking Sex with the Pleasure Mechanics, and the Better Sex Podcast, Hosted by Jessa Zimmerman. Each of these appearances were invaluable venues to refine and hone the arguments, concepts, and frameworks presented herein.

Special recognition is due to Angie Gunn, who was an early booster for this project. I had the pleasure of presenting pieces of what became this project with Angie at the 2018 AASECT Annual Conference and Angie's profound knowledge of sex therapy, gender therapy, and trauma work influenced, in particular, what ultimately became Chapter 4, on Coming into Compassionate Relationship.

Writing a book is a solitary activity even without a global pandemic that requires social distancing! As I've embarked on this writing adventure, so many people have walked this journey with me and kept it from feeling solitary. To them and for their support, love, and friendship, I am deeply grateful and indebted: Melissa Vise, Jayne Reino, Chelsea Fisher, Ricardo Wilson, Meredith McCoy, Doug Braun-Harvey, Joe Kort, Brian Gibney, Rafaella Fiallo, Dalychia Saah, Molly Adler, Jackie Dondero, Gwen Lotery, Paul Chilkov, Dana Johnson, Neal Castleman, Deborah Schnepf, Stacy Lewis, Chema Jimenez, Tom Swafford, Mike Giancola, Austyn James, Sara Mindel, Kelli Cronin, Julie Bindeman, Jenna Benyounes, Susanna Brisk, Tamara Pincus, Rosemary Moulton, Mike Giordano, Kristin Hodson, Caz Killjoy, Luna Matatas, Joanna Walling, Harper Jean Tobin, Lisa Spiedel, Sam Tryon, Alycia Williams, Signey Olson, Katie DePalma, Thibaut Clement, Nam Le Toan, Antoine Quint, Hélène Cottet, Solène Nicolas, Laura Wiseman, Megan Doherty, Joëlle Simeu, Kristin Vallacher, Kitty F. Davies, Turner Willman, Hannah Harris-Sutro, Daemonum X, Raechel Anne Jolie, Tal Eli, Rhea Ashley Hoskin, Mina Harker, Moxxy Cox, and Meg Metcalf.

While I speak often in this book about chosen family, community networks of care, and intergenerational wisdom, I would horribly remiss if I did not acknowledge the love and support of my mother, Leslie Field, her partner, Morris Weiner, as well as my in-laws, Daniel and Helen Horowitz.

Special mention and call out must be made for the efforts of Chris Maxwell Rose, Rae McDaniel, Bianca Palmisano, Katie Richard, Mac Peyton, Lauren Elizabeth Hapeman, Leigh Freilich, and Jessica Begans for reading and offering tremendously helpful feedback on drafts of book content, particularly at moments when my imposter complex raged. These magnificent humans challenged me, guided me, and provided me with necessary encouragement along the way.

My dear friend Rob Santos very kindly reviewed and responded to practically every word of this book between May and August 2020. Rob is among the most thoughtful and theoretically savvy humans I am fortunate to know and it was an privilege to benefit from his wit and wisdom. He is also an amazing friend.

Finally, I am tremendously grateful to the fourteen colleagues who generously contributed vignettes and activities to Chapter 6.

To Sarah, my best friend, wife, and my life partner. Thank you for being a sounding board, a whip-smart reader, and partner-in-reverie. You are my light and I love and adore you more than words can express! You have always helped make dreams I didn't know were possible realizable. More muppetry and mayhem, please?

CONTENT WARNING

This book contains: descriptions of/references to trauma (collective, intergenerational, insidious, and event-based); brief references to genocide, settler colonialism, and cultural erasure; brief references to police brutality; descriptions of/references to sexual assault; descriptions of/references to sexual and gender-based harassment; references to/experiences of homophobia, (trans)misogyny, transphobia, and other forms of minority stress; references to/depictions of intense D/s dynamics and kink play; and references to gender-based violence, discrimination, stigma, and murder.

INTRODUCTION

Lucie Fielding

When I first embarked on a process to affirm my gender identity—a process sometimes referred to as a *transition*—I had many questions. Many of them had to do with what sex would be like as I moved through transition. What would sex feel like? What would sex look like? Would I be able to orgasm? How would I be able to orgasm? What were my dating prospects? Would I be fuckable or even fuck-*able*? The medical and mental health providers I spoke to were, for the most part, affirming of my process. They suggested trans-inclusive and body positive books such as *Fucking Trans Women* and *Girl Sex 101*.[1] They helped me process the feelings behind my anxieties around "fuckability." And they offered me reframes that allowed me to understand transition as a "process" rather than as an "event," or series of events with a defined beginning and end. But they were often limited in their ability to support me in finding answers to my questions. And some of what I was told was inaccurate, lacking in nuance, or just plain wrong.

My providers' limitations were, in part, a function of how little training mental health and medical providers receive in sexual health.[2] Few counseling, clinical psychology, social work, nursing, or medical programs provide coursework focused on human sexuality, let alone require it.[3] And when present in programs, instruction in sexual health and human sexuality is often limited in scope, confined to sexual problems, sexual dysfunctions, and discussions of sexuality as "a source of identity," e.g., sexual orientation.[4] Further, as Theodore Burnes, Anneliese Singh, and Ryan Witherspoon noted in their analysis of responses from a recent survey of 25 counseling psychology doctoral programs in the United States, providers are emerging from graduate and professional programs with very little exposure to sex-positive constructs or frameworks, namely, frameworks that approach sexuality as "a source of wellness, inclusivity, and joy."[5]

My providers' limitations were also, in part, a function of how sparse the research base is with respect to trans folx and their erotic lives. Writing in 2012, Arlene Istar Lev and Shannon Sennott asserted that "[despite] the public gaze on transsexual bodies and the clinical pathologization of the transgender identities, there has been little attention paid to the actual sex lives of transgender, transsexual, and other gender nonconforming people."[6] Unfortunately, not much has changed in the scholarly and clinical literature since that time.

Despite my providers' limitations, I write this book from the fortunate position of having answered most of the questions that had bedeviled my early explorations of gender identity. I learned that sex could be transcendent, that I could be multi-orgasmic and polymorphously perverse, and that I am indeed fuckable and fuck-able. I learned how to find immense pleasure in my body and I learned that my body is capable of so much more than I had imagined.

I owe that learning in large measure to a supportive spouse, marvelous partners, affirming providers, and the intergenerational wisdom stored in the queer and trans communities with which I have been fortunate to engage. And a huge part of that learning is attributable to a very specific kind of privilege I possessed: the fact that when I approached these questions about my gender transition, I was simultaneously training to be a sex therapist. As such, I had access to a vast array of sexual health knowledge and I was able to question what I was being told by my providers and to think critically and creatively. I am mindful, having both been in the therapist's chair and on the consulting room couch, that not everyone possesses the sexological knowledge to ask questions of their providers and, even more crucially, not everyone feels empowered to question them. Even if many modalities de-center the person of the clinician as expert, many clients will not feel themselves empowered to challenge or call in their therapist, let alone their endocrinologist.

This book was born out of a desire to use my privilege—the knowledge and experience I have from being both a trans clinician and a trans client/patient to help providers increase capacities and comfort with respect to hosting sexual health conversations with trans and non-binary clients. At present, many trans and non-binary folx acquire sexual health information from peers and a small number of zines and books. These community-based resources are vital and necessary. However, clinicians also need to be able to provide accurate and affirmative sexual health information and support, particularly when the treatment they offer has a bearing on erotic expression.

Who Is This For?

In introducing her Wheel of Consent framework, sexological bodyworker Betty Martin challenges her clients to examine their intentions about a given touch or sexual activity by asking themselves a crucial question, "Who is this for?" This question guides how I have examined my intentions for this book. On the one hand, this is a book geared toward a professional audience. Neither in tone, nor in language, nor in content is this a community-facing text and my aim is to address my colleagues across the multidisciplinary team (MDT) of psychotherapists, medical doctors, nurse practitioners, physical therapists, bodyworkers, surrogate partners, professional dominants, sex coaches, and sex educators who work with, affirm, and support gender expansive folx. I am a therapist and an educator, so the conceptual frameworks, vignettes, and treatment interventions introduced in this book will necessarily reflect those professional identities. However, my hope is that medical professionals will be able to draw inspiration from this text as well and find in it tools and strategies that they can adapt for their practices. And the list I provided above includes a lot of folx who may not normally be included in what is often thought of as an MDT. I do this intentionally. I would not be offering this book to you were it not for professional dominants, surrogate partners, and pelvic floor PTs. And many of the exercises and interventions I offer you herein are drawn from conversations and trainings with these providers, adapted, of course, to reflect professional codes of ethics that prohibit sexual touch and discourage non-sexual touch except in cases where the clinician is able to ethically justify the clinical appropriateness and utility of the touch.

But although this book is written for providers, it is ultimately *for* our clients as well as their partners and families. Very few books, articles, and other sex education sources have been geared towards them. Instead, trans and non-binary folx are far too often placed in the position of having to extrapolate from cis het experiencing, to engage in erotic life hacks. We need to change this dynamic so that trans and non-binary folx can have tools to assist them in exploring with excitement their embodied sexual lives. By the same token, cis folx can benefit from the wisdom, ingenuity, and playfulness that is already present in trans, non-binary, and queer communities. Perhaps there is something cis folx can learn from *us* about erotic embodiment, desire, sex, and sexuality.

I hope that this book will be a first step in dismantling some of the toxic discourses that have helped keep trans sexualities and erotic embodiments in the dark for far too long. And more than that, I hope that this book will spark erotic imagination and greater empathic attunement within the provider—client relationship.

Defining Our Terms

Any text focused on trans experiencing necessarily seems to include a section on language. Language, like gender and sexuality for many folx, is fluid. Terms come in and go out of fashion constantly, and with whiplash-inducing speed. Indeed, terms and language related to gender identity and expression have shifted just in the two years it took to get this book into your hands.

Trans, Transgender, Non-Binary

For the most part, when referring to the population considered in this book, I use the expression "trans and non-binary folx." Sometimes, I shorten this simply to "trans." And both of these expressions refer to any of us who do not identify with the sex we were assigned at birth and/or the gender some may assume of us as we move through the world. I use the longer expression "trans and non-binary folx" primarily because I want to be as expansive as possible. But terms are fraught and there is enormous variation within the trans community in terms of how folx identify, how they characterize their experience, and how they define what it means to be trans. And like in any community, there are tensions and plenty of deeply unfortunate boundary policing to go around.

There is also the problem of so-called "umbrella terms." As the author b. binaohan points out, the use of terms for describing gender expansiveness are often steeped in a logic of homogenization. Terms used in this very book replicate this totalizing logic. binaohan explains, terms like *trans, transgender, transsexual,* and even *non-binary* were terms designed to be "broadly inclusive" while also "[serving] a political utility for uniting a diverse group of people to fight with solidarity out of shared interests for the same sorts of social goods."[7] The problem with an ethic of broad inclusivity is that it may serve to "[override] individual identification out of a need for a hegemonic identity for the 'common good'" and "[legitimize] one type of experience over others."[8] And you might be able to guess whose experiences are legitimized over others! White, Western embodiments and perspectives are held up as the norm, while other cultural traditions are left out of the picture.

Accordingly, even as I use terms and expressions like trans and non-binary in this book, I wish to keep in mind the heterogeneity of trans experiencing as well as the inexhaustible variety of ways folx, both in the present and in the past, have played with, subverted, and embodied gender. Terms such as trans, transgender, genderqueer, and non-binary may have been recent innovations, but gender non-conformity and non-binary genders have existed in some form in just about every culture and society on the planet for millennia.

Cis

Cis is a Latin prefix that translates to "on this side of," as in its use in the compound terms "cisgender," "cis woman," and "cis folx." Trans, another Latin prefix, translates to "across" or "on the other side of." Both cis and trans have also become umbrella terms in their own rights. Cis, whether as a standalone term, or as a prefix to another term (such as woman, man, or individual), refers to anyone whose gender identity matches or aligns with the sex they were assigned at birth (e.g., male, female, intersex). Cis is an activist term and a way of indicating that everyone, whether cis or trans, has a relationship to gender. Cis helps make that relationship visible for folx who are not trans and non-binary, as it allows one to recognize that a privilege of being cis is that one is rarely placed in the position of having to actively examine or think about one's gender identity. I also use the expression "cis het" throughout this text. This is shorthand for someone who is both cis and straight.

Queer

Queer is a term that originated as a slur. I've certainly had it spat in my face more times than I can possibly count. I recognize, as a result, that this word may cause discomfort in some readers. But *queer* is also a term that has been reclaimed by many in LGBTQIA2S+ communities. It has, indeed, become a badge of pride, and carries a great deal of political and theoretical weight. No single word, as Catherine Lord and Richard Meyer write in their book *Art & Queer Culture*, "can accommodate the sheer expanse of cultural practices that oppose normative heterosexuality. In its shifting connotation from everyday parlance to phobic epithet to defiant self-identification, 'queer' offers more generous rewards than any simple inventory of sexual practices or erotic object choices."[9] As this quote suggests, the term "queer" is necessarily oppositional, in a way that gay, lesbian, or bisexual are not, necessarily. Queer embodiments, queer identities, and queer practices are understood to offer a direct—and radical—challenge to cis heteropatriarchal norms, cisnormativity, compulsory heterosexuality, and monocentrism (the cultural privileging of monogamy). Finally, use of the term "queer" also serves to mark out this project as one influenced by generations of queer theory. As Jack Halberstam writes in *The Queer Art of Failure*, queer and queerness are a means of "articulat[ing] an alternative vision of life, love, and labor," and a way of offering "different ways of being in the world and being in relation to one another than those already prescribed for the liberal and consumer subject," a way for us to imagine possibilities for undoing, unbecoming, subversion, and resistance.[10]

"X" Marks the Spot!

You might also notice that I employ the word "folx" throughout the text. Why not "folks"? They are pronounced the same way, and both folx and folks are gender-neutral ways to refer to groups of people. The letter "x" is an orthographic symbol that has become synonymous with gender-inclusivity, and is also used in words like Latinx (a term that is a gender-neutral variant of the gendered forms of Latino and Latina), and the honorific Mx.

Embodiment

This book is not about what constitutes trans sexualities; nor is it a how-to book on the (many) ways trans and non-binary folx can—and do—experience eroticism. It is, rather, a project with the aim of giving providers pleasure-centered tools for better engaging trans and non-binary clients in discussions of sex, desire, sexuality; and for helping them experience erotic embodiment. Of these terms, the word *embodiment* might be the least familiar to readers. Embodiment refers "to the experience of living in, perceiving, and experiencing the world from the very specific location of our bodies."[11] To focus on erotic embodiment in this book as I do is in part to consider the phenomenological experience of having and moving through the world with a "desiring, heaving, sexual body."[12] It is to understand that sex and the erotic happen within—and sometimes between—bodies. It is to understand sex as joyously messy, awkward, carnal, and visceral. And it is to center in erotic experiencing, "what people actually do, think, and feel when expressing sexual feelings or use their bodies in sexual ways."[13]

Moreover, to focus on embodiment is also to consider that "bodies and sexuality, as experienced and made sense of, are not simply natural but exist, are apprehended, and are understood within social structures of power," structures that would seek to "imbue bodies and bodily processes" with particular, culturally constructed "meanings and significance, both inside and out."[14] We don't merely inhabit and do things with/to our bodies. Rather, erotic embodiment considers the many ways that our "social and historical environments enter into and become entangled with" our sexual bodies, how, "by living day to day in a society that makes certain demands on our bodies and psyches, we come to internalize these norms and discourses and embody them."[15] That is, how we have sex, how we use our bodies to have sex, and what we consider sex to be in the first place, are all subject to regulation, surveillance, and input from the societies and cultures in which we have sex and experience our sexualities. For example, as I will discuss in Chapter 1, cultures have a lot to say about which bodies are able to be coded or read as desirable. Or, we might consider how certain roles in sex get glommed onto gender (e.g., some folx mistakenly associate bottoming with passivity and receptivity, which is, in turn, associated with femininity).

The Embodied Psyche

In many "systems of thought," Susan Stryker writes, "no place is shunted to the periphery of consideration with greater alacrity than is the body."[16] It is common in psychotherapeutic thought to distinguish between psyche and soma, a distinction that arises in no small part from a Western philosophical tradition of mind–body dualism. Psyche (ψυχή) is the Ancient Greek term for the soul; whereas soma (σῶμα) is the term for the body. Psychology, or the study of psyche, has tended to place a superabundant emphasis on the mind—its structures, its processes—while leaving the body and its vicissitudes to the realms of medicine and bodywork. The very notion of "talk therapy" reifies this mind–body split while placing a premium on cognition and cognitive processes.

Throughout this text, I will often use the term *embodied psyche.* In employing this term I seek to collapse the mind–body split and view psyche as inseparable from—and, indeed, unintelligible, without—the body. Psyche is soma and soma is psyche. The body, as I will discuss in greater detail in my elaboration of what I will call the *somatic-imaginal* (Chapter 4), has an imagination, and it often communicates sensation and feeling through image and story. To speak of an embodied psyche, then, is to place an emphasis on what the body is imagining and what stories, scripts, and images it embodies and has embodied. In so doing, I seek to place myself in dialogue with—and in the tradition of—somatic psychotherapies—therapies that have sought to "unify human beings into an organic and inseparable whole for the purpose of healing, growth, and transformation" and value "the physical body as a structural blueprint for our consciousness and our essential aliveness."[17]

Clients, Patients, and Consumers, Oh My!

Across disciplines we have many names for the folx who work with us. Those in community mental health and social work settings may refer to these folx as *consumers.* Those in medical professions are apt to refer to the folx they work with as *patients.* And many educators, therapists, coaches, bodyworkers, and professional dominants are likely to refer to them as *clients.* I refer to the individuals and relational units I work with as clients, and this book follows suit.

Location of (My)self

Location of self, which I shall have occasion to discuss at great length in Chapter 2, is the name of a process that allows a provider to initiate a conversation with their client "about similarities and differences in their key identities, such as race, ethnicity, gender, class, sexual orientation, and religion," and how these facets of identity will, almost necessarily, "influence the therapy process."[18] Designed by family therapist thandiwe Dee Watts-Jones, location of self functions as a way for the provider to communicate, from the beginning of the provider–client relationship, that continual reflections and discussions of identity are "meaningful and embedded in the work."[19] Identities represent a crucial "lens through which we understand the world," and how we are understood as we move through that world.[20] Engaging in location of self can, thus, be a vital practice for building a therapeutic alliance with our clients. Likewise, I feel it just as important to locate myself in this book for the reader, primarily as a way to indicate the many ways that my own social and professional locations impact the book you are about to read.

I am a white, visibly able-bodied, queer, polyamorous, kinky femme in her early 40s who was assigned male at birth (AMAB). I use the pronouns she/her/hers as well as they/them/theirs, and I experience a frisson of glee when someone interchanges those pronouns in a sentence. Of the identities I hold, "femme" is perhaps the one I most cherish, and femme is both my queer identity and my gender identity. Historically, as Rhea Ashley Hoskin and Allison Taylor explain, "the term 'femme' has been used to reference queer femininities, often specifically how queer women do femininity."[21] But femme is so much more than an aesthetic, if one, like butch, that has always "included an element of political resistance."[22] Femme is an identity and embodied enactment in and of itself, and one with a rich history, a lineage of queer writers such as Joan Nestle, Dorothy Allison, Amber Hollibaugh, Julia Serano, Hunter Shackelford, adrienne maree brown, Leah Lakshmi Piepzna-Samarasinha, Alok Vaid-Menon, Kai Cheng Thom, and Raechel Anne Jolie. And in claiming femme as my identity, I do so with the intention of locating myself within that powerful lineage and naming its influence on how I view the world, how I embody, how I engage in activism, and how I love and lust. To identify as femme is also to say that I am not a woman, but am, rather, non-binary. When gendered spaces are the only ones available to me, I will always gravitate to ones designated for women, but "woman" is not a gender that has ever felt quite, hm, right. Femme, on the other hand, fits like a leather glove molded directly onto my hand.

As I indicated in the first section of this introductory chapter, this book emerges from experiences navigating interactions with mental health and medical providers as a trans, queer, and kinky client and patient. I have chosen to change my gender marker and birth name on all government documents where I am able to do so and I've undertaken hormone therapy (HT) as well as breast augmentation surgery (top surgery). But I've also chosen not to pursue either facial-feminization surgery (FFS) or vaginoplasty (bottom surgery). I recognize the fact that I *have* the choice as to whether or not to pursue a given medical or mental health procedure/treatment, given my class position and privilege. But I have chosen to engage in a certain procedures and not others for a number of reasons. Above all, the ways I hold gender dysphoria in my embodied psyche mean that undertaking certain courses of treatment would not alleviate or address said dysphoria. I am delighted with the body I have and the ways I have learned to use it. I have made certain choices with respect to how I embody my gender and sexuality, and those choices have a direct bearing on how I conceptualize trans sexualities and erotic embodiments in this text. Your choices and your clients' choices may very well differ from mine. And that's ok.

I was raised within a significant amount of class privilege and am now someone with multiple postgraduate degrees living in the middle class. My existence as a white, queer, fairly-high SES femme means that I hold a great deal of privilege as I navigate spaces. My PhD, combined with my whiteness, opens doors that might otherwise be harder to breach. And I am well aware of the fact that so many of the trans figures afforded platforms to speak look and sound a lot like I do. It is for this reason that Chapter 6 is designed the way it is, namely so as to center the experiences and perspectives of folx who occupy different social and professional locations from my own.

I was born in Houston, Texas and I've lived and worked for the most part in urban environments, but I now find myself living in the rural South and practicing in Charlottesville, Virginia. You may very well know Charlottesville because of the University of Virginia, but you might also remember it as the site of the Unite the Right rally in August 2017. There is a rich history of rural and Appalachian queers, but as the Unite the Right rally exposed for all the world to see, there is also a troubling history there associated with the terrible legacies of slavery, Jim Crow, and structural white supremacy. Indeed, I began practicing in Charlottesville in July 2017, just a few weeks before the Unite the Right rally would gather there, and my first years as a clinician were indelibly marked by that experience. The rural environment presents challenges to me as a human, particularly as a queer and trans femme who often feels isolated and cut off from community. But I also know that my work is particularly important in this environment as one of a handful of trans clinicians in the state who are sex-positive and knowledgeable about kink/BDSM and consensual non-monogamies. My visibility matters here, and I always keep in mind the privilege it is to serve the communities I serve.

Finally, at time of writing, I am a trainee under supervision and not a licensed therapist. I have worked in a variety of practice settings, including a sexual and intimate partner violence agency and shelter, a university counseling center, a community mental health organization; and I currently work under my clinical supervisor in a group practice. Throughout my work as a mental health professional, I have tended to specialize in providing sex therapy and gender therapy. Despite the breadth of my experience and the depth of my knowledge of theory, histories of sexualities, sex therapy, and gender-affirming care, I cannot claim the mantle of seasoned clinician. For this reason, I have purposely designed and structured this book so that when it comes to clinical vignettes, treatment planning, and clinical interventions, I am not the only voice offering examples and insight. This is particularly the case in Chapter 6, as you will see.

Book Features

To aid in working through the concepts I introduce in this book, I have included a couple of features. I outline those below.

Bringing Theory to Practice

Peppered throughout Chapters 1–5, you will find text boxes with headers that begin with "BTToP," which stands for Bringing Theory to Practice. The BTToP chapter subsections consist of activities, value clarification exercises, and interventions designed to enliven concepts or theoretical elements introduced and explored in the chapters. The inclusion of these BTToP subsections will hopefully go some way toward demonstrating how the clinical stances and conceptual frameworks explored in the book might show up in the room and how they might be applied to clinical practice.

Glossary

At the very end of the book, I have included a glossary of key terms related to gender and sexualities. I recognize, after all, that some terms used in this book might be more familiar to some readers than to others.

Vignettes and "Client" Material

At several points in this book, I employ client vignettes to help place chapter content within a clinical context. The clients named and the client material discussed are composites, and details have been altered to ensure that anonymity and confidentiality are carefully preserved. I have derived much of this clinical material from my own experiences as a client (rather than as a therapist), or from stories told to me by friends and other professionals. Vignette writing is complicated under any circumstance, but it is even trickier because I serve small communities within an already small community. I recognize that vignettes can help the reader understand how to apply the theories in this book, but I have worked to ensure that this function takes a backseat to my legal and ethical duties to my clients.

Book Structure

In her TED Talk, "The Danger of a Single Story," novelist and feminist Chimamanda Ngozi Adichie discusses how complex concepts, situations, individuals, communities, and cultures are all too often reduced to single, unitary narratives. These narratives, she laments, "show a people as one thing, as only one thing, over and over again, and that is what they become."[23] Single narratives are cloaked in a definitiveness that serves to "flatten" experience and "overlook the many other stories" that form—and might (in) form—us.[24] They foreclose conversation. They are also steeped in power, an insidious power that burrows deeply into the cultural imaginary and simultaneously erases its traces. For, as Adichie noted, power is implicated in the process of how stories "are told, who tells them, when they're told, [and] how many stories are told."[25] Single narratives come to dominate us, colonize us, and rob us of our humanity and our complexity. Chapter 1, Unimaginable Bodies, teases out a few of the many ways the sexual bodies of trans, non-binary, and gender non-conforming folx have been storified within a set of dominant discourses that fail to imagine the heterogeneity and possibility of trans sexualities and erotic embodiments. I consider four structuring narratives: the failure to view trans bodies as capable of desirability and desire-ability; trans narratives as ones steeped in trauma, stigma, and oppression; a clinical discourse centered on sexual losses and trade-offs; and a clinical focus on sexual function as opposed to pleasure.

If Chapter 1 in many ways frames the stakes of that which adrienne maree brown has called an "imagination battle,"[26] Chapters 2–5 function in part as strengths-based reframes of the four problematic clinical stances and imaginative failures reviewed in Chapter 1. Each of these chapters proposes a conceptual framework that is pleasure-centered, trauma-informed, culturally humble, and steeped in ethical practice.

In Chapter 2, I propose and describe a foundational clinical stance I call ethical curiosity. Trans bodies are often subjected to a dehumanizing and denuding gaze as they move through the world, sometimes even at the hands of providers. To speak of an ethics of curiosity is to recognize that members of marginalized groups and vulnerable or underserved populations often have to perform a great deal of emotional labor for their care providers and that this labor is not only depleting but also a source of rupture in the therapeutic alliance. In order to avoid a clinical gaze that clients often experience as invasive, I propose a model of curiosity that is empowering and respectful of client autonomy and privacy. Following a conceptual discussion of the distinguishing features and principles of ethical curiosity, I will provide the reader with examples of how providers can deploy ethical curiosity in clinical practice.

Chapter 3, Coming into Passionate Relationship, describes how providers might help clients re-vision their relationship to—and with—their sexual bodies. All of us grow up with narratives of how our bodies are supposed to function and how we are supposed to find pleasure, but for trans and non-binary individuals these narratives pose particular problems, as they can provoke dysphoria and fail to map onto how we want to be in the world sexually. As a result, we often need to unlearn cultural scripts that would seek to define our sexual lives. This chapter proposes a model of how to do this work with clients through processes of mystification which can help break apart limiting narratives and promote curiosity and new ways of engaging with—or re-visioning—their bodies.

Chapter 4 arises out of the recognition that for many of our clients, their bodies have not been safe places to be. Their bodies may hold or have been the site of trauma and the kinds of explorations that I discuss in Chapter 3 might very well feel daunting or unsafe. In this chapter, I propose a conceptual framework for feeling bounded and finding safety in the body, coming into compassionate relationship with the embodied sexual self.

If, as I will discuss in Chapter 1, the sexual lives of trans and non-binary clients are too often discussed purely in terms of sexual function and placed within a narrow conceptualization of sexual health, Chapter 5 will provide readers with a conceptual framework for expanding their erotic imaginations, one steeped simultaneously in pleasure-positivity and social justice frameworks. Here, I propose that clinicians focus on re-centering pleasure in the discussion of trans sexualities and on evoking client capacities for erotic creativity.

I bring the book to a close in Chapter 6 by bringing theory to practice, namely, showing some of the ways the principles, concepts, and clinical stances articulated in Chapters 1–5 might be applied in work with trans, non-binary, and gender expansive clients. Here, I have chosen to step back and de-center my voice in favor of other perspectives. The reader will find contributions from an array of providers working at the intersection of gender-affirmative care and sexuality, sexology, and sexual health. Some contributors offer vignettes that will allow you to see how they are working with trans sexualities in their practices. Other contributors present activities and exercises that you might adapt for your own work with your trans and non-binary clients.

Notes

1 Mira Bellwether, *Fucking Trans Women: A Zine About the Sex Lives of Trans Women* (CreateSpace Independent Publishing Platform, 2010); Allison Moon, *Girl Sex 101* (Lunatic Ink, 2014).

2 Peggy J. Kleinplatz, "Advancing Sex Therapy or Is That the Best You Can Do?," in *New Directions in Sex Therapy: Innovations and Alternatives*, ed. Peggy J. Kleinplatz, 2nd ed. (New York, NY: Routledge, 2012), xxviii.

3 Theodore R. Burnes, Anneliese A. Singh, and Ryan G. Witherspoon, "Graduate Counseling Psychology Training in Sex and Sexuality: An Exploratory Analysis," *The Counseling Psychologist* 45, no. 4 (May 2017): 504–527, https://doi.org/10.1177/0011000017714765; Eli Coleman et al., "Summit on Medical School Education in Sexual Health: Report of an Expert Consultation," *The Journal of Sexual Medicine* 10, no. 4 (April 2013): 924–938, https://doi.org/10.1111/jsm.12142; S. Andrea Miller and E. Sandra Byers, "Psychologists' Continuing Education and Training in Sexuality," *Journal of Sex & Marital Therapy* 35, no. 3 (May 2009): 206–219, https://doi.org/10.1080/00926230802716336; S. Andrea Miller and E. Sandra Byers, "Practicing

Psychologists' Sexual Intervention Self-Efficacy and Willingness to Treat Sexual Issues," *Archives of Sexual Behavior* 41, no. 4 (August 2012): 1041–1050, https://doi.org/10.1007/s10508-011-9877-3; Marie Murphy, "Everywhere and Nowhere Simultaneously: The 'Absent Presence' of Sexuality in Medical Education," *Sexualities* 22, no. 1–2 (February 2019): 203–223, https://doi.org/10.1177/1363460717708147; Alan W. Shindel and Sharon J. Parish, "CME Information:Sexuality Education in North American Medical Schools: Current Status and Future Directions (CME)," *The Journal of Sexual Medicine* 10, no. 1 (January 2013): 3–18, https://doi.org/10.1111/j.1743-6109.2012.02987.x; Christina Warner et al., "Sexual Health Knowledge of U.S. Medical Students: A National Survey," *The Journal of Sexual Medicine* 15, no. 8 (August 2018): 1093–1102, https://doi.org/10.1016/j.jsxm.2018.05.019.

4 Burnes, Singh, and Witherspoon, "Graduate Counseling Psychology Training in Sex and Sexuality," 511.

5 Ibid., 514.

6 Arlene Istar Lev and Shannon Sennott, "Transsexual Desire in Differently Gendered Bodies," in *Handbook of LGBT-Affirmative Couple and Family Therapy*, ed. Jerry J. Bigner and Joseph L. Wetchler (New York, NY: Routledge, 2012), 113.

7 b binaohan, *Decolonizing Trans/Gender 101* (biyuti publishing, 2014), 26.

8 Ibid., 27 and 28.

9 Catherine Lord and Richard Meyer, *Art and Queer Culture*, 2nd ed. (London: Phaidon, 2019), 9–10.

10 Jack Halberstam, *The Queer Art of Failure* (Durham, NC: Duke University Press, 2011), 2.

11 Deborah L. Tolman, Christin P. Bowman, and Breanne Fahs, "Sexuality and Embodiment," in *APA Handbook of Sexuality and Psychology, Vol. 1: Person-Based Approaches.*, ed. Deborah L. Tolman et al. (Washington: American Psychological Association, 2014), 760, https://doi.org/10.1037/14193-025.

12 Ibid., 760.

13 Ibid.

14 Ibid., 759.

15 Ibid., 761.

16 Susan Stryker, "Dungeon Intimacies: The Poetics of Transsexual Sadomasochism," *Parallax* 14, no. 1 (2008): 38.

17 Christine Caldwell, ed., *Getting in Touch: The Guide to New Body-Centered Therapies* (Quest Books, 1997), 1.

18 thandiwe Dee Watts-Jones, "Location of Self: Opening the Door to Dialogue on Intersectionality in the Therapy Process," *Family Process* 49, no. 3 (2010): 405.

19 Ibid., 405.

20 Ibid., 410.

21 Rhea Ashley Hoskin and Allison Taylor, "Femme Resistance: The Fem(me)inine Art of Failure," *Psychology & Sexuality* 10, no. 4 (October 2, 2019): 282, https://doi.org/10.1080/19419899.2019.1615538.

22 Ibid., 282.

23 Chimamanda Ngozi Adichie, *The Danger of a Single Story*, TED Talk (Oxford, UK, 2009), 9:25 – 9:37, https://www.ted.com/talks/chimamanda_ngozi_adichie_the_danger_of_a_single_story?utm_campaign=tedspread&utm_medium=referral&utm_source=tedcomshare.

24 Ibid., 13:04–13:11.

25 Ibid., 9:37–10:11.

26 adrienne maree brown, *Pleasure Activism: The Politics of Feeling Good*, Emergent Strategy (Chico, California: AK Press, 2019), 10.

1

UNIMAGINABLE BODIES

Lucie Fielding

Before we can begin to discuss clinical approaches for how trans sexualities and erotic embodiments might be better integrated into gender-affirmative practice, we must first delve into the dominant narratives that have, to date, shaped how we, as providers, consider and conceptualize the sexualities and erotic lives of trans and non-binary folx. These are narratives that have been featured in the clinical literature since practically the advent of gender-affirmative clinical practice. As such, they greet our clients the moment they walk through our doors—they are the absent presences on our couches; they charge and hang in the air; they settle like dust particles on every surface of our office spaces. Moreover, in addition to lodging themselves in us—how we conceptualize, how we work—they are also carried by our clients and tend to show up lurking behind many of the concerns they bring with them into the room.

I will explore and unpack four of these structuring narratives: the "unimaginability" of trans bodies; trans narratives as ones defined by trauma and oppression; a discourse centered on sexual losses; and a clinical focus on sexual function. My argument is that a deconstruction of cultural and historical narratives that have structured how we conceptualize trans sexualities can, ultimately, enrich clinical practice and create space in us to promote alternative, client-centered, and pleasure-oriented narratives for joining with our trans and non-binary clients and supporting their pursuit of erotic embodiment.

Imaginable Bodies

Although we often see who we desire and are attracted to as a highly subjective set of tastes and preferences ("I like who I like!"), these tastes and preferences do not exist within a vacuum. Rather, they are subject to social construction and are intimately bound up in structures of power. This is what some Black, fat, feminist thinkers have called the politics of desirability.[1] The politics of desirability accounts for the fact that our desires and attractions occur within contexts that privilege some and marginalize others. Capitalist systems tell us that we are not "enough"—thin enough, "fit" enough, happy enough, productive enough, or even queer or trans enough. Cultural standards of beauty, attractiveness, and desirability communicate in ways subtle and decidedly unsubtle that beauty and desirability are solely the province of white, light-skinned, cis, thin, able-bodied, high SES, tall, fit and toned folx.[2] We can see desirability politics in action when on dating platforms such as Grindr and Tinder folx outright state racialized dating preferences, or even body type and gender expression preferences.[3] And just as racism, colorism, ableism, ageism, and fatphobia often inform whether one is perceived as desirable, so does one's gender identity.[4]

Trans and non-binary folx often report experiencing a phenomenon referred to colloquially as "dating while trans," a discrimination faced while seeking romantic, play, and/or sexual partners based generally in one's trans identity and often more specifically in a trans or non-binary person's ability to "pass/blend" as cis. In fact, the mere disclosure of one's gender identity seems to have a clear negative impact on whether a trans or non-binary dating prospect is seen as attractive.[5] In a recent study published in the *Journal of Social and Personal Relationships*, researchers found that across a sample (n= 958) of cis heterosexual and LGBTQ folx, 87.5% indicated that they would not consider dating a trans person, with cis heterosexual men and women being the populations most likely to exclude trans and non-binary folx from their dating pool.[6] Moreover, for those respondents who indicated a willingness to consider a trans or non-binary individual as a dating prospect (n=120), trans masculine individuals were favored far more than trans feminine folx. Studies like this confirm: dating while trans is a thing; desirability and attractiveness are heavily inflected by cisnormativity, transphobia, and transmisogyny.[7]

The lens of desirability politics applies chiefly to interrogating the extent to which sexual and romantic desire and seemingly subjective measures of physical attraction are culturally constructed. In short, it examines desirability, a subject's *ability to be desired*. Building upon this framework, I propose we also consider *desire-ability*, a given person's capacities for desiring, experiencing desire. The lens of desire-ability emerges from work in disability studies and discussions of sex and ageing.[8] In this framework, only certain bodies within a given socio-cultural landscape are sexualized and afforded the capacity to desire sex or possess an erotic imagination. As Ana Cristina Santos and Ana Lúcia Santos assert in their qualitative study of disabled cis women's narratives in Portugal, "sexual engagement is inaccessible to those bodies that do not fit a particular aesthetic or functional ideal," namely, that of cis, heterosexual, younger than middle-age, thin, able-bodied folx.[9] Put simply, trans and non-binary folx are not only excluded from being objects of desire, but are not imaginable as beings able to experience sexual desire.

From the earliest days of gender-affirmative care in the United States, desire-ability has been a capacity denied to trans and non-binary clients. According to Harry Benjamin, for example, most trans folx were thought to "have no overt sex life at all," at least prior to medical interventions, and particularly bottom surgeries.[10] Moreover, trans folx, per Benjamin, were thought to perceive their genitals and sexual characteristics as "disgusting deformities that must be changed by the surgeon's knife."[11] Benjamin ultimately positioned hatred of the sexual body and aversion for engaging in sexual activity as a "central feature" of trans experiencing, and as a primary diagnostic criterion for determining whether a patient is a "true transsexual."[12] This would later form the basis for access criteria to gender-affirmative care up to and through the first decade of the twenty-first century in some clinical settings.[13]

Considered together, desirability and desire-ability point to a particular kind of privilege, one I refer to as *erotic privilege*. Erotic privilege is a type of privilege afforded to certain kinds of bodies within a given culture. These bodies, in a Western European and American cultural idiom, are typically white, cis, able-bodied, thin, tall, and between the ages of 18–35. Bodies that do not conform to—or, literally, *embody*—one or more of these cultural ideals are erotically marginalized and deemed "unimaginable."[14] These bodies are simultaneously erased and subjected to intense objectifying or fetishizing scrutiny; and they afforded neither desirability nor desire-*ability*.

Think, here, of how often fat bodies become the butt of jokes in many Hollywood comedies, or how the mere thought of people having sex after 60 becomes a source of derision, discomfort, and outright disgust. I often think of a September 2016 opinion piece in the *New York Times* by poet Jennifer Bartlett, written partly in response to Jessica Valenti's memoir *Sex Object*.[15] Bartlett, who has cerebral palsy, spoke to having a very different experience of the male gaze or sexual advances than Valenti does, asserting that Valenti, an able-bodied cis woman, universalizes the experience of male sexual advances as problematic and invasive. Bartlett notes, "I've never been aggressively 'hit on' in a bar, despite the fact that I have frequented them alone throughout the years. In fact, I've rarely been approached in a bar at all."

A couple of years ago I was walking down the street in LA with my wife. We were holding hands and as we passed a gaggle of guys on the corner, one of the guys looked me up and down, whistled, and catcalled, "Lookin' fine, ladies!" I'd never been catcalled before, and before I could collect my feminist wits about me, I turned back to the guy who had just catcalled us, and with a huge grin on my face, exclaimed, "Thank you!" It was only a few steps down the street, when the glow of having been sexually objectified had worn off a bit, that I turned to my wife and said, "I probably shouldn't have thanked the guy for catcalling me, huh?" "Yeah," she responded, sighing with bemusement.

I'm not saying that unsought sexual attention is a good thing. And having experienced sexual and gender-based harassment in the workplace too many times to count, I'm not saying that sexual harassment is a good thing either— the times I've experienced it have felt pretty damned dehumanizing in fact. Rather, I want to highlight that within this particular cultural moment, not everyone has the same access to being viewed as a desirable, desire-able sexual being; some sexual bodies are more imaginable than others. The implication, here, is that as providers working affirmatively with trans and non-binary clients, we need to acknowledge and make visible some of the structural barriers many of our clients face in dating or even gaining access to sex-positive spaces and communities.

Biases, assumptions, and stereotypes around desirability and desire-ability also have an insidious way of showing up in our clients' erotic self-concept, part and parcel of dynamics of internalized transphobia. For example, the recent documentary by Sam Feder, Amy Scholder, and Laverne Cox, *Disclosure* (2020) powerfully shows how messages and assumptions about the desirability and desire-ability of trans bodies are embedded in popular culture.[16] It is easy to believe oneself undesirable and incapable of experiencing desire when one is constantly spoon-fed images of trans bodies provoking violence, disgust, and even literal vomiting, as in the case of films of my childhood and adolescence such as *Soapdish* (1991), *The Crying Game* (1992), and *Ace Ventura: Pet Detective* (1994). Negative images, attitudes, and prejudices can, over time, become internalized. So, in addition to the microaggressions and macroaggressions many trans and non-binary folx experience, and the stresses of doing even the most routine activities, such as going to the bathroom, some of us have the added joy of experiencing a voice inside us that insists on adding to society's chorus to tell us that our bodies are repulsive, that we are un-fuckable, that we are less-than, or that our desires and needs are not as important as those of other people in the world.

When I first began affirmatively exploring my gender identity I had a ton of questions about sexual experiencing. And many arose from my own internalized transphobia. When I would question whether I would be attractive or "fuckable" for prospective partners, this essentially spoke to a part of my internal system, one that already viewed myself as un-fuckable or undatable as a trans person. I had to work to dismantle and unlearn these beliefs about myself, and, by extension, other trans folx out in the world.

When we go into dating, play, and sexual activity with internalized transphobia prominently running the show, it can be horrendously easy to dissociate during sex or play and not check in with partners, even when something is not feeling great; or to go into play negotiation from a place that minimizes our desires and needs. It can also be easy to approach dating, sex, and play from a scarcity mindset. A scarcity-based belief structure can lead us to think we should count ourselves lucky should someone, anyone, find us desirable, even if that someone is abusive or dismissive of our needs. Thus, we date and play believing that the experience is the best we could possibly expect or deserve, because we should be grateful for the sexual attention from someone as such attention is a limited resource.

In addition to calling out dynamics of desirability and desire-ability in the wider culture and naming and bringing compassion when a client internalizes said dynamics, we must also examine our own biases and assumptions around attraction, desirability and desire-ability as providers. If we cannot imagine our clients as sexual beings who are desirable and desire-able, then how are we to sit with our clients as they work to imagine into themselves as sexual beings? In the BTToP section that follows I've included a list of questions designed to help you unpack and work through biases, assumptions, stereotypes, and counter-transference around desirability, desire-ability, and erotic privilege.

Erotic privilege is not simply visible within the cultural imaginary (e.g., the bodies and identities that are featured as sexual beings in advertising, beauty magazines, books, film, television, and music). It can also be observed within the research base. Trans bodies—like those of BIPoC folx, elders, disabled folx, and fat folx—are all-too-often not "seen" or recognized by researchers and scholars. As Breanne Fahs and Sara McClelland argue in their elucidation of the field of critical sexuality studies, these bodies are often viewed as "abject bodies" in the literature, bodies that are "ignored, out of bounds, or pushed out of bounds," or are consistently imagined in "one-dimensional" terms.[17]

Following feminist philosopher Nancy Tuana, I assert that this absence, this "ignorance," should not be "theorized as a simple omission or gap" but, rather as "an active production," a function of an "epistemology of ignorance," one that is "constructed and actively preserved, and is linked to issues of cognitive authority, doubt, trust, silencing, and uncertainty."[18] The erasure of trans erotic experiencing is often enacted in the design phase of sexological research and writing. That is, erasure and silences are produced and reproduced in the research questions we pose as well as every time we imagine "experiences as universal and/or easily communicated to another person."[19]

Open just about any book written in the last ten years or so on sex education, sexology, sex research, or sex therapy. Flip to the introduction and see if the author attends to the sexual health or sexualities of trans and non-binary folx. Usually, you won't find much. Some of those books at least contain a brief apologia on why trans and non-binary folx were not included, as in this passage from the introduction to Emily Nagoski's otherwise stupendously wonderful book, *Come As You Are*:

> *First, most of the time when I say "women" in this book, I mean people who were born in female bodies, were raised as girls, and now have the social role and psychological identity of "woman." There are plenty of women who don't fit one or more of those characteristics, but there's too little research on trans* and genderqueer sexual functioning for me to say with certainty whether what's true about cisgender women's sexual wellbeing is also true for trans* folks. I think it probably is, and as more research emerges over the coming decade we'll find out, but in the meantime I want to acknowledge that this is basically a book about cisgender women.*[20]

I often recommend *Come As You Are* to my clients. But I always offer a disclaimer about its focus and exhort them to extrapolate from the book's otherwise excellent presentation of current research and conceptual frameworks in contemporary sexology to their own embodied experience. The point is, though, neither I nor my clients should have to engage in that extrapolation, at least, not all the time. But that's what an array of populations who possess unimaginable bodies have to do. Trans and non-binary folx constantly have to engage in life hacks from cis erotic experiencing because, with very few exceptions, an entire research base and body of work in sex education effectively doesn't imagine trans folx as sexual beings that have a right to accurate, comprehensive sexuality education tailored to their needs and their bodies. This book is, in essence, an exercise in flipping this particular script, challenging us to perhaps imagine into what it would be for us as providers, and particularly those of us who are cis het, to extrapolate a bit from trans experiencing.

BTToP: Imagining Desirability

The following are a set of questions intended to help you begin to unpack biases, assumptions, stereotypes, and counter-transference around desirability and desire-ability. This exercise is specifically designed to examine your own relationship to erotic privilege and reflect on how erotic privilege might impact your work with your clients. As such, you might experience discomfort. That's ok. Simply notice that discomfort and try to bring some curiosity to it. You might notice where the discomfort lives in your body, how it is held by it. Are there particular sensations, images, feelings, or thoughts that accompany the discomfort?

1. What messages have you picked up in your life about desirability and desire-ability?
2. How have the following people or groups influenced your beliefs or assumptions about desire and what bodies are desirable and desire-able?
   - Family members;
   - Friend groups;
   - Sexual or romantic partners;
   - Your communities;
   - Media (film, television, social media, magazines, porn, etc.)
3. How do you benefit from erotic privilege? How would you consider yourself "erotically marginalized"?[21] What experiences bring these intersections of erotic privilege and marginalization into relief?
4. A scarcity mindset is informed by what we are taught about desirability and desire-ability. In your dating and relationship life have you ever noticed yourself engaging with scarcity? How did/do you manage, or think through, scarcity?
5. Bring to mind an image of a person you find sexually and/or romantically attractive. Notice what characteristics this person has. Are they cis or trans? What age are they? Do they belong to particular ethnic/racial groups? How are they dressed? Notice their body size and shape. Are they disabled or visibly able-bodied? Now, ask yourself why this image and these characteristics are most readily available to you and why we as a culture may value them.
6. Bring to mind an image of a trans or non-binary person. Notice what characteristics this person has. Notice whether your images are of trans and non-binary folx who might be assumed to be cis. What age are they? Do they belong to particular ethnic/racial groups? How are they dressed? Notice their body size and shape. Now, ask yourself why this image and these characteristics are most readily available to you.
7. How do you transmit to others messages about their desirability and desire-ability?

"Death and Oppression"

As a population, trans and non-binary folx experience high rates of stigma, discrimination, harassment, and violence. Indeed, the disparities, discrimination, and negative outcomes trans folx face have been well-documented in the literature.[22] The most recent data from the National Center for Transgender Equality's (NCTE) transgender survey paints a disturbing portrait of the barriers, hardships, and challenges many in the trans community face, from "pervasive" patterns of violence and harassment in social, scholastic, and professional settings to large economic disparities between trans and non-binary respondents and the larger US population. And trans folx experience higher rates of physical and sexual assault and violence than the larger US population, rates that may very well directly inform work with trans and non-binary clients around sexual health and erotic embodiment.[23]

Studies focusing on trans populations have also documented high correlations between psychological distress as well as poor (mental) health outcomes and experiences—or crucially, expectation of experiences—of stigma, violence, and discrimination.[24] These outcomes range from higher rates of suicidality and substance abuse, co-morbidities such as depression and anxiety as well as a hesitance to report gender-based violence or seek medical or mental health treatment.[25] The higher prevalence of mental health challenges faced by trans and non-binary folx are consonant with the minority stress model proposed by Ilan Meyer and expounded upon specifically for trans populations by Rylan Testa and colleagues.[26]

The minority stress model relies on the hypothesis that the higher incidence of health challenges and negative health outcomes documented among trans and non-binary populations in comparison to the larger US and Western European population is attributable to the "hostile and stressful social environment" LGBTQIA2S+ folx are subjected to as a result of their gender and sexuality minority status.[27] In particular, Meyer specified that minority stress arises out of both distal and proximal stressors. Distal stressors, or stressors external to the individual that are objectively measurable, would include micro- and macro-aggressions and social rejection as well as forms of discrimination specific to trans, non-binary, and gender non-conforming folx such as "being unable to access legal documents or medical care because of differences in records regarding their sex or name, discrimination when obtaining medical care, and being unable to access safe restrooms in public places."[28] Testa and his colleagues also delineated a distal stressor they termed "nonaffirmation," which is "when one's internal sense of gender identity is not affirmed by others," e.g., being addressed using pronouns that do not affirm one's gender identity or being deadnamed.[29] Proximal stressors are those that emerge from "individual perceptions and appraisals," and include the expectation and fear of experiencing violence and discrimination as well as the concomitant hypervigilance that needs to be maintained to protect the individual from those expected negative experiences. Perhaps the most significant proximal stressor is "the internalization of negative societal attitudes," namely, internalized transphobia.[30]

Experiences of minority stress are exacerbated by dynamics of intersectionality.[31] That is, our social locations are multifaceted, and gender is only one facet of our *identity constellation*. Gender "both influences and is influenced by other significant markers of power and privilege (e.g., race/ethnicity, sexual orientation, social class, religion/spirituality, ability status, immigration status)."[32] And, in turn, trans folx's intersections of identities "greatly impact access to resources, vulnerability to discrimination, and experiences with others, including their health care providers."[33] Thus, as a white, relatively high SES, visibly able-bodied, queer, non-binary femme, I may be subject to gender-based violence, harassment, and discrimination; transphobia; trans misogyny; homophobia; heteronormativity; and femme erasure. But these experiences of discrimination and stigma are often magnified for BIPoC trans folx, lower SES folx, and disabled folx. As Sand Chang and Anneliese Singh note, "when examining the barriers that exist in employment, housing, health care access" BIPoC trans, non-binary, and gender non-conforming folx experience the highest barriers to accessing necessary care and services as well as the greatest health disparities, compared to white folx and the US population at large, data further borne out in the results from the NCTE's 2015 Trans Survey.[34] Gender-based discrimination is further inflected by dynamics of colonialism, ableism, and white supremacy.

The challenges—the discrimination, the stigma, the structural barriers, the violence—trans and non-binary folx face merely in trying to navigate daily life are very real, and they need to be highlighted. To do otherwise would be to invalidate our clients' lived realities. Moreover, dynamics of minority stress as well as a sensitivity to the institutional barriers many trans and non-binary folx experience absolutely need to be factored into how we, as providers, work with and serve our trans and non-binary clients and work as advocates to promote social change.

But there's an essential difference between naming disparities and dynamics of oppression or working to dismantle barriers, and centering narratives of discrimination and disparity to the exclusion of other topics of study. Indeed, as Stephanie Budge and colleagues note, existing research on trans and non-binary folx has "primarily focused on their negative experiences and has disproportionately examined coming-out processes and identity development stages."[35] To this point, a recent content analysis of more than a decade of academic scholarship and research on trans and non-binary folx found that the largest research topic in scholarly articles between 2002–2012 related to psychological distress as well as health risks and disparities.[36] With respect to the sexual lives of trans and non-binary folx in particular, it is striking that such a large percentage of the research base on trans sexual health focuses on HIV-related health risks, risky sexual behavior, and sexual function.[37]

On a more anecdotal level I am struck by how many workshops on gender-affirmative care I've witnessed are dominated by long discussions of discrimination, stigma, and oppression. To listen to cis folx talk about trans experiencing is to get the idea that we are a sad, troubled population. When asked during a podcast interview why she focused on serving trans communities, for example, one cis clinician described trans folx as "these poor people," "These people are really struggling so much. I just find it amazing that our society is still giving them such a hard time as a whole population."[38] While I, and most other trans folx, can report numerous experiences of minority stress, this does not represent the whole or even the majority of our experiencing of self and community.

An almost exclusive focus on the disparities, the co-morbidities, the risk factors, the stigma and discrimination cannot be the only lens through which we come to understand trans experiencing, particularly as we work to facilitate a coming into (com)passionate relationship with the embodied sexual self (see Chapters 3 and 4). I am particularly concerned about how these research foci impact how we show up "in the room" and the projections we carry with us in our work with our trans and non-binary clients. If our understanding of sexual health is defined primarily by health disparities and risk factors, for example, how does this serve to foreclose conversation around possibilities for embodied sexual joy? Or how does an almost exclusive focus on what a friend, activist Turner Willman, has called the narrative of "death and oppression" further limit our clinical imaginations and desiccate landscapes of experience? I'd like to invite us to consider grounding our praxis in fostering and evoking trans ingenuity, resilience, and capacities for tapping into intergenerational wisdom.

BTToP: Intergenerational Wisdom

In recent years, mental health professionals have developed the notion of intergenerational trauma.[39] While, as Resmaa Menakem writes, trauma is often thought of "as something that occurs in an individual body, like a toothache or a broken arm," it also "routinely spreads *between* bodies, like a contagious disease."[40] This is to say that trauma is often collectively, communally experienced and can be passed intergenerationally. But resilience can also be passed intergenerationally and experienced collectively! And one of those mechanisms of collective, communal resilience is what I call in this book *intergenerational wisdom*.[41]

Our clients access the wisdom that is held in queer and trans communities through a variety of ways. There are what we might consider official histories—books on queer and trans liberation that document histories that go back for centuries of queer, trans, and gender expansive individuals and communities. Fortunately, many of these works have become more mainstream, beginning with Leslie Feinberg's *Transgender Warriors* and extending into the present with Susan Stryker's accessible *Transgender History*, C. Riley Snorton's *Black on Both Sides*, Tourmaline's edited volume *Trap Door: Trans Cultural Production and the Politics of Visibility*, and Matthew Reimer and Leighton Brown's *We Are Everywhere: Protest, Power, and Pride in the History of Queer Liberation*.[42] There are also rich archival collections that house periodicals, zines, correspondence, images, and ephemera that make visible queer and trans history and the lives of the people who lived it, such as the Digital Transgender Archive, the Lesbian Herstory Archive, the John J. Wilcox Archives, and the Leather Archives. These works and collections can help our clients understand that they are not alone, that they belong to a rich and proud tradition of resistance, joy, and creativity.

Yet while these sources of knowledge can help our clients imagine possibilities for their lives, they rarely speak to the specific ways in which trans individuals find sexual pleasure in their bodies. This type of knowledge is often passed through word of mouth, on social media, or in small-batch publications such as zines. I think here of *Fucking Trans Women*, the *Trans Sex Zine*, and the magazine *Original Plumbing*, all of which I've recommended to clients. Here, the pathways of intergenerational knowledge transmission are more tenuous and ephemeral. They depend on trans and non-binary individuals talking to the right person at the right time, or on knowing which social media accounts to follow, or even on knowing which platforms are not censoring certain types of speech. This last item is a constantly moving target, as so much social media content is subject to the whims of the platforms on which they are housed and how they choose to define and enforce so-called "community standards" provisions. This became a great deal harder in April/May 2018 with the enactment of FOSTA-SESTA in the United States, which ultimately led to a targeting of sexual content on social media and the shuttering of all so-called "adult content" on the platform Tumblr, formerly a rich repository of content on queer and trans sexualities.[43]

Intergenerational wisdom, in short, is passed like a cherished family recipe, a codex of resilience surreptitiously slipped into the hands on oil-stained, well-worn paper, crumpled and smoothed out many times over. It is the ingenious mad science that gifted trans feminine folx with *muffing* from a practice otherwise used by medical professionals to check for hernias (discussed at length in Chapter 3), or the ways of flagging queerness and specific kink interests collected in the "hanky code."

To give a recent example of both intergenerational trauma and intergenerational knowledge transmission dynamics at work, this book was completed in the shadow of the COVID-19 global pandemic. In the early days of the pandemic and as shelter in place orders finally began to proliferate in many states, my clients were, like all of us, experiencing an array of feelings—fear for their own health and the health of friends and family members; devastation at the loss to livelihood as well as food and housing security; rage at the Federal government's often callous, lackluster, and un-empathic response; crushing uncertainty about the future. Even those who were blithely operating as if nothing was wrong and that things would go surely back to "normal" in two to four weeks were having a trauma response.

The COVID-19 pandemic recalled for many the HIV/AIDS crisis of the 1980s and 1990s, which, like the COVID-19 pandemic, included a failed and flailing national response as well as a complete lack of regard for the concerns, experiences, and lives of marginalized populations. In another parallel, a few of my clients wondered aloud if intimacy and touch would be made indelibly suspect for an entire generation. For, once again, contact, connection, and touch were being coded as risky and a means of sparking contagion.

In the shadow of that earlier epidemic, notes for a future were recovered, even as "soul wounds" from that time were re-opened.[44] As Somatic Therapist Marika Heinrichs wrote on Instagram:

> *Queers know about loving in the midst of virus, of fear, of death. We know how to keep connecting as if our lives depend on it. Because they do. We have loved through terror and plague and kept moving towards each other. [...] We have skills and wisdom that are transferable. We have this knowledge in our lineages. We have something to offer. Let us never forget that our queerness is a gift, a blessing, a spell for survival in these times.*[45]

Thus, many in the queer community organized mutual aid and care networks, given their understanding that if help was not coming from the government, it would have to come from community instead.

During this pandemic, we also relearned that connecting with others (even if done virtually) and caring for them was a way to help ourselves and build stronger and more resilient communities. Thus, for example, the dating app Lex was used by many queer and trans folx around the world to seek out connection and pleasure where physical touch was not possible and social distancing was the order of the day. Lex users wrote personals for pervy pic exchanges and to engage in sending letters and care packages to pen pals.

"Our communities are fabulously sexual and inventive," wrote activist Amber Hollibaugh of queer communities in the midst of the HIV/AIDS epidemic of the 1980s and 1990s, "and we can support each other in taking the steps each of us needs to be safe, erotic, and powerful."[46] As I will discuss in the next section, our task as providers ultimately comes down to a particular form of resourcing with our clients, a tapping into that which Michel Foucault called *subjugated knowledges*: deep wells of intergenerational wisdom, queer lineage, and ancestry that are always already present in queer and trans communities; an inheritance of struggle, but also a life-affirming movement toward ecstasy and connection.[47]

"Love's Inscription"

"The body has two histories," writes Jordy Rosenberg in his novel *The Confessions of the Fox*:

> *There is the history that binds us all. The terrible history that began when the police first swarmed the streets of the cities and the settlers streamed down the decks of their ships [...] There is no trans body, no body at all—no memoir, no confessions, no singular story of "you" or anyone—outside this broad and awful legacy.*[48]

This is the history shaped by the legacy of colonialism and white supremacy, one which, as b. binaohan notes, has resulted in many of us not having "access to our cultural heritage and histories. Many of us live in the diaspora. And even those that don't live in the diaspora, white colonialism has done a very excellent job of erasing or rewriting our histories in many areas of the world."[49] Rosenberg's narrator, thus, reminds us of the burdens of intergenerational trauma that trans bodies hold. But then, he writes, there is "the second history of the body," described as "love's inscription":

> *Some inscriptions we wear like dreams—fragments of a life untethered from this world, messages from a future reflected to us like light off broken shards. [...] Some inscriptions are utterances, battles. [...] I'm not*

*saying this battle was fought for us. [...] And yet, because of it, and many
others like it, now we inhabit our own skin.*[50]

Here, Rosenberg shifts to a history that includes one of resilience,
intergenerational wisdom, and the ecstasies borne out of the struggle for
collective liberation—those who struggled, survived, and thrived so that
we might "inhabit our own skin." In my work with queer and trans clients,
I like to remind them that they are part of a lineage, that they are someone's
legacy and that someone will eventually be their legacy. To hone that sentiment: queer lineage is queer futurity, which is to say that embedded in the
queer and trans body, and passed between them intergenerationally, is what
José Esteban Muñoz called the "ideality" of queerness, namely, "the warm
illumination of a horizon imbued with possibility" that "can be distilled from
the past and used to imagine a future."[51]

Connecting oneself to communities and to the intergenerational wisdom
contained therein, as Rosenberg suggests, is a form of meaning-making
Emily and Amelia Nagoski call "engag[ing] with something larger than
yourself."[52] Engaging with something larger than oneself, they write, "helps
us tolerate the uncertainty, the mortality, the helplessness or loneliness" that
often co-occur with stress and traumatic activation, and thereby, promotes
resilience and thriving. For some folx, the something larger is their spiritual
and religious beliefs. For others, this author included, the something larger
can be our (chosen) families, our communities, and collective struggle.

One element of the minority stress model that is not as often highlighted
as the processes of stress and stigma, is that "not all of the effects of minority
stress are negative."[53] Ilan Meyer, argues that "resources such as group solidarity and cohesiveness" or "establish[ing] alternative structures and values
that enhance their group" can go a long way to ameliorating or protecting
"minority members from the adverse mental health effects of minority
stress."[54] In other words, connecting up to queer and trans communities,
identifying social supports, and finding kinship by leaning into pride in one
or more facets of one's identity constellation can be a key to alleviating and
mitigating the impact of minority stress.[55]

This drawing of strength and resilience from community and the collective constitutes a facet of what Stephanie Budge and her research team
refer to as *facilitative coping*, which they operationalize as mechanisms
"whereby individuals seek social support, learn new skills, change
behaviors to positively adapt, and find alternative means to seek personal
growth and acceptance" during moments of adversity and acute stress or
when an individual may be "newer [to] identity development."[56] Externally
focused facilitative coping mechanisms include: researching gender identity and trans history, attending support groups, attending outreach
events, finding places and experiences that increase comfort, connecting

to online networks for support, and increasing political awareness.[57] Each of these external processes of connecting up to community, seeking social support, and fostering identity pride, Budge and her team assert, enhance an individual's ability to find agency and self-efficacy within themselves, and led to shifts allowing for an "embracing of change and flexibility" to engage in meaning-making and modify "thoughts, behaviors, perspectives, and other life patterns adaptively to cope with changes and stressors related to their identity process."[58]

The ultimate goal of externally focused facilitative coping processes is to evoke a client's capacities for exploration and for identifying alternative ways of being in and moving through the world, a nurturing of that which philosopher Perry Zurn terms *trans curiosity*. While acknowledging the objectifying, fetishizing, exploitative, reductive, and totalizing possibilities of curiosity, possibilities I shall elucidate in greater detail in the next chapter, Zurn articulates a vision of curiosity that is deployed as "a tool of resistance by which trans people foster the rich self and social life typically denied them by institutionalized forms of curiosity."[59] Trans curiosity, Zurn explains, "is a series of material, intergenerational, and transhuman acts of exploration" and "plays an undeniably integral role" in helping trans folx lay claim "to wholeness, to community, and to history."[60] And it is a rich history to which our clients might lay claim![61] We, as providers, are in a position to help our clients connect up to this history, to begin to see themselves not as the fetishized or objectified other often presented within the cis imaginary, but rather as individuals embedded in communities, indelible parts of a legacy of struggle, but also of resilience and ingenuity.

BTToP: Exploring Community Resilience

As Sand Chang, Anneliese Singh, and lore dickey suggest, you might engage your trans and non-binary clients in assessments of resilience both at intake and throughout your work with them.[62] I've included in this BTToP section a series of questions you might ask your clients to "integrate a strengths-based perspective," connect them to social supports and community resources, and begin an exploration of facilitative coping skills available to them.[63] The hope here is that you might begin to help your client elicit awareness of the heterogeneity of trans experiencing as well as evoke their capacities for trans curiosity.[64]

- What kinds of support around desire/sexuality/eroticism/kink/embodiment would be helpful to you at present?
- How are you connected to affirming communities, media, people?

- When you're having a rough time of it or you're feeling unsafe; or you've something to celebrate or be excited about, who are the people in your life you turn to? Who is in your inner circle of support, particularly in matters of dating and sexuality? With whom in your life do you feel you can most fully be yourself?
- In what kinds of environments do you feel the most seen and heard, particularly as you've navigated gender identity and embodiment?
- When do you feel most like yourself? What are some practices, rituals, or activities you engage in when you are feeling—or are wanting to feel—most like yourself?
- In what contexts do you feel sexy and attractive? What are some practices, rituals, or activities you engage in when you are feeling—or are wanting to feel—sexy/attractive?
- What do you most cherish or are most proud of in the identities you hold?

Landscapes of Loss

Trans and non-binary folx, asserts Harper Jean Tobin, "are rarely seen as happy, healthy people in satisfying sexual relationships," at least in the popular imagination.[65] In recent years there have of course been intensely positive depictions of the erotic lives of trans and non-binary folx, but these tend to be the exceptions rather than the rule. More often than not, as Tobin points out, trans folx are imagined as largely desexualized hero(ine)s, lonely and single, the "freaky fetish object," or the "conniving deceiver."[66] I think of the sexual and romantic fate—at least as of the fifth season (2019–2020)—of Nia Nal on the television show *Supergirl*. Introduced in the show's fourth season (2018–2019), Nia Nal is the first trans superhero on television. While representing a huge milestone in terms of positive trans representation in popular culture, Nia Nal's sexual life has never been depicted to the same degree as that of other queer characters, such as Batwoman/Kate Kane or White Canary/Sara Lance, on the CW network's DC superhero lineup. She is briefly afforded a romantic relationship with another character of the show, the charmingly cerebral Braniac 5, but even this relationship sours near the beginning of season 5, leaving her single and pining.

Historically, of course, the sexual lives of trans and non-binary folx have been depicted in even bleaker terms. The clinical literature, for one, tends to minimize or even outright deny "sexuality as a factor in trans experience."[67] Indeed, as first Sandy Stone and, most recently, researcher J.R. Latham have shown, a denial of trans eroticism formed the backbone of how medical and mental health professionals determined access to gender-affirmative care.[68] Clinicians were placed in the position of gatekeeping "the permissible range of expressions of physical sexuality," with aversion to sexual expression viewed as a hallmark of trans experiencing.[69]

This discourse serves to crystalize in the cultural imaginary the idea that being trans implies a sex life that is qualitatively *less than* cis sexualities. And by doing so, they establish trans lives as being built around a set of tradeoffs and false dilemmas. The false dilemma, here, is presented as a choice between alleviating gender dysphoria via various kinds of treatment (e.g., talk therapies, HT, and surgical interventions) and retaining a familiar and fulfilling sexual life. Put another way, the resolution of gender dysphoria has often seemed to imply and involve sexual losses, or, at least, a series of tradeoffs.

A discourse of tradeoffs and losses can be perceived when we speak of the reduced access to dating and sex-positive spaces many gender diverse people face due to discrimination and exclusion; changes in couple sexuality and relational identity; and, finally, the functional consequences of gender confirmation surgeries.[70] And, vexingly, this all manifests in the room with our clients! Consider how one of the contributors to *TransSex Zine* frames the tradeoff as they began HT, "I felt like I was making a choice between the possibilities of finding comfort and pride in my body, and anyone wanting to fuck me."[71]

One of the most striking examples of how a discourse of loss is embedded in gender-affirmative clinical practice is to be found in guidance on potential side effects we provide clients seeking HT, and particularly feminizing HT. A commonly cited side effect of HT is a shift in libido/sex drive—depressed in feminizing HT; increased in masculinizing HT.[72] Despite the nearly ubiquitous presence of this indication as part of informed consent, it is scientifically inaccurate and un-nuanced guidance, and we really need to stop describing desire and arousal side effects of HT in terms of sex drive.

This is because sex is not a drive. Strictly speaking, a drive is a homeostatic "biological mechanism" that supports and ensures our survival by, in the words of Emily Nagoski, "keep[ing] the organism at a healthy baseline— not too warm, not too cold, not too hungry, not too full."[73] If we do not satisfy drives of hunger, thirst, or fatigue by eating, drinking or sleeping our tissues will experience damage, and we will eventually die. Thus, sex cannot be considered a drive because, as the American ethologist Frank Beach quipped, "No one has ever suffered tissue damage for lack of sex."[74] Instead, sexual desire is better described as an incentive motivation system. If drives are motivational systems that compel us to resolve a negative tension in the body and return to a baseline, an incentive motivation system is what pulls us toward "something worth working for" and is resolved when the incentive is gained or obtained.[75] And unlike drives, incentive motivation systems vary from person to person.

Nagoski delineates between what I refer to as two *desire templates: spontaneous desire* and *responsive desire*. We are perhaps most familiar with thinking of sexual desire in terms of spontaneous desire, as this is the desire template that we are most likely to see represented in popular culture. Spontaneous desire feels like it appears suddenly, out of thin air—"you're sitting at lunch or walking down the street, maybe you see a sexy person or think a sexy thought, and pow! you're saying to yourself, 'I would like some sex!' "[76] This is a perfectly normal desire template and one that Nagoski estimates typifies the experiencing of approximately 75% of cis men and 15% of cis women.[77] However, many clients who report a desire differential in their relationships often come to me under the mistaken impression that spontaneous desire is the preferred or most valid way of experiencing desire, "I wish sex with my partner were more spontaneous," these clients might exclaim.

Others are more apt to experience desire responsively. Folx who experience responsive desire may "find that they begin to want sex only after sexy things are already happening."[78] Responsive desire is keyed to "the circumstances of the present moment" and one's "brain state in the present moment."[79] Examples of contexts might include: partner characteristics (such as their physical appearance or smell); one's own mental and physical wellbeing (e.g., whether one is experiencing high levels of stress or not, or whether one has a health at every size [HAES] approach to their body image); or relationship characteristics (e.g., whether one trusts one's partners, the presence of a power dynamic, or whether one feels a sense of emotional connection).

One prominent not-so-sexy context for many trans and non-binary folx is gender dysphoria itself. To say the least, it is hard to imagine being comfortable being intimate, naked, or playful with oneself or a partner when negative feelings about one's body or how that body is perceived or interacted with are at the forefront of our psyches! Engaging in certain types of sexual activity can activate dysphoric feels in such a way that we might leave our bodies and dissociate.[80] For example, when a partner plays with my clit (the term I use for my genitalia), pumping or jerking motions tend to be intensely distressing, whereas flicking or swirling motions feel yummy and allow me to drop back into my body and be present for the experience. When our bodies are affirmed or when we have "the right hormones in our bodies" and/or "a body that reflects our sense of self," we can, as Tobi Hill-Meyer and Dean Scarborough suggest, "be more present and connected to ourselves," and thus we might find ourselves able to be open to desire and embodied erotic experiences.[81]

If sexual desire is characterized as a drive motivational system that can go up and down then the presence of either an increased desire for sex or a decreased desire for sex can be experienced as a loss. For trans and non-binary folx who take testosterone, the prospect of increased libido and spontaneous clitoral glans erections might be distressing. Some folx on T, as

Hill-Meyer and Scarborough note, feel as if their desire becomes capacious and overwhelming, "we suddenly fantasize about everyone and everything we see, all the time, uncontrollably, and want sex nonstop."[82] The expansion of the contexts in which desire and arousal are experienced might feel like one is losing control over desire. For trans and non-binary folx who take estrogen and other androgen-blockers, the prospect of a decrease in libido might be equally distressing. It might seem, indeed, like a loss of sexual desire—or unwanted sexual desire—is just part of what is necessary to achieve an overall sense of embodied gender euphoria.

Why does there need to be a tradeoff or a loss? What if, instead, we attended to variation, to changes in desire templates and context? What if, indeed, the alleviation of gender dysphoria didn't imply sexual losses, but rather the opening onto new possibilities for embodied ecstasy, facilitated by gender euphoria? There are so few empirical studies specifically devoted to the phenomenology of trans desire, but we could easily imagine that the changes in desire so many trans and non-binary folx report as they connect to their embodied sexual selves might be better characterized as shifts in desire templates (from a spontaneous desire-dominated template to a more responsive desire template, and vice versa) or variations in the contexts to which desire may be responsive.

As I will continue to discuss in the next section, shifts in rhetoric on our part might seem minor, but the pay-offs for our trans and non-binary clients can be profound. As Tobin reminds us, "[we] all have the right to sexual pleasure, regardless of our gender identity, our anatomy, or the steps we have or have not taken to outwardly affirm that identity."[83] The language and rhetoric we use as providers can help affirm that right. If we rely on false dichotomies and eschew nuance (as in a reliance on drive theory) we effectively foreclose in-depth conversation and exploration between client and clinician about the possibilities of arousal, desire, pleasure, and erotic embodiment, regardless of how a body is shaped or configured. We must always keep in mind that the ways we can "connect sexually are virtually unlimited and they aren't—or don't need to be—limited by our identities," a theme I shall take up in greater detail in Chapter 3.[84]

BTToP: Informed Consent and Desire

When clients express concerns over shifts in desire or if you are engaging in informed consent prior to them starting HT, you might consider using language I've included below. This language was generously provided by Emily Nagoski and used here with her permission, modified slightly so as to incorporate a conceptual model on understanding sexual desire, proposed by Kristen P. Mark and Julie A. Lasslo:

> W*e know desire depends on a wide range of individual, interpersonal, and socio-cultural factors. Hormones might be involved, but so are mood, relationship factors, personal history, and cultural-societal factors such as gendered expectations as to role and expression as well as cultural sexual attitudes and value systems. If you experience changes in sexual arousal and desire as you go through this process, it's likely that the most effective interventions will be more like therapy and less like medical intervention, since most of the changes people experience in sexual desire throughout their lives are not biological but related to their overall wellbeing, their relationship, partner characteristics (e.g., attractiveness), and the values related to your cultures of origin and affiliation with respect to sexual expression.*[85]

I suggest viewing this language as more of an enhancement to an informed consent process, a way of nuancing what is included in clinical guidance and standards of care, rather than a wholesale replacement of said guidance. Although the research base doesn't yet reflect the experiencing of trans and non-binary clients, we can still provide insight and psychoeducation extrapolated from the larger science of sexual desire and arousal with confidence.

Fully Functional

"You are fully functional, aren't you?" asks a scantily clad Tasha Yar (Denise Crosby) of her colleague, the lovable android Lt. Commander Data (Brent Spiner) in the second episode of the freshman season of *Star Trek: The Next Generation*, "The Naked Now" (1987).[86] In the episode, the crew of the Enterprise-D becomes infected by a pathogen that lowers inhibitions. "The Naked Now" is not, by any stretch of the imagination, one of the series' best episodes, but this scene, Yar's question of Data, and his stammered, flummoxed response ("I am programmed in multiple techniques, a broad variety of pleasuring") has stuck with me. I am particularly struck by the phrasing of Yar's question to Data and the discourse of function deployed therein. What does it mean to be "fully functional"? To what aspect of functionality is the question directed? Is she asking whether Data possesses genitalia? Is she also asking whether any such genital structures present function in such a way so as to engage in sexual activity?

And notice anything about Data's response? He speaks of programmed capacities for engaging in sexual behavior and for giving pleasure in a variety of ways, but what about Data's pleasure? Data's capacity for experiencing himself "a broad variety of pleasuring" is never considered. Here, the character is afforded desirability, but not desire-ability; Data is pleasurable, but not pleasure-able. Data's pleasure is utterly disregarded; all that his prospective partner cares about is whether he is "fully functional," whether he can perform in particular, societally scripted, compulsorily heterosexual, ways as a lover.

In many ways, we are all Data—asked to "perform" sexually within a set of "normal operational parameters" with very little regard for our own pleasure. As Peggy Kleinplatz has observed, sexology, sex therapy, and sexual medicine paradigms all too often define treatment goals "in terms of remedying technical difficulties in performance" and "stop at the level of normative, standard functioning."[87] Doing so either utterly ignores questions of pleasure or limits pleasure to orgasmic potential and achievement. This is a problem in the field that affects all bodies and all genders. But trans and non-binary bodies face particular challenges within paradigms that emphasize function and performance. The discourse of function, I contend, is yet another way the scholarly literature on trans experiencing forecloses conversations about trans sexual expression and desire, shuts down the possibility for imaginal play, and limits the erotic horizons of trans and non-binary folx.

In the clinical literature, notions of function are often closely tied to outdated, phallocentric and genitally focused conceptions of sex. To see this in action we might consider how the American Sexual Health Association (ASHA) talks about function. The entry on sexual functioning on the ASHA website defines "healthy sexual functioning" as the ability "to experience sexual pleasure and satisfaction when desired" and asserts that sexual functioning is an "important part of overall sexual health."[88] The page goes on to describe a rather expansive conception of how sexual pleasure can be experienced, "from solo masturbation to oral sex to sensual massage to a range of other possibilities." So far, so good. Links are established between sexual health and sexual function, as well as sexual pleasure, but sex and sexual pleasure are not reduced to genital experiencing—e.g., the reference to sensual massage, which need not involve genital touch. Unfortunately, the ASHA entry on sexual functioning quickly goes off the rails from there. While the first part of the entry presents sexual pleasure broadly, the rest focuses on genital experiencing and places sexual function within the context of the "sexual response cycle."

The sexual response cycle refers to the pioneering sexological research of William Masters and Virginia Johnson, who proposed a model of human sexual response comprised of four phases: excitement (arousal), plateau, orgasm, and resolution (a refractory period).[89] The sexual response cycle they proposed is susceptible to a number of critiques. First, the model is resolutely linear in its approach, with each phase following the last in the same order every time. Second, while arousal is included in the model, neither pleasure nor desire is present. Rather, the model centers sexual response—and, by extension, healthy or normative, sexual function—on the achievement of orgasm. Pleasure, here, is completely subordinate to orgasm, which, in turn, largely limits the definition of what constitutes "sex" to behaviors that result in a genital orgasm. And finally, the model is entirely focused on physio-logical factors informing sexual response and ignores cultural and social factors and other forms of what Nagoski calls "context."

To take another example, we can look at the DSM-5, which tends to discuss sexual function solely in the context of the antonym, sexual dysfunction. The DSM-5 characterizes sexual dysfunction as "a clinically significant disturb-ance in a person's ability to respond sexually or to experience pleasure."[90] Ten disorders of sexual function are listed in the chapter: (1) delayed ejaculation, (2) erectile disorder, (3) female orgasmic disorder, (4) female sexual interest/arousal disorder, (5) genito-pelvic pain/penetration disorder, (6) male hypoactive sexual desire disorder, (7) premature (early) ejaculation, (8) sub-stance/medication-induced sexual dysfunction, (9) other specified sexual dysfunction, and (10) unspecified sexual dysfunction. Notice anything about this list? Removing the other specified and unspecified sexual dysfunction disorders, we are left with over half of disorders explicitly referencing genital function or focused on orgasmic potential. As such, the DSM-5's reference to sexual function as a capacity to "experience pleasure" might be seen in a less flattering light. Here, pleasure might be understood as a metonym for orgasm. Another difficulty with the way the DSM-5 speaks of pleasure is that it largely subordinates pleasure to function such that pleasure cannot exist in the absence of function, and, for that matter, genital sex.

To speak of sexual function is, thus, essentially, to speak about genitals, and genitals performing in particular ways—hard, orifice-penetrating pen-ises; wet, supple vaginas capable of receiving penetration. And as Kleinplatz urges us to consider, when the goals of treatment—whether via sex therapy or medical intervention—are narrowly focused on genital function, sexual performance, and the achievement of orgasm, much of what makes sex pleasurable, such as, "embodiment, connection, and integration" is utterly ignored or missed.[91] The complexities and richness of sexual expression and erotic embodiment are disavowed and evacuated of meaning.

While the centrality of "sexual function" in sexual health paradigms is a problem for all bodies, there are particularly harmful implications for trans and non-binary bodies. First, it serves to reify a narrative that trans sexual embodiment is constituted by steps taken in pursuit of a "specific treatment trajectory," namely, medical transition, including hormone therapies and surgical interventions (particularly bottom surgeries such as orchiectomy, vaginoplasty, metoidioplasty, and phalloplasty).[92] As Greta Bauer and Rebecca Hammond point out in a suggestive article that works to highlight some of the social contexts and sexual realities of trans women's lives, we see this playing out in how so many of the articles on trans sexual lives almost exclusively emphasize "postoperative orgasmic potential and sexual satisfaction" among trans folx who have undergone bottom surgeries and the effects of hormone therapies on "sexual desire and function."[93] This focus on orgasmic potential or sexual function, Bauer and Hammond continue, "ignores the sexual health needs of the majority of" trans and non-binary folx "at most points in their lives," considering that many trans and non-binary folx, do not pursue medical transition and, particularly, surgical interventions such as facial feminization surgery (FFS), vaginoplasty, and phalloplasty, both by choice and because of the enormous expense of such surgeries.[94]

In addition to ignoring the sexual health needs of most trans and non-binary clients, a discourse that emphasizes sexual function "flattens out the complexities" of trans people's experiences of sexuality, and "simultaneously disavow[s]" how many trans and non-binary folx can and do embody their sexualities.[95] Trans erotic embodiment is thereby reduced to genitals and heteronormative, cisnormative, ableist conceptions of what sex is and can be in ways that elide questions of pleasure. After all, some trans folx don't use their genitals for sex and many do not engage in sexual activity that involves hard penises going into wet vaginas. And even for those that do engage in genital and/or penetrative sex, a discourse of function serves to define sex in terms of "success" and "performance," while shunting to the side as immaterial questions of embodiment, connection, fulfillment, and pleasure. What sort of ideas of embodied sexuality and eroticism are we purveying here? A rather dismal, sub-standard, and pleasure-less one, I'm afraid, and one which does not delight in variation, exploration, possibility, risk-taking, wonder, and ecstasy.

Frameworks such as Kleinplatz's optimal sexuality model have done a great deal in recent years to teach sex educators, counselors, and therapists how to help clients decouple sex and pleasure from orgasm, function, and performance; as well as how to normalize a range of desires, sexual identities, and ways of engaging with passion and intimacy.[96] Unfortunately, the clinical literature—and by extension gender-affirmative clinical practice—to date has not often afforded trans and non-binary clients the same level of access to a pleasure-positive imaginal landscape to the same extent as cis clients have enjoyed. In Chapter 5, I will explore how we can do so by re-centering our focus on pleasure via a social justice framework.

Conclusion

Each of the narratives I discussed in this chapter constitute what I refer to as an *imaginative failure* when they become constellated within the therapeutic relationship. If, in psychotherapy, an *empathic failure* occurs when a therapist fails, for whatever reason, to empathically attune with their client, an imaginative failure occurs when we, as providers, fail to imagine into the full range of our clients' lives, feelings, and experiences.

The danger of imaginative failures is that they foreclose conversation; they prematurely cut off potential pathways of exploring the client's lived experience or, worse, designate those potential pathways unsafe or off-limits. When conversations are foreclosed, we unwittingly become tools of social control, cutting out alternative ways of being that might form and inform us and our clients.

Our imperative as providers, I submit, is to be able to imagine each and every one of our clients as sexual beings, and to eschew that which adrienne maree brown refers to as "fearful imaginations," imaginations hampered by colonial logics, white supremacy, and patriarchy.[97] In exhorting you to imagine each and every client as a sexual being I am suggesting that we should be able to imagine all bodies, all clients, as capable of desire, desirability, and embodied joy. In the next four chapters my aim is to introduce a set of conceptual stances and frameworks grounded in this imperative. Each of these stances is designed to help us, as providers, avoid imaginative failures and help our clients to embrace curiosity and live passionate, embodied sexual lives.

Notes

1 I am particularly indebted to the work of Hunter Shackelford (http://ashleighshackelford. com). For example, Hunter Shackelford, "Bittersweet Like Me: Lemonade and Fat Black Femme Erasure," *Wear Your Voice* (blog), April 27, 2016, https://wearyourvoicemag. com/bittersweet-like-lemonade-aint-made-fat-black-women-femmes/. See also Caleb Luna, "On Being Fat, Brown, Femme, Ugly, and Unloveable," *BGD* (blog), July 21, 2014, https://www.bgdblog.org/2014/07/fat-brown-femme-ugly-unloveable/.

2 See, for example: Carol L. Glasser, Belinda Robnett, and Cynthia Feliciano, "Internet Daters' Body Type Preferences: Race–Ethnic and Gender Differences," *Sex Roles* 61, no. 1–2 (July 2009): 14–33, https://doi.org/10.1007/s11199-009-9604-x; Chongsuk Han, "No Fats, Femmes, or Asians: The Utility of Critical Race Theory in Examining the Role of Gay Stock Stories in the Marginalization of Gay Asian Men," *Contemporary Justice Review* 11, no. 1 (March 2008): 11–22, https://doi.org/10.1080/ 10282580701850355; Margaret L. Hunter, "'If You're Light You're Alright': Light Skin Color as Social Capital for Women of Color," *Gender & Society* 16, no. 2 (April 1, 2002): 175–193, https://doi.org/10.1177/0891243202016002003; Margo Mullinax et al., "In Their Own Words: A Qualitative Content Analysis of Women's and Men's Preferences for Women's Genitals," *Sex Education* 15, no. 4 (July 4, 2015): 421–436, https://doi.org/10.1080/14681811.2015.1031884; Mya Vaughn et al., "Addressing Disability Stigma within the Lesbian Community," *Journal of Rehabilitation* 81, no. 4 (2015): 49–56; Allison Taylor, "'But Where Are the Dates?' Dating as a Central Site of Fat Femme Marginalisation in Queer Communities," *Psychology & Sexuality*, September 17, 2020, 1–12, https://doi.org/10.1080/19419899.2020.1822429.

3 Denton Callander, Christy E. Newman, and Martin Holt, "Is Sexual Racism Really Racism? Distinguishing Attitudes Toward Sexual Racism and Generic Racism Among Gay and Bisexual Men," *Archives of Sexual Behavior* 44, no. 7 (October 2015): 1991–2000, https://doi.org/10.1007/s10508-015-0487-3.

4 Karen L. Blair and Rhea Ashley Hoskin, "Transgender Exclusion from the World of Dating: Patterns of Acceptance and Rejection of Hypothetical Trans Dating Partners as a Function of Sexual and Gender Identity," *Journal of Social and Personal Relationships*, May 31, 2018, 026540751877913, https://doi.org/10.1177/0265407518779139; Jessica M. Mao, M. L. Haupert, and Eliot R. Smith, "How Gender Identity and Transgender Status Affect Perceptions of Attractiveness," *Social Psychological and Personality Science*, June 27, 2018, 194855061878371, https://doi.org/10.1177/1948550618783716.

5 Mao, Haupert, and Smith, "How Gender Identity and Transgender Status Affect Perceptions of Attractiveness."

6 Blair and Hoskin, "Transgender Exclusion from the World of Dating."

7 For a set of trans and non-binary folx reflecting on dating and the challenges of "dating while trans," see: Nico Lang, "Looking for Love and Acceptance: Dating While Trans in America," *The Daily Beast*, October 15, 2016, http://www.thedailybeast.com/articles/2016/10/15/looking-for-love-and- acceptance-dating-while-trans-in-america.html.

8 Mitchell S Tepper, "Sexuality and Disability: The Missing Discourse of Pleasure," *Sex and Disability* 18, no. 4 (December 2000): 283–290; Cassandra Loeser, Barbara Pini, and Vicki Crowley, "Disability and Sexuality: Desires and Pleasures," *Sexualities* 21, no. 3 (March 2018): 255–270, https://doi.org/10.1177/1363460716688682; Ana Cristina Santos and Ana Lúcia Santos, "Yes, We Fuck! Challenging the Misfit Sexual Body through Disabled Women's Narratives," *Sexualities* 21, no. 3 (March 2018): 303–318, https://doi.org/10.1177/1363460716688680; Maggie L. Syme et al., "'At My Age…': Defining Sexual Wellness in Mid- and Later Life," *Journal of Sex Research* 56, no. 7 (September 2019): 832–842; Joan Price, *Naked At Our Age: Talking Out Loud About Senior Sex* (Berkeley, CA: Seal Press, 2011).

9 Santos and Santos, "Yes, We Fuck! Challenging the Misfit Sexual Body through Disabled Women's Narratives," 307.

10 Harry Benjamin, *The Transsexual Phenomenon*, Electronic Edition (Düsseldorf: Symposium Publishing, 1999), 31, http://www.mut23.de/texte/Harry%20Benjamin%20-%20The%20Transsexual%20Phenomenon.pdf.

11 Benjamin, 11.

12 J.R. Latham, "Axiomatic: Constituting 'Transexuality' and Trans Sexualities in Medicine," *Sexualities* 22, no. 1–2 (February 2019): 20, https://doi.org/10.1177/1363460717740258; Benjamin, *The Transsexual Phenomenon*, 11.

13 Laura Erickson-Schroth and Laura Jacobs, *"You're in the Wrong Bathroom!": And 20 Other Myths and Misconceptions About Transgender and Gender-Nonconforming People* (Boston, MA: Beacon Press, 2017), 57.

14 The concept of "erotically marginalized" is featured and explored in: Damon Constantinides, Shannon L. Sennott, and Davis Chandler, *Sex Therapy with Erotically Marginalized Clients* (New York, NY: Routledge, 2019).

15 Jennifer Bartlett, "Longing for the Male Gaze," *The New York Times*, September 21, 2016, https://www.nytimes.com/2016/09/21/opinion/longing-for-the-male-gaze.html. Cf. Jessica Valenti, *Sex Object* (New York, NY: HarperCollins Publishers, 2016).

16 Sam Feder, *Disclosure*, Documentary (Netflix, 2020).

17 Breanne Fahs and Sara I. McClelland, "When Sex and Power Collide: An Argument for Critical Sexuality Studies," *The Journal of Sex Research* 53, no. 4–5 (May 3, 2016): 393 and 405, https://doi.org/10.1080/00224499.2016.1152454.

18 Nancy Tuana, "Coming to Understand: Orgasm and the Epistemology of Ignorance," *Hypatia* 19, no. 1 (2004): 195.

19 Fahs and McClelland, "When Sex and Power Collide," 394.

20 Emily Nagoski, *Come as You Are: The Surprising New Science That Will Transform Your Sex Life* (New York: Simon & Schuster, 2015), 8.

21 Constantinides, Sennott, and Chandler, *Sex Therapy with Erotically Marginalized Clients*.

22 Stephanie L. Budge, Mun Yuk Chin, and Laura P. Minero, "Trans Individuals' Facilitative Coping: An Analysis of Internal and External Processes.," *Journal of Counseling Psychology* 64, no. 1 (2017): 12, https://doi.org/10.1037/cou0000178.

23 Sandy E. James et al., "The Report of the 2015 U.S. Transgender Survey" (Washington, DC: National Center for Transgender Equality, December 2016).

24 Walter O. Bockting et al., "Stigma, Mental Health, and Resilience in an Online Sample of the US Transgender Population," *American Journal of Public Health* 103, no. 5 (May 2013): 943–951, https://doi.org/10.2105/AJPH.2013.301241; Anneliese A. Singh, Danica G. Hays, and Laurel S. Watson, "Strength in the Face of Adversity: Resilience Strategies of Transgender Individuals," *Journal of Counseling & Development* 89, no. 1 (January 2011): 20–27, https://doi.org/10.1002/j.1556-6678.2011.tb00057.x; Michael L. Hendricks and Rylan J. Testa, "A Conceptual Framework for Clinical Work with Transgender and Gender Nonconforming Clients: An Adaptation of the Minority Stress Model.," *Professional Psychology: Research and Practice* 43, no. 5 (2012): 460–467, https://doi.org/10.1037/a0029597.

25 James et al., "The Report of the 2015 U.S. Transgender Survey"; Cesar A. Gonzalez, Joseph D. Gallego, and Walter O. Bockting, "Demographic Characteristics, Components of Sexuality and Gender, and Minority Stress and Their Associations to Excessive Alcohol, Cannabis, and Illicit (Noncannabis) Drug Use Among a Large Sample of Transgender People in the United States," *The Journal of Primary Prevention* 38, no. 4 (August 2017): 419–445, https://doi.org/10.1007/s10935-017-0469-4; Stephanie L. Budge, Jill L. Adelson, and Kimberly A.S. Howard, "Anxiety and Depression in Transgender Individuals: The Roles of Transition Status, Loss, Social Support, and Coping," *Journal of Consulting and Clinical Psychology* 81, no. 3 (2013): 545–557, https://doi.org/10.1037/a0031774; Nicholas J. Parr and Bethany Grace Howe, "Heterogeneity of Transgender Identity Nonaffirmation Microaggressions and Their Association with Depression Symptoms and Suicidality among Transgender Persons.," *Psychology of Sexual Orientation and Gender Diversity* 6, no. 4 (December 2019): 461–474, https://doi.org/10.1037/sgd0000347.

26 Ilan H. Meyer, "Prejudice, Social Stress, and Mental Health in Lesbian, Gay, and Bisexual Populations: Conceptual Issues and Research Evidence," *Psychological Bulletin* 129, no. 5 (2003): 674–697, https://doi.org/10.1037/0033-2909.129.5.674; Hendricks and Testa, "A Conceptual Framework for Clinical Work with Transgender and Gender Nonconforming Clients."

27 Meyer, "Prejudice, Social Stress, and Mental Health in Lesbian, Gay, and Bisexual Populations," 674; Hendricks and Testa, "A Conceptual Framework for Clinical Work with Transgender and Gender Nonconforming Clients," 462.

28 Rylan J. Testa et al., "Development of the Gender Minority Stress and Resilience Measure," *Psychology of Sexual Orientation and Gender Diversity* 2, no. 1 (March 2015): 66, https://doi.org/10.1037/sgd0000081.

29 Testa et al., "Development of the Gender Minority Stress and Resilience Measure," 66.

30 Meyer, "Prejudice, Social Stress, and Mental Health in Lesbian, Gay, and Bisexual Populations," 676.

31 Kimberlé Crenshaw, "Mapping the Margins: Intersectionality, Identity Politics, and Violence against Women of Color," *Stanford Law Review* 43, no. 6 (July 1991): 1241–1299.

32 Sand Chang, Anneliese A. Singh, and lore m. dickey, *A Clinician's Guide to Gender-Affirming Care: Working with Transgender and Gender Nonconforming Clients* (Context Press, 2018), 3.

33 Chang, Singh, and dickey, *A Clinician's Guide to Gender-Affirming Care.* 3.

34 Sand C. Chang and Anneliese A. Singh, "Affirming Psychological Practice with Transgender and Gender Nonconforming People of Color," *Psychology of Sexual Orientation and Gender Diversity* 3, no. 2 (June 2016): 140, https://doi.org/10.1037/sgd0000153; James et al., "The Report of the 2015 U.S. Transgender Survey," 6.

35 Budge, Chin, and Minero, "Trans Individuals' Facilitative Coping," 12.

36 Bonnie Moradi et al., "A Content Analysis of Literature on Trans People and Issues," *The Counseling Psychologist* 44, no. 7 (2016): 960–95.

37 Greta R. Bauer and Rebecca Hammond, "Toward a Broader Conceptualization of Trans Women's Sexual Health," *The Canadian Journal of Human Sexuality* 24, no. 1 (April 2015): 1, https://doi.org/10.3138/cjhs.24.1-CO1; Moradi et al., "A Content Analysis of Literature on Trans People and Issues," 980.

38 Nazanin Moali, "Coming Out as Transgender from the Sexology Podcast with Dr. Moali," The Sexology Podcast with Dr. Moali, accessed July 31, 2020, http://www.sexologypodcast.com/2018/07/31/coming-out-as-trangender/.

39 Vivian Rakoff, "A Long Term Effect of the Concentration Camp Experience," *Viewpoints*, no. 1 (1966): 17–22; Teresa Evans-Campbell, "Historical Trauma in American Indian/Native Alaska Communities: A Multilevel Framework for Exploring Impacts on Individuals, Families, and Communities," *Journal of Interpersonal Violence* 23, no. 3 (March 2008): 316–338, https://doi.org/10.1177/0886260507312290; Maria Roth, Frank Neuner, and Thomas Elbert, "Transgenerational Consequences of PTSD: Risk Factors for the Mental Health of Children Whose Mothers Have Been Exposed to the Rwandan Genocide," *International Journal of Mental Health Systems* 8 (2014): 1–12. Joy DeGruy, *Post Traumatic Slave Syndrome: America's Legacy of Enduring Injury and Healing*, Revised Edition (Portland, OR: Joy Degruy Publications Inc, 2017); Rachel Yehuda and Amy Lehrner, "Intergenerational Transmission of Trauma Effects: Putative Role of Epigenetic Mechanisms," *World Psychiatry* 17, no. 3 (October 2018): 243–257, https://doi.org/10.1002/wps.20568.

40 Resmaa Menakem, *My Grandmother's Hands: Racialized Trauma and the Pathway to Mending Our Hearts and Bodies* (Las Vegas, NV: Central Recovery Press, 2017), 37.

41 I am indebted to the research and forthcoming work of Vern Harner, a doctoral candidate in social work at the University of Washington, for the concept of intergenerational knowledge.

42 Leslie Feinberg, *Transgender Warriors: Making History from Joan of Arc to Dennis Rodman* (Boston, MA: Beacon Press, 2005); C. Riley Snorton, *Black on Both Sides: A Racial History of Trans Identity* (Minneapolis, MN: University of Minnesota Press, 2017); Reina Gossett, Eric A. Stanley, and Johanna Burton, eds., *Trap Door: Trans*

Cultural Production and the Politics of Visibility, Critical Anthologies in Art and Culture (Cambridge, MA: MIT Press, 2017); Matthew Reimer and Leighton Brown, *We Are Everywhere: Protest, Power, and Pride in the History of Queer Liberation* (New York, NY: Ten Speed Press, 2019).

43 For a full treatment of how FOSTA-SESTA and Tumblr's ban on adult content has played out and how it has, in particular, impacted access to content related to queer and trans sexualities, see Carolyn Bronstein, "Pornography, Trans Visibility, and the Demise of Tumblr," *TSQ: Transgender Studies Quarterly* 7, no. 2 (May 1, 2020): 240–254, https://doi.org/10.1215/23289252-8143407.

44 Menakem, *My Grandmother's Hands: Racialized Trauma and the Pathway to Mending Our Hearts and Bodies*, 10; Eduardo Duran, *Healing the Soul Wound: Counseling with American Indians and Other Native Peoples* (New York, NY: Teacher's College Press, 2006).

45 Marika Heinrichs, "Queers Know about Loving in the Midst of Virus...," Instagram Post, @wildbodysomatics, March 11, 2020, https://www.instagram.com/p/B9nozx-AS5e/.

46 Amber Hollibaugh, *My Dangerous Desires: A Queer Girl Dreaming Her Way Home* (Durham, NC: Duke University Press, 2000), 218.

47 Michel Foucault, *The Archaeology of Knowledge: And the Discourse on Language*, trans. A. M. Sheridan Smith (New York, NY: Vintage, 2010).

48 Jordy Rosenberg, *Confessions of the Fox* (New York, NY: One World, 2018), 315.

49 b binaohan, *Decolonizing Trans/Gender 101* (biyuti publishing, 2014), 73.

50 Rosenberg, *Confessions of the Fox*, 315.

51 José Esteban Muñoz, *Cruising Utopia: The Then and There of Queer Futurity*, 10th Anniversary Edition, Sexual Cultures (New York, NY: NYU Press, 2019), 1.

52 Emily Nagoski and Amelia Nagoski, *Burnout: The Secret to Unlocking the Stress Cycle* (New York, NY: Ballantine Books, 2019), 58.

53 Hendricks and Testa, "A Conceptual Framework for Clinical Work with Transgender and Gender Nonconforming Clients," 462.

54 Meyer, "Prejudice, Social Stress, and Mental Health in Lesbian, Gay, and Bisexual Populations," 677.

55 Chang, Singh, and dickey, *A Clinician's Guide to Gender-Affirming Care*, 101–105.

56 Budge, Chin, and Minero, "Trans Individuals' Facilitative Coping," 13; Chang, Singh, and dickey, *A Clinician's Guide to Gender-Affirming Care*, 104.

57 Budge, Chin, and Minero, "Trans Individuals' Facilitative Coping," 16–18.

58 Ibid., 21.

59 Perry Zurn, "Puzzle Pieces: Shapes of Trans Curiosity," *APA Newsletter* 18, no. 1 (2018): 12.

60 Ibid., 14.

61 Susan Stryker, *Transgender History: The Roots of Today's Revolution*, 2nd ed. (Berkeley, CA: Seal Press, 2017); Genny Beemyn, "US History," in *Trans Bodies, Trans Selves: A Resource for the Transgender Community*, ed. Laura Erickson-Schroth (Oxford/New York: Oxford University Press, 2014), 501–536; Snorton, *Black on Both Sides: A Racial History of Trans Identity*; Gossett, Stanley, and Burton, *Trap Door: Trans Cultural Production and the Politics of Visibility*.

62 Chang, Singh, and dickey, *A Clinician's Guide to Gender-Affirming Care*.

63 Budge, Chin, and Minero, "Trans Individuals' Facilitative Coping," 105.

64 Zurn, "Puzzle Pieces: Shapes of Trans Curiosity."

65　Harper Jean Tobin, "The Perils and Pleasures of Sex for Trans People," in *Sex Matters: The Sexuality and Society Reader,* ed. Mindy Stombler et al., 4th ed. (New York, NY: W. W. Norton & Company, 2014), 22.

66　Ibid., 22.

67　Zowie Davy and Eliza Steinbock, "'Sexing Up' Bodily Aesthetics: Notes towards Theorizing Trans Sexuality," in *Sexualities: Past Reflections, Future Directions* (New York, NY: Palgrave Macmillan, 2012), 266.

68　Sandy Stone, "The 'Empire' Strikes Back: A Posttranssexual Manifesto," *Camera Obscura* 10, no. 2 (May 1992): 150–76; Latham, "Axiomatic," 14; Erickson-Schroth and Jacobs, *"You're in the Wrong Bathroom!": And 20 Other Myths and Misconceptions About Transgender and Gender-Nonconforming People,* 57.

69　Stone, "The 'Empire' Strikes Back: A Posttranssexual Manifesto," 161.

70　Blair and Hoskin, "Transgender Exclusion from the World of Dating"; Jean Malpas, "Can Couples Change Gender? Couple Therapy with Transgender People and Their Partners," in *Handbook of LGBT-Affirmative Couple and Family Therapy,* ed. Jerry J. Bigner and Joseph L. Wetchler (New York, NY: Routledge, 2012), 69– 85; Kevan Wylie, Edward Wootton, and Sophie Carlson, "Sexual Function in the Transgender Population," in *Principles of Transgender Medicine and Surgery,* ed. Randi Ettner, Stan Monstrey, and Eli Coleman, 2nd ed. (New York: Routledge, 2016), 159–166.

71　Brody, "Desirability," *Trans Sex Zine, Volume II,* May 2018, 10.

72　Eli Coleman et al., "Standards of Care for the Health of Transsexual, Transgender, and Gender-NonconformingPeople,Version7," *TheInternationalJournalofTransgenderism* 13, no. 4 (2012): 165–232, https://doi.org/10.1080/15532739.2011.700873.

73　Nagoski, *Come as You Are,* 229.

74　Frank Beach, "Characteristics of Masculine 'Sex Drive,'" in *Nebraska Symposium on Motivation,* vol. 4 (Lincoln, NE: University of Nebraska Press, 1956), 1–32.

75　Nagoski, *Come as You Are,* 231.

76　Ibid., 225.

77　Ibid., 225.

78　Ibid., 225.

79　Ibid., 75.

80　Tobi Hill-Meyer and Dean Scarborough, "Sexuality," in *Trans Bodies, Trans Selves: A Resource for the Transgender Community,* ed. Laura Erickson-Schroth (Oxford; New York: Oxford University Press, 2014), 257.

81　Nagoski, *Come as You Are,* 361.

82　Hill-Meyer and Scarborough, "Sexuality," 363.

83　Tobin, "Sex Matters," 24.

84　Ibid., 27.

85　Emily Nagoski, "Re: Follow up from DC Master Class," November 5, 2018; Kristen P. Mark and Julie A. Lasslo, "Maintaining Sexual Desire in Long-Term Relationships: A Systematic Review and Conceptual Model," *The Journal of Sex Research* 55, no. 4–5 (June 13, 2018): 567, https://doi.org/10.1080/00224499.2018.1437592.

86　Paul Lynch, "The Naked Now," CBS All Access, *Star Trek: The Next Generation,* October 5, 1987.

87　Peggy J. Kleinplatz, "Is That All There Is? A New Critique of the Goals of Sex Therapy," in *New Directions in Sex Therapy: Innovations and Alternatives,* ed. Peggy J. Kleinplatz, 2nd ed. (New York, NY: Routledge, 2012), 101 and 106.

88 American Sexual Health Association, "Sexual Functioning," American Sexual Health Association, accessed August 8, 2020, http://old.ashasexualhealth.org/sexual-health/sexual-functioning/.

89 William Masters and Virginia E. Johnson, *Human Sexual Response* (Boston, MA: Little, Brown, and Co., 1966).

90 American Psychiatric Association, *Diagnostic and Statistical Manual of Mental Disorders: DSM-5* (Arlington, VA: American Psychiatric Association, 2013), 423.

91 Kleinplatz, "Is That All There Is? A New Critique of the Goals of Sex Therapy," 101.

92 Latham, "Axiomatic," 15.

93 Bauer and Hammond, "Toward a Broader Conceptualization of Trans Women's Sexual Health," 1; Mauro E. Kerckhof et al., "Prevalence of Sexual Dysfunctions in Transgender Persons: Results from the ENIGI Follow-Up Study," *The Journal of Sexual Medicine* 16, no. 12 (December 2019): 2018–2029, https://doi.org/10.1016/j.jsxm.2019.09.003; Carolin Klein and Boris B. Gorzalka, "Sexual Functioning in Transsexuals Following Hormone Therapy and Genital Surgery: A Review," *The Journal of Sexual Medicine* 6, no. 11 (2009): 2922–2939; Wylie, Wootton, and Carlson, "Sexual Function in the Transgender Population."

94 Bauer and Hammond, "Toward a Broader Conceptualization of Trans Women's Sexual Health," 1.

95 Latham, "Axiomatic," 14.

96 Peggy J. Kleinplatz and A. Dana Ménard, *Magnificent Sex: Lessons from Extraordinary Lovers* (New York, NY: Routledge, 2020).

97 adrienne maree brown, *Pleasure Activism: The Politics of Feeling Good*, Emergent Strategy (Chico, CA: AK Press, 2019), 10.

2

ETHICAL CURIOSITY

Lucie Fielding

"Fascinating!" he said, leaning forward in his seat, opposite mine. His eyes scanned me, taking in my form, scrutinizing every inch of me. I could have sworn that he licked his lips and rubbed his hands together, but I cannot say for certain. What I am sure of is that I felt in that moment as if he had. He was my first clinical supervisor. I had just come out to him as trans, and, sitting in that chair, facing his queries, his penetrating gaze, every molecule in my body wished that I hadn't.

His questions had been innocent enough, at first. (They seem to always begin that way!) But before I knew it I was being asked whether I would have "the surgery" (meaning, for him, a vaginoplasty), whether my wife and I would be staying together, how she identified sexually, and what sex was like with us. It went on like that for half an hour: a barrage of questions, each followed by a "fascinating!" And when I finally stumbled out of my supervisor's office, I felt like there was not a hot shower long enough to cleanse me. I felt exposed, nauseated, dirty; and I felt a sharp pang of shame. It was the type of shame that would, two and a half years later, greet me following two sexual assaults. It's taken me a long time to learn that my failure to fight back or to flee the space was not something I should be ashamed of in the least. And so, as tears welled in my eyes and I slumped in the chair of my shoebox of an office, exhausted, I instead lambasted myself that I hadn't cut off my supervisor's interrogation the moment he had slipped into sexualizing territory, that I hadn't firmly told him that his questions were not ok.

The thing is, this was neither the first nor the last time something like this would happen to me. And the general contours of this story—with its insistent questions and its fetishizing, objectifying gaze—are not uncommon to many trans and non-binary folx. As Perry Zurn states, trans and non-binary folx "consistently experience themselves as the object of" cis folx's curiosity, whether that takes the form of "long looks, stares, or outright gawking by people on the street [...], the well-meaning, but often invasive questions of friends and family [...], the battery of questionnaires and exams conducted by medical professionals [...], or the spectacularizing attention afforded trans icons across various social media."[1]

And so much of the curiosity that trans and non-binary folx experience from cis people is related to *if* we, *how* we, *with whom* we, and *with what* we fuck; or the shape, character, and function of our genitals. "Have you had 'the surgery'?" "What have you got going on 'down there'?" "How do you go to the bathroom?" "Do you still have a penis?" "Do you still get your period?" As a result of this invasive, objectifying cis gaze, Zurn notes, many trans and non-binary folx "live defensively, constantly parrying unwanted attention, often in a vain attempt to guard not only their privacy but their legitimacy."[2]

Each of the chapters of this book places a heavy emphasis on cultivating curiosity, wonder, and exploration; or evoking a client's capacities for engaging their erotic imaginations. In Chapter 1, for example, I briefly discussed Zurn's concept of "trans curiosity." And in the next two chapters (Chapters 3 and 4) I will introduce two conceptual stances—coming into passionate relationship, and coming into compassionate relationship, with the embodied sexual self—that depend on nurturing curiosity and wonder about one's embodied sexualities. And as providers we are often taught that curiosity is a value worth cultivating in ourselves. Indeed, how often do we, as providers, begin an intervention with something along the lines of, "I'm curious..."? Curiosity in and of itself is not bad and there are many instances when it can be empowering and open us up to possibility. The problem is that it can also be dehumanizing and disempowering and can shut us down. In these instances, curiosity can actually be unethical.

In this chapter, the first of four that explore conceptual frameworks for work with trans sexualities and erotic embodiments, I introduce a clinical stance I call *ethical curiosity*, one that is constituted by three fundamental principles: dismantling entitlement, seeking permission, and treating the client in the room. This stance emerges out of the observation that curiosity is not an ethically neutral value.[3] A curiosity grounded in ethics also recognizes that members of marginalized groups and vulnerable or underserved populations often have to perform a great deal of emotional labor for their care providers (in the form of educating) and that this labor is not only depleting but also a source of rupture in the provider–client relationship. If the clinical gaze can often be perceived as invasive, othering, and de-humanizing, ethical curiosity proposes another model of relating, one that respects and empowers the client.

Mangogul's Ring

In our contemporary understanding of it, curiosity has a positive value, a capacity that speaks to a deep desire to explore and to know. Research psychologist Todd Kashdan defines curiosity as "the recognition, pursuit, and desire to explore novel, uncertain, complex, and ambiguous events" as well as a "feeling of interest in a situation where a potential exists for learning."[4] For Kashdan and others, curiosity is a "fundamental human motive" and a prosocial behavior that ultimately allows one to "expand knowledge, build competencies, strengthen social relationships, and increase intellectual and creative capacities."[5] This book and this author generally promote the view that curiosity is a virtue worth nurturing and developing both interpersonally and intrapersonally. But curiosity is not *intrinsically* good or a virtue, and the desire to know and explore, particularly within the person of the provider, needs some examination, unpacking, and troubling. For, largely missing from the ways that curiosity is explored in the psychological literature are the ways that curiosity can be experienced interactionally and how it can replicate oppressive dynamics that exist within society at large. To put it another way, we often talk about the positive benefits of being a curious person, but we rarely consider the impact of curiosity on the folx who are its objects, on whom curiosity's appetitive gaze is turned. In an interpersonal setting, what the curious person may experience as an opportunity for growth and learning might be experienced by the object of that curiosity as objectifying, tokenizing, or fetishizing. And engaging in curiosity without regard for how the person experiences that curiosity is not only unethical but shuts down possibilities for reciprocity and joining-with.

Curiosity's shadow, particularly with respect to how certain (sexual) bodies can become a focus of a probing, invasive, and essentializing gaze, is nicely emblematized by *Les Bijoux indiscrets,* an erotic novel by the Enlightenment philosopher Denis Diderot.[6] First published in 1748, *Les Bijoux indiscrets,* or, in English, *The Indiscreet Jewels,* focuses on the misadventures of a vaguely non-European potentate, Mangogul, and his efforts to overcome ennui through a penetrating investigation into (cis) female sexuality. The basic plot is that a genie presents the bored prince with a magical ring. The ring, when rubbed and pointed at the women at court, forces their genitalia—their *bijoux,* or jewels—to recount their owner's sexual adventures. What follows is a series of vignettes narrated by these indiscreet and loquacious jewels that reveal and lay bare secret and suppressed sexual stories. Once unmuffled by the ring's power, the genitals, per Diderot's reckoning, were compelled to speak sexual truths that their bearers' mouths would—or could—not speak. (These forced sexual confessions, as one might imagine, were deeply disconcerting for women upon whom the ring was turned.)

Nearly 230 years after the publication of *Les Bijoux indiscrets*, French theorist Michel Foucault used the novel as an allegory for how power operates through discourses of/on sexualities, declaring in the first volume of his *Histoire de la sexualité* that his chief aim was to "transcribe into history the fable of *Les Bijoux indiscrets*."[7] According to Foucault, "we have all been living in the realm of Prince Mangogul: under the spell of an immense curiosity about sex, bent on questioning it, with an insatiable desire to hear it speak and be spoken about."[8] One of Foucault's central assertions is that over the course of the eighteenth and nineteenth centuries a medico-moral discursive apparatus developed to interrogate the contours of pleasure as well as to medicalize cultural anxieties surrounding emergent constructs of sex, gender, and sexuality. This apparatus, which, among other things, culminated in *catalogues raisonnées* of disorders of sexualities such as Krafft-Ebing's *Psychopathia Sexualis* and the creation of Freudian psychoanalysis (the so-called "talking cure"), Foucault argues, emerged from older confessional modes.[9] This new mode re-deployed and secularized the Catholic sacrament of confession with its dogged pursuit of sexual thoughts, urges, and behaviors down to their "slenderest ramifications," but within the exacting language of social science, psychiatry, medicine, and the law—a "regulated and polymorphous incitement to" sexual speech.[10] And, like sacramental confession, the types of confession that would proliferate beginning, roughly, in the eighteenth century would "[unfold] within a power relationship, for one does not confess without the presence (or virtual presence) of a partner who is not simply the interlocutor but the authority who requires the confession, prescribes and appreciates it, and intervenes in order to judge, punish, forgive, console, and reconcile."[11]

Thus, we might consider the so-called fundamental rule of classical psychoanalysis, an instruction Freud gave to all analysands at the beginning of treatment to speak of "whatever comes into their heads, even if they think it unimportant or irrelevant or nonsensical…or embarrassing or distressing."[12] As for the analyst, their corresponding imperative was to receive these images, phantasies, and utterances with "evenly suspended attention" and intervene only sparingly and with well-formulated interpretations of analysand material.[13] Thus, the analyst is given license to ask the analysand to delve into the most intimate details of their lives, while concomitantly maintaining a sense of privacy and propriety over their own, all so that the analyst might serve as a blank screen upon which the analysand might project their unconscious phantasies. The analyst becomes "a receptive organ toward the transmitting unconscious of the patient."[14]

Crucially, Foucault's allegorical deployment of Diderot's *Les Bijoux indiscrets* does much to raise suspicion about the supposedly morally neutral stance of the therapist-confessor, revealing how power operates and replicates itself through the production of speech about sex, but also how the act of taking confession—the act of sitting with—can itself be titillating.

*P*leasure in the truth of pleasure, the pleasure of knowing that truth, of discovering and exposing it, the fascination of seeing it and telling it, of captivating and capturing others by it, of confiding it in secret, of luring it out in the open – the specific pleasure of the truth discourse on pleasure.[15]

I think, here, of a clip from the 1962 remake of Robert Weine's German Expressionist psychological thriller, *The Cabinet of Doctor Caligari* (1920). Beginning with the age at which she first allowed a man to "make love" to her, Dr. Caligari (a psychoanalyst) insistently and mercilessly bombards his hapless analysand with a series of increasingly revealing questions designed to incite sexual speech; here, the detailed narrative of the analysand's sexual debut:

*W*hat did you feel, what did you think? Were you pleased, frightened, ecstatic, disgusted? What did he say? What words did you speak? That's what I want to know. Now, tell me, now, now, all of it, now, tell me, yes!*[16]*

The film's director, Robert Kay, presents psychoanalysis as a nightmarish vision of prurient excess, a psychic sexual assault. Caligari probes relentlessly, insistently, veritably assaulting his young, female analysand with questions while never allowing her to respond. His demand: "tell me now, now, all of it now." Each "now" builds toward crescendo, confirming Caligari's sexual tension, while his exclamatory "yes!" is delivered almost as if it were an orgasmic ejaculation.

Although contemporary psychoanalysis and psychotherapy are, in so many ways, a far cry from how they are represented by both Robert Kay's Caligari and Foucault's ring-bearing analyst-confessors, I maintain that Foucault's critiques remain trenchant and useful. At the very least, they illuminate the shadow side of therapeutic action, and how we, as providers, can all too easily find ourselves operating as unwitting tools of social control or working from a place that serves our desires rather than those of our clients and patients.

"Every time we speak," suggest narrative therapists Jill Freedman and Gene Combs, "we bring forth a reality. Each time we share words we give legitimacy to the distinctions that those words bring forth."[17] This does not constitute an injunction against offering reflections or interpretations or posing questions, but rather a warning that we need to do so with care and as informed, ethical users. For, as the genie warned in depositing the magic ring in Mangogul's hands, "remember that curiosity can be misdirected."[18]

Curiosity and Entitlement

For many trans and non-binary folx, Diderot's phantasy of genitals forced to speak their truths and relate their stories for others' entertainment feels all too real. Trans folx attract a particular form of invasive curiosity about their sexual lives and sexual bodies, what J.R. Latham calls "genital-curiosity."[19] Genital curiosity shows up in so many domains of trans folx's lives, from media and popular culture to interactions with cis friends and family members.

Part of this is the superordinate value placed on "the surgery" as well as a fascination with how trans and non-binary folx date and have sex. As the actress and activist Laverne Cox states in *Disclosure*, a documentary she co-produced, "This focus on surgery became the ways in which trans people have really been talked about for 60 years."[20] One of the more discomfiting things *Disclosure* does is highlight the media's decades-long, obsessive genital-curiosity. The film shows clips of talkshow hosts, from Tom Snyder interviewing Christine Jorgensen in 1982 about the significance of gender-affirmative surgeries, to Katie Couric interrogating the model Carmen Carerra in 2014 about her "private parts"— asking they're "different now, aren't they?"[21]

This curiosity arises out of a deep sense of entitlement. It is an entitlement to hear about medical history and to probe trans sexualities (as well as the trans subject's feelings about said medical history and sexuality). Interviewers often claim to speak for a faceless general public who "want to be educated," as Couric declares in her interview with Carerra.[22] But is this education really necessary? Interviewers rarely ask about the genitals of their cis subjects; doing so would be impolite, after all. In media appearances, trans and non-binary people are offered no such consideration of their right to privacy. Reflecting on the experience of being interviewed by cis folx, activist and writer Janet Mock explains that she feels as if she is tasked with carrying "the burden of people that, they're expecting me to communicate all these things, but also to give all this private information about my body and my journey and my life."[23] This is done, she suggests, because her interviewers occupy "a space of entitlement" but cloak that entitlement in the position that, "Well, our viewers really want to know. This is something people really wanna know."[24]

The same objectifying, de-humanizing curiosity and entitlement to know also show up in interactions with friends, family, and colleagues. Zurn notes that the "relative position of intimacy with a trans person" can give groups and individuals the impression that they have their own sense of entitlement, a "right to full disclosure, warranting any demand for information they can muster, whether regarding names or pronouns, hormones or surgery, sexual practices or dysphoria."[25] Again, the disposition of cis folx's genitalia are regarded as a private matter that is not particularly important to anyone other than their partners. And yet somehow it is viewed as acceptable to ask trans and non-binary folks these questions and acquiring such private information is often seen as somehow relevant to understanding how trans a person truly is, or where they are in the course of their transition.

For my part, when I began my transition, many friends and family members were particularly interested in knowing about the status of my relationship with my wife, asking whether we were "ok" and whether we would choose to separate or remain together. Some of this was genuine concern for how my wife was dealing with my transition, but some of it was an unstated set of misgivings about whether these friends and relatives could see themselves as remaining in a relationship with a trans person. Friends and family members also inquired about whether I would ultimately pursue a vaginoplasty, assuming that this would be my end goal for gender affirmation. This came along with a scrutiny of images of me, seeking hints of physical traits or mannerisms that would betray gender presentations and expressions culturally consonant with the gender I was assigned at birth. Finally, I found that my transition, my gender identity, quickly became public property, in a sense. When introducing me to new people, family members would sometimes divulge my history, including what my deadname is, the gender I was assigned at birth, and when I opted to pursue elements of social and medical transition. Did a colleague of a family member really need to know that I am trans, or did that family member simply decide that their friend and colleague was *entitled* to that information at the outset?

To be sure, as Sam Orchard rightly points out in an article and accompanying set of comics he composed for *Dude* magazine, "[depending] on the context and scenario, certain questions might be totally okay to ask."[26] It is entirely appropriate to ask about how a sexual partner wants to be touched, what they want certain body parts to be called, and how they like to fuck.

But for the most part, the scrutiny trans and non-binary bodies seem to attract is unnecessary and invasive. And, indeed, beside the point! The preoccupation cis folx have with "the surgery" and how we use our genitals objectifies and fetishizes trans people, such that we don't get to talk about our real, lived experiences.[27] As Julia Serano puts it in *Whipping Girl*, by focusing on genitalia, this invasive, prurient curiosity reduces "us to the status of objects of inquiry" and cis folx can "free themselves of the inconvenience of having to consider us living, breathing beings."[28] As such, the specific needs and concerns of certain populations of trans and non-binary people can be rendered "invisible, including the needs of trans refugees, migrants, sex workers, drug users, poor trans people, and homeless trans people."[29] Also left out?—the complexities and heterogeneity of trans desire, eroticism, pleasure, and relationships. Genital curiosity, as Amy Marvin notes, pulls us in to "wonder" about trans worlds and experiencing, "but not in order to actually see ourselves from the vantage points of [those worlds], or really understand it in careful, particular, and historical complexity."[30] In short, a direct line might be drawn between the kinds of imaginative failures I explored in the last chapter and genital curiosity.

Because genital curiosity is a phenomenon with which most trans and non-binary folx are all too familiar, they often go into social interactions or spaces of public accommodation girding their loins for inappropriate questions, denuding stares, and ill-informed statements. In public, I perceive a host of non-verbal cues that translate to a person attempting to assign a gender to me, a process some of my trans clients refer to as "clocking." I know these cues because I know I give them off too sometimes, in spite of my continued efforts to unlearn them. Many of us do, cis or trans, but it rarely feels good for the person whose body is being psychically processed so that it can be fit into a ternary of gender boxes: male, female, or, unassignable. The gawking, the stares, the non-verbal assignments of gender are uncomfortable in and of themselves to perceive, but they also can lead to physical violence and verbal assault. To this day, each and every time I enter a restaurant or store or bathroom I make a mental map of my surroundings, hypervigilant to potential areas of threat and identifying escape routes to safety.

Therapeutic interactions can also be fraught for many trans and non-binary clients. Under the historically prevailing diagnostic model of care, a primary role of the provider, and particularly the qualified mental health practitioner, is to assess whether their client meets the diagnostic criteria for Gender Dysphoria in the DSM-5, criteria which includes evidence of "clinically significant distress or impairment in social, occupational, or other important areas of functioning."[31] This enshrines a power dynamic that puts the provider in the position of inciting speech via a probing, assessing curiosity, and entitles them to expect specific performances of presentation and expression from their clients. That is, in order to access particular forms of desired medical care (e.g., particularly gender-affirming surgical interventions, but, in some cases, even hormone therapies), clients have had to learn the particular stories "they must tell to achieve their goals."[32] This is a very real example of how an entitlement to curiosity is written into the standards of care for trans folks. There is no instance I can think of where cis individuals have to prove something about themselves to a mental health provider to access desired or needed medical interventions.

As providers, we have to anticipate and work to create spaces to address the stress occasioned by our curiosity, a work that starts from the first moment an individual or relational unit inquires about working with us.

It begins with intake paperwork and extends to how we hold space in the room itself from the first session onwards. The first principle grounding that holding of space is actively working to dismantle our burning desire to know about particular aspects of a client's story and personal history, a principle that I begin to unpack in the next section.

Dismantling Entitlement

At the heart of a process of dismantling our entitlement to know is a guiding question, "Who is this for?" This question can be broken down further as we enquire why we feel we need to know certain information, what assumptions or dominant narratives we might be bringing to our work with trans and non-binary clients, and when we should ask them for information vs. when we should do our own research.

It is important to recognize that dismantling entitlement is not so much a set of hard and fast rules as a process and a way of thinking about what we do and do not ask of our clients. These are never easy questions to answer; I struggle with these issues in working with clients, despite the fact that my trans identity may make me in many ways intimately familiar with what some of my trans clients are facing. For instance, in one-off sessions in support of a client's desire for top or bottom surgeries, I sometimes find it difficult to know when and how far to probe with respect to the client's motivations for surgery. This is all to say that dismantling the power and privilege that has been invested in us while continuing to serve clients is a practice and a process, an art rather than a science. Dismantling entitlement—and each of the principles discussed in this chapter for that matter!—constitutes a framework, a guide to promote a curiosity that can open up avenues of discussion rather than unwittingly shut them down.

Why am I asking this? Other ways of phrasing this question might be: is there a clinical value to this particular query? Does this serve the client's needs, or my own? What purpose does this question have? If I bring my awareness to my body and check in with it, do I find myself experiencing a thrill? Or perhaps titillation? A kind of excited thirst for "understanding"?

One way we can get at our motives for a particular line of inquiry is by bringing awareness to our bodies in the present moment and noting sensations, images, feelings, or thoughts that might be surfacing. When a client says something that piques your curiosity, or tickles at the edges of intuition, you might examine, for example, how you're holding yourself, or moving. Are you leaning forward in your chair, for example, a physical stance that can communicate interest and curiosity? Depending on the client or the content being brought into the room, this leaning in might be viewed as an act that communicates an intent to engage, to join with; or it might be viewed as an invasive stance, a crossing of physical boundaries that might evoke a startle response in the client. What about your heart rate? Is your heart beating faster, suggesting hyperarousal, as if you are on pins and needles awaiting the client's or patient's answer to a query with antici-patory relish, perhaps even titillation? Sometimes, our bodies' interoceptive signals are experienced as images that bubble up to the surface, images that elude language or are pre-verbal. I refer to this phenomenon in Chapter 4 as the *somatic-imaginal*.

What assumptions am I bringing to this interaction? In addition to discerning the motives behind our desire to know, we must also attend to the ways that our curiosity is shaped by—and can reinforce—repressive cul-tural norms. For example, as Chang and Singh assert in a paper laying out principles of affirming psychological practice with BIPoC gender expansive folx, notions of masculinity and femininity are steeped in and "based on White and/or Western dominant cultural norms."[33] And such expectations of "what femininity and masculinity look like on a client," they argue, can "consciously or unconsciously inform" a provider's approach when working with trans and non-binary folx, particularly for clients "who either do not fit these norms [and expectations] or who may be struggling to reconcile these norms" with their own identity constellation.[34] For instance, trans women are often expected to perform or embody a kind of hyper femininity. This cultural expectation negates the possibility that trans women might be butch or androgynous. A clinician working with a trans woman might thus invest a lot of their curiosity in the presence, or absence, of their clients' feminine attributes as proof of their transness and thereby impose certain cultural norms and expectations on their client. To avoid such a process, Chang and Singh suggest providers "refrain from assuming that they know what a client means when they" identify themselves using specific gender identities (e.g., "I'm non-binary" or "I'm a man") and instead ask as a follow-up to such a statement, "What kind of _____ (e.g., man, woman, [non-binary] person) are you or would you like to be?"[35]

Another way of imagining into this question is to think about how our curiosity can be a tool through which dominant discourses can act. We might ask: whose curiosity is being satisfied? Whose desire to know is operative in the present moment? For, as Michael White and David Epston suggest, as providers, we cannot allow ourselves to complacently "take a benign view of our own practices."[36] After all, most of the modalities and practices deployed in the US and Western Europe were designed by white, Western European and US cis het men operating within cisheteropatriarchy, white supremacy, and colonial logics. As such, they reflect, replicate, and reify the assumptions, biases, and normative values of those constructs. As I will argue in the next chapter, we cannot really help embodying the cultures in which we move. But we *can* be critical consumers and actors! We can do the hard decon-structive work of seeking to ensure that systems of power do not simply use us as unwitting conduits for their replication. We can take accountability when we fuck up—and, we will all fuck up. We can re-vision how we work so as to practice radical mental health and radical sexual health. And we can thereby "come up with our own understandings for how our psyches, souls, and hearts experience the world, rather than pour them into conventional medical frameworks" that might conceive of our work with trans and non-binary clients in terms of "success," "function," "performance," "productivity," and specific treatment and transition pathways.[37] We can, in short, resist.

Who needs to educate me about material a client is bringing into the room? Embedded in the entitlement to know is the idea that subjects of curiosity are entitled to ask others to educate them on some of the basic elements of their experiencing. It is often the case that those who are marginalized know more about the dominant culture than vice versa. For instance, as a Jewish person, I know a lot more about Christian traditions than many Christians know about Jewish practices and history. As a result, clients from marginalized backgrounds will come into the room knowing that they may have to explain elements of their life and identities to their providers, a burden that clients from the dominant culture do not share. This can be intensely frustrating—even anxiety-provoking—for our clients and can damage the therapeutic alliance. Moreover, this means that clients are spending their valuable time in session helping providers get up to speed when a simple Google search or, at most, the pursuit of additional training, education, and experience will do. Thus, from the instant our clients enter our offices and consulting rooms, we must disabuse them of any duty to be our teachers, to be the expert on trans-ness or non-binary-ness, or queerness, disability, or Blackness.

We must educate ourselves in the heterogeneity of trans and non-binary experiencing. This book can serve as part of this education, but certainly should not be the sum total of it. It can be important to learn about the global history of gender diversity.[38] Relatedly, we might work to develop an understanding of how these histories of gender diversity—and gender-affirmative care!—intersect with histories of (settler) colonialism, Westernization, white supremacy, and the mass displacement of indigenous populations.[39] And we might endeavor to recognize and understand the health disparities, discrimination, social stigma, and minority stress to which our trans and non-binary clients might very well be subject, just as we would seek to recognize how white supremacy and institutionalized racism impact BIPoC populations. Finally, we should acquaint ourselves with the medical and gender-affirming interventions some of our trans and non-binary clients might pursue (e.g., "low-dose T," "metoidioplasty" or "zero-depth vaginoplasty," and various binding and packing options) as well as some of the terms and colloquialisms that members of trans communities are using in the present moment.

Of course, there are many elements of trans and non-binary experiencing that we can research and learn, but the client sitting in your office is not a community; they are an individual with particular needs holding a particular identity constellation. There are some things that no amount of research can tell us and that only our client can share with us. While it is not a client's job to educate us about any single facet of their identity constellation, we *can* bring our curiosity to learning their histories, the stories they have told of themselves, the stories others have told about them, the particular ways they embody their identity constellation, the facets of their identity constellation in which they instill pride and the facets that are not particularly meaningful to them. Curiosity directed in this way and for these purposes steeps the relationship in a dynamic of mutuality, active learning, shared inquiry, and discussion.[40] Both provider and client take a stake in the work. The invitation to learn from and engage in a participatory, active process might be facilitated by a framework called location of self, a framework I outline in the next section.

BTToP: Dismantling Entitlement Vignette

As a means of illustrating the principle of dismantling entitlement I offer a vignette supplied by a colleague of mine, Allison (she/her), a licensed marriage and family therapy therapist (LMFT) based in Southern California. Allison is a white, cis, bisexual woman who is in a long-term monogamous relationship with another cis woman. A few years ago, she began to work with a client who had found her on a directory of queer therapists. The client, Elena (she/her), is a Latinx, married trans woman who had recently opened up that marriage, joined a local sex-positive group (Sex Positive Los Angeles), and was beginning to go on dates. Elena sought out Allison because she is queer and because of her experience as a gender-affirming marriage and family therapist so that Elena could process her experiences as she began to seek out community and navigate multiple relationships.

At the time, Allison, like many therapists, had limited experience working with consensually non-monogamous (CNM) clients. She knew, as soon as Elena filled out her inquiry form and identified herself as polyamorous, that she needed to broaden her scope of competence around consensual non-monogamies if she were to see Elena from an ethical perspective. As such, before she even saw Elena for an intake session, Allison sought recommendations for books and articles on polyamory and scheduled a consultation session with a colleague well-versed in working with CNM clients for just after the intake. In addition to doing the work this way, Allison also Googled the term "Latinx," as she was unfamiliar with it and wished to ensure that Elena was not placed in the position of educating her about this aspect of her identity constellation.

At intake, as Elena began to go over her presenting concerns, a nagging set of thoughts began to bubble up into Allison's consciousness—Allison found herself wondering about Elena's wife, Meg, and how she was handling Elena's dating. She wondered to herself, "How did the conversation about opening up go down? Was it a mutual decision?" "Is Meg dating anyone?" "How's Meg dealing with Elena talking about her experiences dating?" In that moment, as she scribbled notes furiously on her notepad and worked to stay present with her client, a part of Allison was, in essence, identifying with Meg. Allison only knew of Meg's existence because she was identified as Elena's wife on the client information form. And Elena was Allison's client, not Meg, and not the relational unit. Still, in Allison's mind, Meg, the absent third, was spectrally conjured into the room as if she were a client or explicitly part of Elena's presenting concerns.

Allison did not foist her curiosity about Meg onto Elena, however, and worked diligently to direct her curiosity inward instead. "What is present for me here in this moment?" "What cultural norms are being activated in me?" "Do I really need to know the answers to any of my questions about Meg and her relationship with Elena at this time?" As she turned these questions over and brought her awareness to the sensations, images, feelings, and thoughts that were coming up for her, Allison recognized that part of her identification with Meg stemmed from messages she'd internalized about relationships. All Allison had known in her personal life were monogamous relationships and all her clients to date had, at least while they had been working with her, identified as monogamous. And nothing in Allison's training as a relationship therapist had prepared her to work with ethically and consensually non-monogamous relationships. Indeed, if anything, her training had instilled in her biases and assumptions about the value of monogamy to successful relationships.

A lot of times things come up in client sessions that intrigue us, that activate our desire to know. But our focus as providers must always remain on the client—their material, their concerns, their feelings and experiencing—rather than satisfying our burning questions. For, a lot of the time, as Allison later found out, our questions have a way of coming up in the natural flow of our work with a client or patient. Asking about Elena's relationship with Meg was not appropriate in the moment, but a few sessions later, Elena wanted to talk about how to go about renegotiating an agreement with Meg. In this context, then, some of Allison's questions about Elena and Meg's relationship became relevant, as Elena had explicitly raised them.

Location of Self

In any listing and bio, or whenever I introduce myself to clients during the intake session, I tend to disclose the identities I hold. Sometimes this takes the form of what we, in the queer and kink communities, refer to as *flagging*, as when I talk about offering relationship counseling/therapy on my website and refer to relationship structures and models beyond that of cis het monogamous couplings, namely, "couples, triads, D/s relationships, polycules, etc." This, I hope, signals to relationship units that are kinky and/ or consensually non-monogamous that I am affirming of and knowledge-able about D/s dynamics or various forms of ethical non-monogamy, even if I don't directly say that I am myself polyamorous and kinky. Often, though, I come right out with it as I did in the introduction to this book. I will say, "I am a white, witchy, Jewish, visibly able-bodied, kinky, polyamorous, queer, non-binary femme." I do this as part of what family therapist thandiwe Dee Watts-Jones describes as *location of self*.[41]

As Watts-Jones describes it, location of self is a process in which "the [provider] initiates a conversation with a [client] about similarities and differences in their key identities, such as race, ethnicity, gender, class, sexual orientation, and religion, and how they may potentially influence the therapy process."[42] Location of self, in the first instance, involves the provider self-disclosing their social location, the various facets of their identity constellation. The provider's disclosure of their social location is designed to further the creation of the client–provider relationship, to humanize the provider, "bridge gaps in social power between therapists engaged in cross-cultural therapy," and, most of all, to open the door to dia-logue.[43] The provider's socially locating self-disclosure, in sum, serves as an opening and invitation, communicating that intersections of power, priv-ilege, and oppression are "meaningful and embedded in the work"; inviting the client to reflect upon and discuss their constellation of identities; and signaling the provider's comfort with discussing intersectionality during work together.[44]

The challenge of location of self is that it "requires a willingness to go into places that most of us," provider and client, "still feel uneasy about engaging, interpersonally and personally."[45] As sex therapists Doug Braun-Harvey and Michael Vigorito note with respect to conversations about sexual health—another topic that can generate a great deal of discomfort in both provider and client!—provider avoidance of challenging or culturally sensitive topics may inadvertently serve to "[replicate] the client's similar avoidance of uncomfortable affect states" and create an "unnecessary burden and disincentive" for clients to initiate conversation on these topics.[46] And we want our clients to feel as if they can freely explore topics as vital to their experiencing as their identity constellation and their sexualities!

Engaging in location of self, beginning with how the provider describes themself within bios and extending into the first session with a new client/patient and beyond, can be a powerful way of fostering connection, and is part and parcel of what activist communities call "doing the work." As with other members of close-knit communities, trans and non-binary folx often "choose their therapists because they are familiar, because they respect and appreciate their background, values, and conduct."[47] My clients have often told me that they come to me precisely because I so clearly socially locate. One client, Alix (they/he/ze), a white agender individual, told me at the end of a 30-minute consult appointment that "I can actually breathe in here!" When I asked Alix if they would mind elaborating on this comment, ze told me, "It's just that, with other therapists, I always had to be on guard. But with you I know that you're not going to ask me a lot of uncomfortable questions and I'm not going to have to spend most of my session explaining myself to you. You get it."

I recognize that many of you reading this book are not trans or non-binary. The very fact that I am trans may, of course, help prospective trans, non-binary, and/or queer clients make an initial inquiry with the sense that I likely share certain aspects of experiencing with them, including both experiences of minority stress and experiences of navigating sex and relationships (platonic, sexual, romantic, professional). At the very least, they might assume that choosing a therapist from within the queer and trans community I am far less likely than a cis het therapist to be transphobic, cisnormative, "or ignorant of issues specific to [LGBTQIA2S+] people."[48]

But as Laura Kessler and Charles Waehler point out, the very fact of my membership in trans, non-binary, and queer communities may bring up multiple relationship considerations that a straight and/or cis clinician might not encounter. For one, these particular facets of my identity constellation may lead me to "underestimate the degree of power [I] hold in the therapeutic relationship and in [LGBTQIA2S+] communities."[49] For example, I sometimes feel the lure of a projective identification in which I become unconsciously cast in the role of "elder," "sibling," "parent/Mommy," and, worst of all, "authority." And this can be a challenging set of transferential projections to have hanging in the room. After all, while occupying the energy of an elder sibling, or parent, might sometimes mark me out as a kind of aspirational ideal, it can also come with it a host of insecurities about not "measuring up" as well as some oppositional dynamics (e.g., sibling rivalry).

And even the aspirational ideal piece is hard to hold; for, as I remind my clients at every opportunity, I have no special insight into their worlds or the particular ways they embody their identity constellation. Mine is an idiosyncratic set of social locations—I have not lived their life and I have made particular choices in my life. I have no idea what it is to have a vulva, for example, or to experience menstruation. I don't know what it is to massage my chest after wearing a binder all day, or what it is to cruise in gay male spaces. My whiteness and my specific class location mean that I have no way of conceiving, really, the particular vectors of oppression or vulnerability that trans folx of color or folx who daily encounter food or housing insecurity experience. And although I may inject estradiol weekly like many of my trans feminine clients do, I do not have their physiology, and the effects of spironolactone and estradiol may manifest in different ways in my body. There is no such thing as being queer or trans enough, femmes can be thems, and there is no one, true way to be trans. As Watts-Jones notes with respect to therapists working with clients of the same race and/or ethnicity, "while I usually see my ethnicity/race as an asset in working with those of African descent, I will also say it could be a liability if I assume that I know their experience, or overlook differences."[50]

This is a roundabout way of saying that being cis and/or being straight is in no way a hindrance to joining with our trans and non-binary clients and patients. Occupying these gender and sexual identities merely means that the location of self process can potentially facilitate an even more powerful moment of joining with your trans and non-binary clients. Or, perhaps not more powerful, but perhaps powerfully different or equally powerful! After all, as the prefixes cis and trans were originally meant by activists to convey, every single one of us, cis or trans, has a relationship to gender.[51] A vital part of engaging in location of self is the way that it allows the provider to identify, name, and "give thought to [...] [the] similarities or differences in the identities the client(s) and I occupy," either as they create limitations or opportunities in therapy.[52] Here, the cis provider might give their gender identity and how they came to that identity, perhaps noting places where they are non-conforming with respect to how they perform or present their gender. They might also note the training they've received in gender-affirmative care, and how they work to dismantle gatekeeping structures, deploy an informed consent model, or the ways they have actively worked as fierce advocates for their clients within their community. They might explain how they came to practice gender-affirmative care, their passion for the work. The purpose, here, isn't to "apologize" for or explain away cis-ness, but to be transparent with the client about ways in which gender impacts all of our lives.

When we engage in location of self we communicate that issues of oppression, privilege, and identity are "always relevant to some degree in therapy."[53] We also promote the imaginal reality in which our clients can cross the thresholds of our consulting rooms and find that rare place where they are held and affirmed in the fullness of their infinitely expansive embodied selves. And maybe, just maybe, like Alix, they will feel into that imaginal space and let themselves breathe with ease.

BTToP: Intake Forms and Location of Self

Apart from engaging in self-disclosure of my identity constellation I also signal an interest in engaging in a location of self process on my client information form. Here, I request from all clients the following:

Please tell me about any aspects of your identity that are central to who you are (e.g., race/ethnicity, religious or spiritual identity, disability status, gender identity, sexual orientation/identity, erotic identity, relationship orientation).

I view this prompt as an invitation, rather than a means of collecting demographic information. Although some demographic information may be crucial to collect for certain fields on electronic health record systems, my priority with this question is to empower the client to identify themselves in whatever ways they might choose. In part, this is because, as Sand Chang and Anneliese Singh point out, for some trans and non-binary folx one aspect of their identity constellation, such as their racial/ethnic background or sexual orientation/identity, or even their gender identity, "may be very salient in their day-to-day lives and identities, whereas for others," that same aspect "may not be as salient as another aspect of identity, such as religion or disability status."[54] An open-ended question like the one I use above can help the client articulate their own relationship(s) to various identity labels and community affiliations and can be used as one of many ways of guiding how you, as their provider, might relate to the identities they find the most salient.

Seek Permission

If we return to *Les Bijoux indiscrets* and how genitals are often asked to "speak" in contemporary society, one particularly troubling aspect of how Prince Mangogul conducts his examination of his female courtiers' sexualities is that when he turns his magical, speech-inciting ring on women's "jewels," he often does so from a hiding place. Moreover, his incitements to sexual speech are undertaken without any regard for gathering consent; he merely turns his ring on the unwitting women to extract their sexual stories. He not only feels entitled to his courtiers' stories, but treats these women as instrumental, as objects of desire without their own agency and autonomy. Permission is not sought, negotiation is not undertaken, check-ins are never contemplated.

In the domains of sexual communication and consent education, sex educators will often discuss how gathering consent is not a one-time thing or a two-part transaction that involves a request and a verbal response of "yes" or "no." Rather, as Allison Moon describes consent gathering in *Girl Sex 101*, consent relies on consensus—namely, "All parties must agree on the activity"—and is instantly revocable—that is, each party to an activity is "allowed to change [their] mind at any point, even midway into an activity."[55] Consent is also an ongoing process. Partners will not only engage in negotiation and informed consent practices prior to engaging in sexual activity, but will often check in during and after a given activity. The second principle of ethical curiosity ports these insights from sexual communication and consent education into clinical practice.

From both a legal and an ethical perspective, clinicians are required to provide their clients and patients informed consent. As part of informed consent, the clinician is obliged to provide their client with information regarding the risks and benefits of treatment; potential side effects involved in a given treatment; possible consequences of engaging in a particular treatment pathway; the contours and limits of confidentiality; provider background and qualifications; and information about fees, payment, and billing practices. As the American Counseling Association's Code of Ethics puts it, this model enshrines the principle that clients "have the freedom to choose whether to enter into or remain in a counseling relationship."[56] Although many providers may note, verbally as well as within their intake documents, that informed consent—like transition!—is a process rather than an event, in practice informed consent is gathered primarily at the beginning of treatment. The choice whether to engage in or remain in a specific course of treatment or within a provider–client relationship draws from another ethical value, articulated explicitly within the ACA's ethics code, namely, that of the responsibility of the clinician to foster and continually evoke their client's capacities for autonomy and self-determination, i.e., "the right to control the direction of one's life."[57]

This is all to say that at the core of our ethical codes is an imperative to continuously and rigorously seek consent, all as part of an effort to promote the client's capacities to direct their own care and engage in collaborative goal-setting so as to evoke the client's "knowledge of their own beliefs, personal value systems," and their "individual conceptualization of their own gendered experience."[58] As such, and to satisfy this ethical imperative, I suggest adopting a threefold practice of permission-seeking, checking in, and engaging in aftercare.

Permission-seeking refers to both the process of informed consent gathering, treatment planning, and collaborative goal-setting that occurs at the beginning of a unit of treatment as well as an analogous process at the beginning of sessions where you expect that sensitive or activating or culturally charged topics may arise. And a crucial piece of this permission-seeking is that consent is not blanket consent; consent is gathered and negotiation/discussion undertaken each session as well as for each activity within a given session.

One way to understand the nature of ongoing permission-seeking and informed consent gathering is in terms of Bion's dictum that the provider should go into each session without either "memory or desire," which is to say, that every session "must have no history and no future."[59] By this, Bion essentially asks the provider to treat each new session with a client as its own entity, assuming that nothing from previous sessions necessarily carries over into the present session while concomitantly resisting the urge to impose one's desire for specific outcomes on a given session. In a sense, I think Bion's dictum is a pretty tall order. After all, sometimes recalling information gathered from previous sessions helps deepen connection, as when I might recall a small detail about a client's life—a place name, a partner's name, a favorite color—or set out the coloring books and pencils that they enjoy using in session. And, let's face it, we wouldn't get too far with insurance (or our licensing boards, for that matter!) if we completely, say, neglected to reflect on treatment planning and collaborative goal-setting. But I follow the spirit of Bion's directive. I assume, for example, that in the time that has elapsed since a previous session, things have happened for and to my client and that these extra-therapeutic experiences have impacted them. I further assume that whatever I might go into a session planning to cover will likely not happen. I must hold the goals a given client and I have collaboratively set gently and provisionally. With this in mind, the beginning of each session is an opportunity to seek permission from a client, to see if they are up to delving into particular content, to ask them what they might wish to work on.

In addition to permission-seeking at the beginning of a session, I suggest checking in with clients periodically during sessions. These check-ins can take a number of shapes, shapes many of you are probably already deploying in your practice. When a client has happened upon a sensation, image, feeling, or thought that is particularly charged I will use this as an opportunity to check-in by asking, "That churning feeling in the pit of your stomach, would it be ok if we sat with this a bit longer?" or "Do you think you could close your eyes and check in with your body? What is your body trying to communicate right now?" In IFS parts work, we might be accustomed to asking to speak to particular parts. In the Hakomi practice developed by Ron Kurtz, the practitioner might ask the client if they might engage together in "little experiments."[60] Or, similar to the pleasure/pain scale (e.g., "on a scale of 1 to 10, where is this in terms of pain?"), I often introduce to clients an arousal scale prior to engaging in trauma processing and then refer to the scale periodically during the actual processing. This scale might sound like this, "On a scale of 1 to 10, where 1 is a 'breezy walk in the park on a sunny day' and 10 is, 'if you say one more word I'm liable to either charge out of this room or try to get up from this seat and punch you,' where are you right now?" In this particular context of checking in, I don't want to even approach the higher end of the scale; even a "4" is probably a sign to me that I might want to dial the work back a bit in intensity. Here, I'm trying to keep work with a client on the upper range of their window of tolerance at a given time—just enough to perhaps work to gently expand said window, but not enough to send the client into a hyperarousal state or a hypoarousal state.[61]

The final element in the principle of seeking permission is aftercare. Aftercare is a term that originates in kink/BDSM and refers to the moments after a scene or play has ceased. The methods of working with clients I discuss in this book along with other therapeutic activities such as trauma processing can be intense for our clients (and for us, their providers). After all, so often the therapeutic situation can be a holding environment (*pace* Winnicott) wherein sensations, images, feelings, and thoughts can be brought into the room that might otherwise be too overwhelming or frightening to be experienced on one's own. For this reason, I would advocate incorporating aftercare into your sessions, provided you're not doing something similar already.

When I know I'm engaging in particularly tough/intense work with a client I will often ensure that I hold a tight container and begin at least 15 minutes before the end of session to help the client ground, bring their awareness back to the present, and regulate. Here, I might engage the client in a visualization or grounding activity, or give them a stress ball or a coloring book to play with. I might also take the client through a list of self-care strategies they might engage in once they reach the end of their days and can decompress. And sometimes I invite the client to literally shake off the session content, either by shaking the body or by engaging in a five-minute dance party (they choose the music). In many instances, I process particularly intense experiences with clients, perhaps evoking their observing egos, either immediately following the intense work or at the very beginning of the next session.

And as providers, we need to think about how we might reset, center, and engage in self-care following intense work. I will sometimes clear my office by using a singing bowl. And I'm never averse to a five-minute dance party alone in the office with the door closed. Debriefing for a provider might involve being part of a consultation group, pursuing regular personal therapy, or seeking supervision. Lastly, don't forget to obtain sustenance—brew a cuppa, enjoy a handful of trail mix, and go to the bathroom. We often assist our clients and patients in developing self-care inventories: do you have one? If we are to engage in the work of tending to the soul or being stewards for trauma, it is vital that we remember that aftercare, like self-care in general, "is not a self-indulgence, it is self-preservation, and that is an act of political warfare."[62]

Treat the Client In Front of You

Jack (they/them) is a masc-of-center, Asian-American non-binary person. In the fall semester of their first year at a small liberal arts college in the South with an unusually high percentage of students involved in Greek Life, they began experiencing an acute major depressive episode and a resurgence of self-harm ideation they'd first experienced in high school. At the suggestion of a faculty member, who had observed a noticeable decline in Jack's academic performance along with a withdrawal from participating in class, Jack went to the university's counseling center. Jack was assigned the center's LGBTQIA2S+-affirming counselor, an assignment that initially delighted them. At intake, however, things quickly went off the rails for them. The counselor focused the session squarely on Jack's queer and non-binary identities, attributing the dysphoric mood states they were experiencing to the fact that Jack had not come out to many folx on campus and perhaps wished to explore a gender-affirming transition. Jack continued to see this counselor for another four sessions, thinking that eventually the counselor would attend to their depression, but to no avail.

When Jack finally saw a colleague of mine, they were deeply relieved when their new therapist attended first and foremost to Jack's presenting concern rather than focusing solely on their non-binary identity. The truth, which Jack had tried to convey to the counselor at the counseling center, was that Jack had a robust social support system at the college, and while they found it challenging sometimes navigating a university with a very small population of queer and trans students and a curriculum that was fairly binary in its presentation of gender and sexuality, they felt affirmed in their identity constellation. Moreover, they did not feel as if they wished to pursue any kind of medical transition at that time.

This vignette illustrates the third principle of ethical curiosity: treat the client in the room. For some trans and non-binary clients, identity development or value clarification around transitions are why they come to see us as providers. They may wish us to provide transition support or they may wish to talk about how they are navigating social, cultural, familial, professional, or relational domains with respect to their trans and/or non-binary identities. But, as it was for Jack, for many clients who walk through our doors, the presenting concerns may be unrelated to the client's gender or sexual identities.

I think of Katie (she/her), a friend who is a kinky, queer, white trans woman. At one point, Katie's therapist went on maternity leave for three months and she needed to work with someone new in her absence. The therapist she ultimately opted for worked in ways that excited Katie, particularly as Katie was hoping to do some intensive trauma work and the interim therapist specialized in sensorimotor psychotherapy. At intake with the interim therapist, Katie disclosed that she was kinky and a "pain slut." The therapist thanked Katie for disclosing this important aspect of her life and expressed that although Katie was the first kinky client he'd ever worked with, he was: (1) in no way troubled by kinky content; and (2) sex-positive. The therapist further expressed that he was "completely non-judgmental." A few sessions later, as they were engaging in resourcing, Katie's interim therapist proceeded to propose as a topic of study Katie's appreciation of heavy impact play and receiving marks during said play, suggesting that Katie's kinks might have their origin in her childhood trauma experiences. Here, even if the interim therapist had claimed a stance of non-judgment, he clearly evinced curiosity in the potential for a direct, causal link between Katie's presenting concern—childhood trauma processing—and her consensual kinky urges and behaviors. As with Jack, a mere element of Katie's identity constellation, disclosed at intake, had suddenly become the focus of a clinician's concern.

To be sure, sometimes a client will bring to the consulting room a detail that they minimize, despite said detail being, in reality, far more important than the client wishes to give it credit for. Every time a client utters the phrase, "I don't know if this is important but…" I get the feeling that whatever follows the "but" is probably going to be important. But when it comes to one's identity constellation, oftentimes, as the Freudian proverb goes, "a cigar is just a cigar." As a result, I tend to keep any theories I might hold about the impact of a particular identity facet on the client's presenting concerns to myself, suspended in a kind of psychic stasis. I also use said theories as an opportunity to seek supervision or consultation around any counter-transferential dynamics potentially at play. That is, I work to examine whether a specific quality of the client is activating my own material; pushing on unexamined biases, assumptions, and stereotypes; and/or provoking certain images, feelings, or sensations to surface.

To return to Jack's vignette and their first therapist in the university counseling center, in many ways their initial therapist might have been correct to suspect or surmise that Jack's depression had at least something to do with the fact that they were a queer, non-binary student in an environment in which they were likely to experience minority stress. The clinician's imaginative failure was really in acting from a place that assumed that Jack's non-binary and queer identities should be a focus of concern, and not just as a psychosocial factor.

Relatedly, we must be able to sit with a client in the heterogeneity and specificity of their identity constellation, in the fullness of their embodied being and imaginal possibility. One thing that irks me about how many so-called multicultural counseling texts are written is that they many times provide breezy, totalizing generalities about specific cultural identities. As Paul Gorski and Rachael Goodman write in the introductory chapter to *Decolonizing "Multicultural" Counseling through Social Justice*, many multi-cultural counseling frameworks rely on highlighting "superficial aspects of a culture," all the while "homogeniz[ing]" these groups "in order to fit into simplistic identity development models."[63] And so, articles and books provide guidance on how to "understand" Asian-American clients, engage in counseling with LGBTQIA+ clients, or supervise transgender trainees.[64] The problem, Gorski and Goodman continue, is that:

> *There is as much diversity within Asian Americans or within the [LGBTQIA+] community than there is between any two groups. Also, people experience these identities within a sociopolitical context that has very real implications for their psychological well-being. Moreover, to which chapter should we turn if we want to know how to understand and counsel a lesbian Asian-American low-income Muslim client? Is the Hmong community more or less the same as the Chinese, or Pakistani, or Malaysian community as far as counseling practice goes? Is it enough, anyway, to know a little bit about this or that identity group, paying no attention whatsoever, to intersectionality, or to religious, regional, economic, or other differences ... within these enormous groups?[65]*

The point is that in sitting with a given client, our task is to sit with the whole person, and not just a sketchy facet of their identity constellation. When we fail to do so, we may fall into the trap of reducing our clients and patients to a caricature or to a single story. We may also end up replicating the kinds of totalizing narratives I explored in Chapter 1.

Conclusion

Western history is littered with tales of genitals being compelled to tell stories. In the late 19th century, men who had sex with men were described as having pointy penises.[66] In the 18th century, women's susceptibility to mental illness was attributed to their overheated constitutions and wandering uteruses.[67] Jewish and Black men have been ascribed particularly large penises, with size metonymously referencing a supposed societaly-destabilizing hypersexuality.[68] The indeterminate genitalia of intersex folx were, in early modern Europe, monstrous.[69] And then there is the myth of the hymen as an enduring symbol of a vulva holder's supposed sexual purity, or virginity.[70]

Genitals have something to tell us—something secret; something that cannot simply be divined; something that must be brought into the light; something that must be policed, regulated, controlled, managed, and put in its place; something we must, for the sake of society's moral upkeep, *know*. This history reveals that the curiosity about the sexual lives of some individuals cannot be separated from constructions of power and privilege. Because whose genitals have something to tell us? And whose genitals are afforded the grace of remaining silent? Those genitals and reproductive organs compelled to speak their truths most often belong to members of marginalized groups and communities. And trans and non-binary folx are merely the latest beneficiaries of our invasive genital curiosity, our deep desire to catalogue, classify, probe, and know.

Our curiosity, as providers, can be a powerful tool in working with clients. We might find, as Harlene Anderson did, that through our "earnest efforts to learn" a client's "language" and sit with them in the richness of their internal worlds that we are able to "[participate] in therapy conversations in a different way and [develop] new kinds of relationships with our clients—listening, hearing, and responding in unique ways."[71] The next two chapters will place an emphasis on working with clients to develop capacities for curiosity and wonder as they work to come into (com)passionate relationship with their embodied sexual selves. But, as with many of the powerful tools of our trade as providers, curiosity must be wielded with care and bounded with ethics so as to avoid engaging with clients in ways that are objectifying and essentializing. Deployed without an ethical framework, our curiosity can end up harming our clients or placing to the side their autonomy and their capacities of self-determination; our curiosity can unwittingly be used to serve our own ends or function as a tool of social control.

In this chapter, I have proposed a conceptual stance which grounds the provider's curiosity within an ethical framework. Being an ethically curious provider, I suggested, relies on three principles. First, even if curiosity arises out of an intense desire to know, we must temper this desire by dismantling any sense that we are *entitled* to knowledge from our clients. Part of this, I argued, involves the provider resisting any urge to have the client educate them about any single aspect of their identity constellation while simultaneously, through the location of self process, inviting discussion of intersectionality in the work. Second, ethical curiosity requires a robust, constantly renewed process of seeking permission. And, finally, a practice of ethical curiosity asks that we treat the client in front of us, and not, as

Anderson put it, "trying to collect the client's narrative and place it in our therapists' theoretical and experience maps, to make sense of it [...] from our therapists' logic and expertise," as if we know better.[72]

Like all of the conceptual frameworks discussed in this book, ethical curiosity is not a clinical stance designed solely for affirming work with trans and non-binary folx. Indeed, I would argue that bounding our curiosity within an ethical framework might very well help enhance and deepen our work with all clients, trans and cis, queer and straight, disabled and able-bodied. But, I also contend that a particular ethical praxis is demanded of us, as providers, in the context of how we deploy our curiosity with our trans and non-binary clients and patients. The present moment, in which the sexual bodies, and particularly the genitalia, of trans and non-binary folx are all too often being incited to speak, calls upon us to embody humility, consistently seek permission, see the complexity of the whole person, and dismantle any burning impulse to know. And it calls upon us to ensure that the spaces we hold are ones of care and containment rather than places where discriminatory structures replicate and reinforce themselves.

Notes

1 Perry Zurn, "Puzzle Pieces: Shapes of Trans Curiosity," *APA Newsletter* 18, no. 1 (2018): 11–12.

2 Zurn, 12.

3 Perry Zurn, "Busybody, Hunter, Dancer: Three Historical Models of Curiosity," in *Toward New Philosophical Explorations of the Epistemic Desire to Know: Just Curious about Curiosity* (Cambridge: Cambridge Scholars Press, 2019), 26–49.

4 Todd B. Kashdan et al., "The Five-Dimensional Curiosity Scale: Capturing the Bandwidth of Curiosity and Identifying Four Unique Subgroups of Curious People," *Journal of Research in Personality* 73 (April 2018): 130, https://doi.org/10.1016/j.jrp.2017.11.011.

5 Ibid., 143 and 130.

6 Denis Diderot, "The Indiscreet Jewels," in *The Libertine Reader: Eroticism and Enlightenment in Eighteenth-Century France*, ed. Michel Feher, trans. Sophie Hawkes (New York, NY: Zone Books, 1997), 344–541.

7 Michel Foucault, *The History of Sexuality, Vol. 1: An Introduction*, trans. Robert Hurley (New York: Vintage, 1990), 77.

8 Foucault, *The History of Sexuality, Vol. 1*, 77. N.B. Foucault, writing from his social location as a white, cis, gay male, attends neither to gender nor exoticism and orientalism in his reading of *Les Bijoux indiscrets*. But Diderot's story, importantly, imagines cis female sexuality as a dark continent that needed to be colonized by—and made visible and legible to—cis men.

9 Richard von Krafft-Ebing, *Psychopathia Sexualis: With Especial Reference to the Antipathic Sexual Instinct; a Medico-Forensic Study*, trans. F. S. Klaf (New York: Arcade Publ., 1998); Josef Breuer and Sigmund Freud, *Studies on Hysteria*, vol. 2, The Standard Edition of the Complete Psychological Works of Sigmund Freud (London: Vintage, 2001).

10 Foucault, *The History of Sexuality, Vol. 1*, 19, 33–34.

11 Ibid., 61–62.

12 Sigmund Freud, "Freud's Psycho-Analytic Procedure," in *A Case of Hysteria, Three Essays on Sexuality and Other Works*, vol. 7, The Standard Edition of the Complete Psychological Works of Sigmund Freud (London: Vintage, 2001), 251.

13 Sigmund Freud, "Recommendations to Physicians Practising Psycho-Analysis," in *Case History Schreber, Papers on Technique, and Other Works*, vol. 12, The Standard Edition of the Complete Psychological Works of Sigmund Freud (London: Vintage, 2001), 111–112.

14 Ibid., 115.

15 Foucault, *The History of Sexuality, Vol. 1*, 71.

16 Robert Kay, *The Cabinet of Caligari*, DVD, Horror (20th Century Fox, 1962).

17 Gene Combs and Jill Freedman, *Narrative Therapy: The Social Construction of Preferred Realities* (New York: W. W. Norton & Company, 1996), 29.

18 Diderot, "The Indiscreet Jewels," 354.

19 J. R. Latham, "Trans Men's Sexual Narrative-Practices: Introducing STS to Trans and Sexuality Studies," *Sexualities* 19, no. 3 (March 1, 2016): 353, https://doi. org/ 10.1177/1363460715583609.

20 Sam Feder, *Disclosure*, Documentary (Netflix, 2020), 52:39–52:43.

21 Ibid., 1:28:53–1:29:37.

22 Ibid., 1:29:59-1:30:02.

23 *Activist Janet Mock Flips the Script on Reporter: Asks Her to Prove Her Womanhood*, YouTube Video (YouTube: Fusion, 2014), 1:32 – 1:40, https://www. youtube. com/watch?reload=9&v=ISsdSvJhniQ.

24 *Activist Janet Mock Flips the Script on Reporter*, 2:27–2:55.

25 Zurn, "Puzzle Pieces: Shapes of Trans Curiosity," 12.

26 Sam Orchard, "But How Do You Go Pee?," *DUDE Magazine*, July 2011, 25.

27 Feder, *Disclosure*, 1:29:41–1:29:54, 1:30:12–1:30:30.

28 Julia Serano, *Whipping Girl: A Transsexual Woman on Sexism and the Scapegoating of Femininity*, 2nd ed. (Berkeley, CA: Seal Press, 2016), 187.

29 Amy Marvin, "Transsexuality, the Curio, and the Transgender Tipping Point," in *Curiosity Studies: Toward a New Ecology of Knowledge*, ed. Perry Zurn and Arjun Shankar (Minneapolis, MN: University of Minnesota Press, 2020), 189.

30 Ibid., 198.

31 American Psychiatric Association, *Diagnostic and Statistical Manual of Mental Disorders: DSM-5* (Arlington, VA: American Psychiatric Association, 2013), 453.

32 Donileen R. Loseke, "The Study of Identity As Cultural, Institutional, Organizational, and Personal Narratives: Theoretical and Empirical Integrations," *The Sociological Quarterly* 48, no. 4 (September 2007): 672, https://doi.org/10.1111/j.1533-8525.2007.00096.x; Sarah L. Schulz, "The Informed Consent Model of Transgender Care: An Alternative to the Diagnosis of Gender Dysphoria," *Journal of Humanistic Psychology* 58, no. 1 (January 2018): 79, https://doi.org/10.1177/0022167817745217. See also Sandy Stone's *Post-Transsexual Manifesto*. Stone describes at length how diagnostic criteria first articulated by clinicians like Harry Benjamin (in his 1966 book *The Transsexual Phenomenon*) served to determine "the permissible range of expressions of physical sexuality," and how trans patients responded by learning specific narratives to access gender-affirming care in clinics. Sandy Stone, "The 'Empire' Strikes Back: A Posttranssexual Manifesto," *Camera Obscura* 10, no. 2 (May 1992): 161.

33 Sand C. Chang and Anneliese A. Singh, "Affirming Psychological Practice with Transgender and Gender Nonconforming People of Color.," *Psychology of Sexual Orientation and Gender Diversity* 3, no. 2 (June 2016): 142, https://doi.org/10.1037/sgd0000153.

34 Ibid.

35 Ibid.

36 Michael White and David Epston, *Narrative Means to Therapeutic Ends* (New York, NY: Norton, 1990), 29.

37 The Mindful Occupation Collective, "What Is Radical Mental Health?," in *We've Been Too Patient: Voices from Radical Mental Health*, ed. L.D. Green and Kelechi Ubozoh (Berkeley, CA: North Atlantic Books, 2019), 139.

38 Sand Chang, Anneliese A. Singh, and lore m. dickey, *A Clinician's Guide to Gender-Affirming Care: Working with Transgender and Gender Nonconforming Clients* (Context Press, 2018), 35; Laura Erickson-Schroth and Laura Jacobs, *"You're in the Wrong Bathroom!": And 20 Other Myths and Misconceptions About Transgender and Gender-Nonconforming People* (Boston, MA: Beacon Press, 2017), 117.

39 See, for instance: Joanne Barker, ed., *Critically Sovereign: Indigenous Gender, Sexuality, and Feminist Studies* (Durham, NC: Duke University Press, 2017); Jessica Hinchy, *Governing Gender and Sexuality in Colonial India: The Hijra, c.1850–1900* (New York, NY: Cambridge University Press, 2019); C. Riley Snorton, *Black on Both Sides: A Racial History of Trans Identity* (Minneapolis, MN: University of Minnesota Press, 2017). For an excellent exploration of how gender constructs intersect with historical traumas linked to settler colonialism and thereby appear in clinical settings, see Alex Iantaffi, *Gender Trauma: Healing Cultural, Social, and Historical Gendered Trauma* (London, UK: Jessica Kingsley Publishers, 2020).

40 Harlene Anderson, "Myths about 'Not-Knowing,' " *Family Process* 44, no. 4 (2005): 500.

41 thandiwe Dee Watts-Jones, "Location of Self: Opening the Door to Dialogue on Intersectionality in the Therapy Process," *Family Process* 49, no. 3 (2010): 405–420.

42 Ibid , 405.

43 Ibid., 408.

44 Ibid.,, 405.

45 Ibid., 418.

46 Douglas Braun-Harvey and Michael A. Vigorito, *Treating Out of Control Sexual Behavior: Rethinking Sex Addiction* (New York: Springer Publishing Company, 2016), 11.

47 Ofer Zur, *Boundaries in Psychotherapy: Ethical and Clinical Explorations* (Washington, DC: American Psychological Association, 2007), 25.

48 Laura E. Kessler and Charles A. Waehler, "Addressing Multiple Relationships Between Clients and Therapists in Lesbian, Gay, Bisexual, and Transgender Communities.," *Professional Psychology: Research and Practice* 36, no. 1 (2005): 68, https://doi.org/10.1037/0735-7028.36.1.66.

49 Ibid., 68.

50 Watts-Jones, "Location of Self," 412.

51 Julia Serano, *Outspoken: A Decade of Transgender Activism and Trans Feminism* (Oakland, CA: Switch Hitter Press, 2016), 92.

52 Watts-Jones, "Location of Self," 411.

53 Ibid.

54 Chang and Singh, "Affirming Psychological Practice with Transgender and Gender Nonconforming People of Color," 143.

55 Allison Moon, *Girl Sex 101* (Lunatic Ink, 2014), 61.

56 American Counseling Association, "ACA Code of Ethics" (American Counseling Association, 2014), 4, https://www.counseling.org/docs/default-source/default-document-library/2014-code-of-ethics-finaladdress.pdf?sfvrsn=96b532c_2.

57 American Counseling Association, 3.

58 Schulz, "The Informed Consent Model of Transgender Care," 85.

59 Wilfred R. Bion, "Notes on Memory and Desire," *The Psychoanalytic Forum* 2 (1967): 272.

60 Richard C. Schwartz and Martha Sweezy, *Internal Family Systems Therapy*, 2nd edition (New York, NY: The Guilford Press, 2020); Ron Kurtz, *Body-Centered Psychotherapy: The Hakomi Method: The Integrated Use of Mindfulness, Nonviolence and the Body* (Mendocino, CA: LifeRhythm, 2007).

61 Daniel Siegel, *The Mindful Therapist: A Clinician's Guide to Mindsight and Neural Integration*, Norton Series on Interpersonal Neurobiology (New York, NY: W. W. Norton & Company, 2010), 51–52.

62 Audre Lorde, *A Burst of Light and Other Essays* (Mineola, NY: Ixia Press, 2017), 130.

63 Rachael D. Goodman and Paul C. Gorski, eds., *Decolonizing "Multicultural" Counseling through Social Justice*, International and Cultural Psychology (New York, NY: Springer New York, 2015), 4–5, https://doi.org/10.1007/978-1-4939-1283-4.

64 See, for example, Yea Sun Eum Kim, "Understanding Asian American Clients," *Journal of Ethnic & Cultural Diversity in Social Work* 12, no. 3 (February 3, 2004): 91–114, https://doi.org/10.1300/J051v12n03_05; Monica McGoldrick, Joe Giordano, and Nydia Garcia-Preto, eds., *Ethnicity and Family Therapy*, 3rd ed. (New York, NY: The Guilford Press, 2005); Pamela Hays and Gayle Y. Iwamasa, eds., *Culturally Responsive Cognitive-Behavioral Therapy: Assessment, Practice, And Supervision* (Washington, DC: American Psychological Association, 2006); Joe Kort, *LGBTQ Clients in Therapy: Clinical Issues and Treatment Strategies* (New York, NY: W. W. Norton & Company, 2018); Daran Shipman and Tristan Martin, "Clinical and Supervisory Considerations for Transgender Therapists: Implications for Working with Clients," *Journal of Marital and Family Therapy* 45, no. 1 (January 2019): 92–105, https://doi.org/10.1111/jmft.12300.

65 Goodman and Gorski, *Decolonizing "Multicultural" Counseling through Social Justice*, 5.

66 Vernon Rosario, "Pointy Penises, Fashion Crimes, and Hysterical Mollies: The Pederasts' Inversions," in *Homosexuality in Modern France*, ed. Jeffrey Merrick and Bryant T. Ragan (New York, NY: Oxford University Press, 1996), 146–176.

67 Vernon Rosario, *The Erotic Imagination: French Histories of Perversity*, Ideologies of Desire (New York, NY: Oxford University Press, 1997); Thomas W. Laqueur, *Solitary Sex: A Cultural History of Masturbation* (New York: Zone Books, 2004).

68 Sander Gilman, *Difference and Pathology: Stereotypes of Sexuality, Race, and Madness* (Ithaca, NY: Cornell University Press, 1985).

69 Lorraine Daston and Katharine Park, *Wonders and the Order of Nature, 1150–1750* (New York, NY: Zone Books, 1998).

70 Emily Nagoski, *Come as You Are: The Surprising New Science That Will Transform Your Sex Life* (New York: Simon & Schuster, 2015).

71 Anderson, "Myths about 'Not-Knowing,'" 502.

72 Anderson, 502.

3

COMING INTO PASSIONATE RELATIONSHIP

Lucie Fielding

Beginning with Freud's influential, if flawed, psychosexual stages of development, we have understood that our relationship to our sexual bodies changes throughout the lifecycle.[1] Indeed, our embodied lives are replete with transition, and quite apart from any decision to engage in any form of gender transition. We age and move through psychosocial stages of development. We acquire illnesses and disabilities. We experience stress and traumas that, sooner or later, write themselves on our bodies.[2] And as we do so, our relationships to sex, sexuality, and our sexual bodies shift. Our desires may morph. Bodily function will necessarily undergo changes. Our very definitions of what constitutes "having sex" may take on new meanings. We recognize that sex at 70 is not only possible, but can be intensely rich, playful, and pleasurable; but that it will also likely look and feel different than it did when we were 20. Likewise, pregnancy, menopause, cancer, and serious injury will often introduce challenges to our sexualities and our embrace of the erotic, but they also offer opportunities to re-examine what feels good as well as the contexts to which our desire is responsive.

"Transition, the passage from one state to another, always involves gains and losses," asserts psychoanalytic psychotherapist Griffin Hansbury.[3] I take this as a truism, but as explored in Chapter 1, the ways we speak of these transitions, these thresholds of initiation, are too often shaped by a negative cognitive bias that prioritizes the losses while not affording much space for understanding—or delighting in—the gains. We pathologize. We label. We diagnose. We rely on normative understandings of what constitutes normal function and what constitutes dysfunction. We internalize cultural scripts that seek to tell us what is normal, what sex should look like, and who possesses desire and desire-ability. The challenge—and the opportunity—transitions place before us, I contend, is to consider—and perhaps even mourn—the losses, and also to celebrate the gains; or, put another way, to shift from a discourse of loss to one of variability.

Take the idea of second adolescence, an archetypal energy that is often described as typifying or accompanying transitional states and coming out processes, particularly within trans narratives. We can choose to focus solely on the negative associations many of us have with adolescence and describe transitions as times of extreme awkwardness and of what we, in an Eriksonian mode, might describe as "role confusion" or an "identity crisis."[4] But adolescence, in addition to being a time of awkwardness and acne, can also be a time of intense experimentation and exploration, and particularly embodied exploration. The awkwardness is real; but so is the exploration. Adolescence can be a time to exclaim with dawning awe, "Holy shit! My body can do that?!?"

Life transitions of all shapes and sizes, I argue, can be opportunities "to discover a whole new landscape of pleasure" in our bodies, to approach our bodies with curiosity and "while cultivating a beginner's mind."[5] This chapter introduces a conceptual framework for helping our clients embrace the opportunity of second—or third, or fourth!—adolescence, as well as the challenge that changes in our relationship to our embodied sexual selves place before them. I describe this embrace as *coming into passionate relationship with the embodied sexual self.* But before we can attend to this conceptual framework, we should talk about piña coladas.

Do You Like Piña Coladas?

Have you ever actually listened intently to the lyrics of Rupert Holmes' 1979 single, "Escape?"[6] You know, the piña colada song!

No? Take a moment and do so.

I'll wait.

The song begins in bed. As his partner sleeps, a man flips through a newspaper, scanning the personal ads. He does so, he explains, because he "was tired of my lady, we'd been together too long/ Like a worn-out recording, of a favorite song."[7] He writes to the paper and inserts a response to a personal ad from a woman who seemed to tick off more boxes for him than his current partner, with whom he'd fallen into "the same old dull routine."[8] The pair arrange to meet at a bar. Lo and behold, on the appointed day, the woman from the ad walks in, only for the man to realize that she is, in fact, his current partner. They laugh for a moment, he reports, and he says, "I never knew."[9]

The relational dynamic chronicled in "Escape" is a common one, perhaps one of the most common presenting dynamics in relationship therapy and counseling. It goes something like this: ardor, passion, and playfulness tend to mark the beginning of a sexual or romantic relationship. As renowned relationship therapist Esther Perel describes it in her book *Mating in Captivity,*

> *You meet someone through a potent alchemy of attraction. It is a sweet reaction and it's always a surprise. You're filled with a sense of possibility, of hope, of being lifted out of the mundane and into a world of emotion and enthrallment. Love grabs you, and you feel powerful.*[10]

The sex of this period can be amazing, imaginative, varied, athletic, and plentiful. But, as numerous chroniclers of the phenomenology of romance and the erotic have found, this state of affairs doesn't tend to stick around all that long. Sooner or later, the passion of romance, of limerence, of NRE (New Relationship Energy) gives way to the cozy comforts of *intimacy*. Here, we find in our partners companionship, steadiness, reliability, a sense of home, a secure base. We nest, we snuggle into familiarity. The problem, as "Escape" illustrates so well, is that with the ascendance of intimacy passion often seems to fade. And, unfortunately, as passion and romance wane, complacency and staleness can set in.

Perel describes the shift from passion to intimacy as a paradox:

> *Love rests on two pillars: surrender and autonomy. Our need for togetherness exists alongside our need for separateness. One does not exist without the other. With too much distance, there can be no connection. But too much merging eradicates the separateness of two distinct individuals. Then there is nothing more to transcend, no bridge to walk on, no one to visit on the other side, no other internal world to enter. When people become fused—when two become one—connection can no longer happen. There is no one to connect with. Thus separatedness is a precondition for connection: this is the essential paradox of intimacy and sex.*[11]

Passion and intimacy are both *relational energies*. One is not better than the other, but they do tend to weave in and out of our relational lives. Intimacy is about closeness, connection, sharing, and knowing. It is perhaps experienced as a kind of softness—a Sunday morning spent lazing about in bed; eye-gazing; making love; being enveloped and enfolded in a tender embrace; getting to that point of comfort in relationship where one does not have to be "ok" all the time. Passion, on the other hand, is about risk, adventure, and not-knowing. It is experienced as a heady rush—the exchange of phantasy, a flush of cheeks, a crush of hands pressing into flesh, the fanning of bosoms, the searing heat of bodies colliding, the effusion of fluids mingling on tongues, moans and sighs and "Oh goddesses!" offered up to the heavens. Passion can feel practically transcendent.

Relational psychoanalyst Stephen Mitchell describes the dynamic of passion and desire fading over time as a "protective degradation," noting that "love seeks, perpetually, a kind of safety that screens out the unknown, the fantastic, the dangerous."[12] Passion, thus, becomes a relational energy we both seek out and crave, and one that we, unconsciously, run screaming from or do our level-headed best to imagine ourselves out of. Passion is "inherently vulnerable," adds Perel. "We feel safer if we can contract the distance between us, maximize the certainty, minimize the threats, and contain the unknown."[13] But the "great irony" of our flight from passion and "our efforts to make love safer," Mitchell asserts, "is that those efforts always make [love] more dangerous," more precarious, and ephemeral (p. 46).[14] For, absent the uncertainty, risk, and vulnerability that typify the passionate relational energy, there is no space, no air, from which the flame of lust and longing can feed.

Loath as I am to admit it, "Escape" has quite a bit to teach us about relational dynamics, passion, and intimacy. I find myself struck, in particular, by that moment wherein the song's male protagonist, faced with the fact that his long-term, intimate partner is, in fact, the mystery woman with whom he had wished to plan his "escape," says, "I never knew." I found myself wanting to scream at the song's male protagonist, "I bet you never asked!" But this exclamation, while perhaps cathartic for me, would have been uncharitable. For, how many of us find ourselves, particularly in the midst of long-term relationships, under the impression that we've learned all there is to know about our partner(s)?

This is a common feature of relationships, and particularly long-term ones, Mitchell and Perel argue. Mitchell goes so far as to assert that the sense of safety and familiarity we often attribute to long-term relationships is "not based on deep mutual knowledge but on collusive contrivance, the predictability not an actuality but an elaborate fantasy," a collaborative act of the imagination.[15] "Our need for constancy," adds Perel,

> *limits how much we are willing to know the person who's next to us. We are invested in having [them] conform to an image that is often a creation of our own imagination, based on our own set of needs. [...] We see what we want to see, what we can tolerate seeing, and our partner does the same. Neutralizing each other's complexity affords us a kind of manageable otherness. We narrow down our partner, ignoring or rejecting essential parts when they threaten the established order of our coupledom. We also reduce ourselves, jettisoning large chunks of our personalities in the name of love.*[16]

Returning one final time to "Escape," the personal ad that serves as the refrain for the song might be seen as a device for felicitous rupture, a potential catalyst for relational *re-visioning*. Both members of the partnership had sought escape from the "worn out recording of a favorite song" that their relationship had become. The personal ad served to shock the couple into the realization that there was so much left to learn about one another, that the escape from the mundane was always already latent in the relationship. It is not entirely clear if the couple will decide to stay together, but what *is* certain is that an opening for passion has been created in the relationship. For, a "worn out recording" has been remastered, revivified—the partners have suddenly learned something new about each other. They now have an opportunity, as Perel writes, "to recover their curiosity and catch a glimpse behind the walls that barricade the other."[17]

From the Interpersonal to the Intrapersonal

In Esther Perel's work, the dynamics of passion and intimacy are examined primarily through an interpersonal lens. Here, coming into passionate relationship involves being able "to bring a sense of unknown into a familiar space," for each partner to recognize "the inherent mystery" of the other.[18] In an interpersonal mode, recognizing the alterity, the radical otherness, of one's partner creates the distance Perel argues is the catalyst for desire. In this book, my aim is to effect a perspectival shift from an interpersonal lens to an *intrapersonal* one. Here, coming into passionate relationship still involves bringing a sense of the unknown to a familiar space, but the familiar space in question is not between people/partners but between our bodies and our selves. The relational dynamic is internalized. Just as staleness can creep into our relationships with our partners, so it is that complacency can set in with respect to our relationship to our bodies, and particularly our embodied sexual selves. We get habituated as to how our bodies, or particular parts of our bodies, are to be used, are to be interacted with, or how they function; we become set in our ways about what sex is supposed to look or feel like and how we go about experiencing pleasure.

For example, folx with penises (and those that have sex with them) often operate under the impression that the only good penis is a rock-hard penis, and that, in the words of Mira Bellwether, "soft penises can't have sex."[19] "We know both statistically and anecdotally," Bellwether adds, "that penises are far from permanently-engorged crotch-rocks, and yet almost all sexual discourse on penises is on erect penises, hard penises, penetrating penises."[20] Moreover, we understand that penises are to be touched or interacted with only in certain ways: stroked, pumped, jerked, or, as I'll talk about at greater length later in the chapter, bobbed. Finally, sexual pleasure or orgasmic experience for folx with penises is often defined in terms of the ejaculation of sperm. This set of assumptions is toxic, and not just for trans and non-binary folx who have penises, but for the many cis male penis-havers who report experiencing that which the DSM-5 refers to as *erectile dysfunction*. These assumptions unimaginatively devalue—and outright dismiss—sex involving a penis that is soft, any kind of sexual activity that is not penetrative, and sexual touch that involves any other part of the penis apart from the shaft or the delta of the frenulum.

In Chapter 1, I discussed the discourse of sexual function. The focus on function, I asserted, centers genital experiencing, and, in particular, penetrative sex (penis-in-vagina, penis-in-anus), in our conceptions of what sex is and how sexual pleasure can be experienced. Add to this the fact that trans and non-binary folx often report complicated relationships to their bodies, and that body dysphoria and gender dysphoria often constellate around genitalia, chest/breast tissue, and the secondary sexual characteristics that tend to manifest at puberty. The discourse of sexual function, thus, can needlessly reduce sexual experiencing to genital touch and pleasure as well as to certain kinds of ways of interacting with bodies. The centering of genitalia becomes a huge way that trans folx' sexual horizons are caught up in the false dichotomy of resolving gender dysphoria and experiencing sexual pleasure and that, by extension, complacency and staleness can settle into trans and non-binary folx' erotic self-concepts.

Coming into passionate relationship explodes tired dichotomies and modes of binary thinking. It gives the lie to the idea that sex has to look or feel a certain way, involve particular acts, or even involve genitals. Steeped in a stance of ethical curiosity, therapy with trans and non-binary folx can promote a play space within the therapeutic container to imaginally explore and re-constitute how desire and eroticism can show up in new ways in the body; and activate a client's capacities for curiosity and awe, perhaps understood, as Perry Zurn puts it, as "searching out subjugated knowledges, and cultivating a [sexual] life of purposeful experimentation and authentic engagement in the project of [erotic] self-creation in community."[21]

Using the language and imagery of narrative therapy, our clients come to our practices embodying a particular problem-saturated narrative, that which some might call the "presenting concern." These are stories our clients have learned to tell about themselves or associate with their bodies, and they are often expressed in labels: co-dependent, sex addict, histrionic, depressive, pervert. I join Michael White and David Epston in holding the foundational assumption that our clients seek out therapy, or treatment, or counseling "when the narratives in which they are 'storying' their experience, and/or in which they are having their experience 'storied' by others, do not sufficiently represent their lived experience, and that, in these circumstances, there will be significant aspects of their lived experience that contradict" their presenting narratives.[22] In other words, our clients come to us with their problem-saturated narratives precisely because they have begun to see fissures in those narratives; they realize on some level, however unconsciously, that the narratives they carry don't fully capture the richness of their embodied lived experience. Here, therapeutic action is understood as a process of helping our clients see and expand the glimmers in the cracks, the places where alternative narratives may be peeking through, ready to be explored, experimented with, and, ultimately, embraced and embodied. Following the narrative model in the remainder of this chapter, coming into passionate relationship will be explored theoretically as well as through grounding examples and exercises through two interrelated processes: mystifying the sexual body (approximate to deconstructing in narrative theory) and re-visioning the sexual body.

Mystification

Coming into passionate relationship with the embodied sexual self is a stance that allows our clients to, ultimately, *re-vision* their relationship to their sexual bodies—to both re-author (or queer) how they storify themselves as sexual beings and to re-map how they relate to or draw pleasure from their bodies. To do so requires acts of imagination as well as some distancing from how they might understand how their bodies work and how their bodies experience pleasure. They must become, as Mira Bellwether colorfully puts it in *Fucking Trans Women*, "sexy mad scientists" and "genital cartographers."[23] This re-visioning is facilitated by what I understand as a process of *mystification*.

To my mind, the art of psychotherapy is a delicate balancing of moments where, in holding space for our clients, we work to demystify client experience and moments where we work to mystify that experience. On the one hand, as when we offer a client psychoeducation or a reframe, or an interpretation, or skills building, we are engaging in a process of *demystification*. That is, we are helping to normalize or contextualize a client's experience; we are helping take a sensation, feeling, image, or thought, and perhaps help the client discharge any fear, guilt, or shame that might be constellated. In a riff on the Jungian maxim to "make the unconscious conscious," our work in a demystifying mode is to make the unfamiliar familiar—or, put even another way, *experience-near*—all to the effect of ensuring that the shame or fear attached to the unfamiliar does not direct our lives.

Thus, we help a client name dynamics, such as the proximal or distal stressors that are playing into a client's experience of minority stress.[24] We engage in processes of social location, provide openings to approach clients with cultural humility, and place client experiences "within the context of intersecting systems of power around gender, race/ethnicity, sexual orientation, and other inequalities."[25] Perhaps, too, we might add, in order to join with said client in a validating moment of shared rage, frustration, and consternation, "You're not sick, the entire fucking [white, cis hetero-]patriarchy is!"[26] Another example of demystifying work might be to engage the client in developing facilitative coping mechanisms, that which Stephanie Budge defines as "a process whereby individuals seek social support, learn new skills, change behaviors to positively adapt, and find alternative means to seek personal growth and acceptance."[27] Here, following Ashley Austin and Shelley Craig's elaboration of gender-affirmative cognitive-behavioral therapies, therapists might also work with their clients to reduce negative self-talk, increase capacities for cognitive reframing, or challenge maladaptive or overreactive cognitive or defensive processes.[28] For a compelling deployment of positive psychology and CBT techniques applied to trans sexualities, see Rae McDaniel's contribution in Chapter 6.

When we engage in a process of *mystification*, on the other hand, we are helping a client complicate or nuance a phenomenon that might, on the face of it, be something the client may take for granted. We are, as therapist and theoretician Darren Langdridge suggests, helping to engage the client in "moving beyond a simple focus on the apparent, through critical engagement with the social world into which client and therapist are thrown."[29] This imaginal, mystifying mode aims to enable the client to "gain an alternative way of seeing,… a way of taking up an alternative position," of "open[ing] up possible ways of living," relating, or being in their bodies.[30] Much like the practice of deconstruction in narrative therapy, mystification is concerned with helping our clients "[interrupt] habitual reality," and, here, the particular habitual reality of how our clients relate to their sexual bodies.[31] Mystification is, essentially, a decolonizing mode of operation, one designed to throw off totalizing, hegemonic discourses designed almost exclusively for cis het folx that demand that trans folx "blend" or "pass" as well as extrapolate their sexualities and their desires from cis folx. We can then help our clients tap into intergenerational wisdom in trans and queer communities and evoke the individual client's capacities for ingenuity and invention. The goal is to help create a space that allows the client to unlock and awaken new pathways for erotic expression, pleasure, and embodied joy.

BTToP: Mystifying the Sexual Body

Experiential activities, such as the Sensate Mapping exercise I'll introduce later in this chapter or those exercises other providers working at the intersection of sexuality and gender-affirmative practice will provide in Chapter 6, can be helpful for engaging clients in mystifying their sexual body. Mystification can often be facilitated at first by reflective questions that allow the client to trouble their existing sense of their sexual body. The purpose of mystifying questions is to create space in the client wherein dominant narratives and cultural scripts can relinquish their hold on the client's imaginary and on embodied erotic experience.

To illustrate what the interplay between demystification and mystification might feel like in a clinical setting I will draw upon work I undertook with Xochi (they/them), a Mexican-American non-binary individual in their mid-30s. Xochi first came to work with me just as they were beginning low-dose T. As the months went on, Xochi began to report changes in their desire and arousal templates. They were experiencing numerous spontaneous erections and they further noticed that their desire was following a more spontaneous desire template. These developments were initially distressing for Xochi, and particularly the fact that they seemed to want to have sex all the time. They feared being consumed by a capacious desire they heavily associated with toxic masculinity.

Initial work with Xochi involved some demystification. We reviewed the potential side effects of HT (hormone therapy), and particularly how spontaneous erections were common. I also normalized Xochi's shifting desire template by discussing spontaneous and responsive desire and discussing context. We then shifted from a demystifying mode to a mystifying one to explore their changing body and what sex—solo and partnered—might look for them as a result.

In order to begin to activate Xochi's erotic imagination, I suggested they read some erotica written by trans and non-binary authors and with a queer and trans lens. One session, they entered excitedly, a copy of Xan West's queer, kink short-story anthology, *Show Yourself to Me* (2015), under their arm and a bookmark conspicuously sticking out of it. They were eager to read a passage from one of the stories out loud to me, a story that has since become one of my favorites, "Strong." In it, the story's narrator discusses gender play and "gender as an elaborate sex toy."[32] They were struck by this image and wanted to explore how they might think of their gender as a sex toy. This led us to a discussion of how they might shift from avoiding and anticipating dysphoria in their sexual experiences to pursuing euphoria. As Xochi and I continued to work together, we focused on how they could make this shift, with West's writing serving as a key touchstone.

I include below a few discussion topics and questions that Xochi and I explored over the course of the next couple of weeks with the hope that they might spark mystifying conversations with your own clients:

1. This shift from wanting to avoid dysphoria to one in which you seek out euphoria and pleasure, is that a big deal to you? A medium deal? A small deal?
2. Where was it that you noticed ideas about masculinity?

3. What messages have you picked up in your life about masculinity? About femininity?
4. Tell me how amazing that experience was, as you began exploring yourself from the perspective of gender being an "elaborate sex toy." What did you notice in yourself? What images or sensations bubbled up into consciousness? What utterly surprised you?
5. How much did you enjoy this difference in how you were able to envision your exploration of your sexuality? Does it feel like there is more possibility for pleasure and wonderfulness in the future? What might that look like?
6. What do you continue to be intrigued or curious about?
7. What feels new and delightful?
8. Who would be surprised and delighted along with you about this experience of pleasure?

The World Re-Mapped

Oftentimes, when we encounter something in the world—e.g., a stimulus or an object—our first impulse may be to name and define it, to identify it as something we already know. Doing so imbues the object with history and freights it with a host of feelings, meanings, and associations. Some of these feelings, meanings, and associations come to us through direct experience over time with a given object (or, more to the point, objects of a similar general look and feel). And ultimately, as Gestalt psychologist Karl Duncker observed, our experience and associations with objects—and, I would argue, activities and phenomena!—can limit our ability to engage in divergent thinking and use an object, interact with a body part, or perform a given activity in ways that are imaginative, non-traditional, and perhaps revelatory and pleasure-enhancing. Duncker identified this foreclosure of the imagination as a cognitive bias, one he called *functional fixedness*.[33] Functional fixedness hobbles us. As sex coach Susanna Brisk notes, our prior experience with objects out in the world "can be the enemy of intuition," as such associations and experiences may simply encourage us to "approach the new as if it were just an extension of the old."[34]

Imagine, here, encountering an object that looks and feels like a "pen." You see a nib. You see the shape is tubular and approximately four inches in length. You grasp it between your fingers and press the end with a nib against a piece of paper. Lo and behold! Ink spills onto the paper. Your perception of the object's pen-ness, honed from experience writing and drawing with similar looking objects referred to as "pens," is confirmed. And so, you name this object "pen" and you interact with it accordingly, as you have with countless other objects identified as "pen." Indeed, it is hard to imagine doing anything else with the object. Functional fixedness has set in!

Other feelings, meanings, and associations are transmitted to us via our family system as well as from the cultures in which we are embedded, something French cultural theorist Michel Foucault referred to as a *discursive field*.[35] Discursive fields are part of the fabric of what I think of as a cultural unconscious. They structure—often without our conscious awareness that they are structuring—how we organize, produce, and consume knowledge; or perceive, respond to, or interact with phenomena.

A good example of this concept in action is provided by cartographic models. For many, the map in Figure 3.1 is likely how we have "always" seen the continents and oceans of Earth depicted. This cartographic model, or projection, was first proposed by the Flemish geographer and cartographer

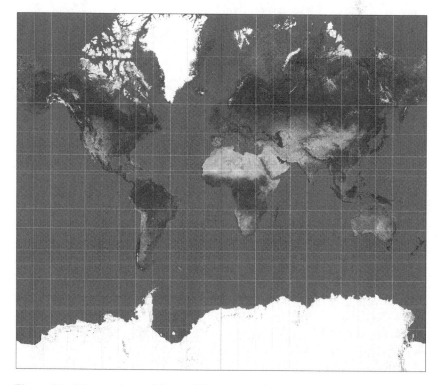

Figure 3.1 Mercator map of the world projection (1569)

Strebe, The World on Mercator Projection between 82°S and 82°N. 15° Graticule. Imagery Is a Derivative of NASA's Blue Marble Summer Month Composite with Oceans Lightened to Enhance Legibility and Contrast. Image Created with the Geocart Map Projection Software., August 15, 2011, Own work, https://commons.wikimedia.org/wiki/File:Mercator_projection_SW.jpg.

Gerardus Mercator in 1569. Now, look at the map depicted in Figure 3.2. This cartographic projection is referred to as the Peters projection, and was presented in the 1970s. Take a few moments and look at both images. Make note of differences as well as the choices made in how land masses are represented in both. What sensations, images, feelings, and thoughts do you notice bubbling up into awareness? Are you aware of any discomfort in your body? How about a thrill of recognition?

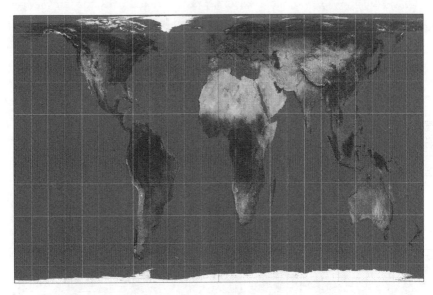

Figure 3.2 The Gall-Peters map of the world projection (c. 1973)

Strebe, The World on Gall–Peters Projection. 15° Graticule. Imagery Is a Derivative of NASA's Blue Marble Summer Month Composite with Oceans Lightened to Enhance Legibility and Contrast. Image Created with the Geocart Map Projection Software., August 15, 2011, Own work, https://commons.wikimedia.org/wiki/File:Gall%E2%80%93Peters_projection_SW.jpg.1

The ways each attend to the relative sizes of land masses reflect the respective values of the cultural milieux in which they were created. At the particular moment in European history in which the Mercator projection was first proposed, many Western European countries were beginning to colonize areas of continents we now refer to as North and South America; build the transatlantic slave trade; and displace, slaughter, and/or enslave the indigenous peoples they had found living in those newly colonized areas. The Mercator projection greatly distorts the size of land masses at the poles, meaning that Alaska, Greenland, and Antarctica are depicted as being far larger than they actually are. Likewise, apart from Antarctica (in fact, the smallest continent after Australia), the objects in the northern hemisphere

(Europe and North America) are depicted as larger than they actually are, relative to those in the Southern Hemisphere (particularly Africa and South America).

The Peters projection was proposed in a vastly different cultural moment. The cultural revolutions of the 1960s had provoked a critique of cultural, social, and political institutions. The Peters projection might be seen as a post-colonial critique of the Mercator projection, highlighting a euro-centric bias built into the Mercator projection, one which has Europe dwarfing and dominating most everything else. That which the Peters projection does is highlight how keyed our perceptions are to our particular socio-cultural locations. As helpful as the Mercator projection's representation of uniform, parallel latitude might have been for the purposes of intercontinental oceanic navigation in an era of sea-based trade and the development of colonial, settler, and imperialist structures, it does reify, reproduce, and operationalize a vision of the world steeped in racist assumptions. The Peters projection represents the same globe, but deploys and relies upon a radically different vision—a re(-)vision—and set of cultural assumptions.

Continuing the cartographic theme, I recall here a proverb established by Marcel Proust in *In Search of Lost Time*, "The only real journey [...] would be to travel not toward new landscapes, but with new eyes."[36] While acknowledging the ableist language of the proverb, Proust's words incite us to engage in mystifying mode of being (and being with!), one that challenges us to deconstruct our experiences, our received knowledges, and to remap the world around us and how we interact with it. And when we clear the cache of the cultural unconscious, when we break out of functional fixedness, we can eschew the knee-jerk impulse to decide "Oh, I know what this is," and approach ourselves and others in the world with, as Brisk puts it, "the 'clean slate' of naiveté."[37] In essence, a mystifying process takes a sex act, bodily structure, or object that may seem familiar and makes it *unfamiliar*. The BTToP section that follows will provide an exercise you can do yourself or with your clients to begin to engage the mystifying mode and a deconstruction of functional fixedness on a sensate level.

As a concept, functional fixedness is most often applied to problem-solving with respect to inanimate objects, as with the pen example discussed above. But to recall the discussion of sexual function in Chapter 1, we might consider how our relationship to our sexual bodies can be beset by functional fixedness, namely, when we consider the discursive field that has developed around body parts and how we are supposed to use or interact with them, as well as what sex should look and feel like. The sensate mapping BTToP exercise may revolve around sensually exploring a small object, but what if we were to apply the same hermeneutic to our bodies, our partners' bodies, and to our erotic imaginations? What opens up when we approach ours and others' bodies "without memory or desire," without expectation, projection, or normative values hung on the experience?[38]

A foundational principle for the work of mystification is established by Mira Bellwether in *Fucking Trans Women*: "The form of someone's body doesn't necessarily determine what that body means, how it works, or what it can do".[39] Just as you, as the Witness in the sensate mapping BTToP exercise in this section, would ask the Cartographer to resist, or outright suspend, the impulse to identify and extend a particular interactional schema to a given object, you might invite the client engaged in a process of mystification to suspend the impulse to ascribe a particular meaning to their body or interact with their body as they normally would, to say to themself, "Oh, I know what this is and what it is supposed to do!"

BTToP: Sensate Mapping Activity

Sensate Mapping is an activity derived, in part, from the modality of Sensate Focus. It is an activity you can do with your clients, as it does not require much, if any, physical touch. It does require a certain amount of intimacy, however, as you will be functioning as a Witness to your client's process. It helps to sit with them in the room in relatively close proximity, perhaps sharing opposite ends of your couch. I conceive of Sensate Mapping as an intermediate step before you begin the work of helping the client re-vision their own erotic relationship to their bodies. The activity is designed to help the client begin to experience the mode of mystification and to perhaps experience a process of emergence, as their relationship with a given object shifts. The hope is that Sensate Mapping can begin to create the kind of imaginal space that is essential for coming into passionate relationship with the embodied sexual self.

In its purest form, Sensate Mapping consists of two rounds of three minutes each. There are two roles: the Cartographer and the Witness, and you and your partner would, ideally, switch roles after the first round. Here, you as the provider will only facilitate a single round, one in which you serve as Witness and the client serves as Cartographer.

What you'll need: a set of objects, preferably small enough that they could be held comfortably in one hand. They can be any type of object, but perhaps the more mundane the objects the better. Think, here, of the pen example I gave at the start of this section.

DIRECTIONS:

1. Kindly invite the Cartographer to sit across from you and to assume a relaxed, comfortable seated pose, in their chair or on a

couch or on a floor. Then, invite the Cartographer to close their eyes and hold out a hand.

2. The Witness will now deposit an object into the Cartographer's open hand.

3. The Cartographer should be invited to bring their curiosity to the object and slowly interact with it however they are moved to do, as long as their eyes remain closed and they confine touch on their body to the area between elbow and fingertips.

4. Remind the Cartographer that they might be tempted to name and identify their object. This is a completely normal impulse. All the same, invite them to resist that identification process, or to engage in it but choose to ignore any identification that takes place. In this way, the hope is that they will begin interacting with the object without relying upon a process of comparison or identification that might encourage them to interact with their object in a set way.

5. The Cartographer may choose to play with a single object for a long time or they may find that they get tired of mapping an object. In this case, they should be invited to hold out their hand to the Witness. The Witness will then remove the discarded object and place a new object in the Cartographer's hand.

6. Engage in this activity for 5 minutes and then process the experience together, using the questions that follow to structure that processing.

QUESTIONS FOR THE CARTOGRAPHER:

1. Were you able to ignore the impulse to identify the object(s) you were given?

2. What did you learn as you interacted with and began to (re-)map the object(s)?

3. What sensations, images, feelings, and thoughts might you have noticed bubbling up into awareness as you moved your hands over the object(s)?

4. What was it like to be witnessed in your process?

Depending on the modality or theoretical orientation you are deploying in your work, you might also want to reserve some time to reflect a bit with your client on what it was like to witness them in their process. You might reflect, in particular, on what you observed and also what you noticed in yourself. What sensations, images, feelings, and thoughts came up for you as witnessed?

Embodying the Social

As discussed in the introductory chapter of this book, embodiment refers "to the experience of living in, perceiving, and experiencing the world from the very specific location of our bodies."[40] This definition plays upon two senses of the verb *to embody*. The first sense is, strictly speaking, the corporeal, visceral experience of being in one's body. This sense of embodiment involves, for example, perceptions concerning our bodies in space drawn from sensory inputs from the musculoskelatal system and perceptions "concerning our internal viscera," respectively.[41]

The second sense of the verb *to embody* brings us to the realm of culture and how embodiment involves "embodying the social": namely, making visible the fact that our bodies are not merely biological or corporeal, but also "exist, are apprehended, and are understood within social structures of power."[42] "The body," as Susan Bordo suggests, "is a powerful symbolic form, a surface on which the central rules, hierarchies, and even metaphysical commitments of a culture are inscribed" and continually reinforced.[43] Nowhere is this constructivist assertion more observable than in how cultural scripts constitute, reconstitute, define, and intersect with our sexual bodies, and particularly our genitals.

As Emily Nagoski writes, "We metaphorize genitals, seeing what they are like rather than what they are."[44] In so doing, cultural values are imposed on our sexual bodies, values that would seek to define—and assign moral meaning to—the specific ways our sexual bodies should work, how they should be used or interacted with, and what they can do. And the vehicle for this meaning-making is often scientific and medical discourse. Take these images, first published in 1538 as part of Flemish anatomist Andreas Vesalius' *Tabulae Anatomicae Sex* (Figure 3.3). They represent sexual and reproductive anatomy, observed from medical dissection. The image on the left represents a penis and gonads. The image on the right represents the vaginal aperture, the vaginal canal, Fallopian tubes, and a uterus. When I teach classes on histories of sexualities, I greatly enjoy the looks of surprise and befuddlement that register on my students' faces as they first contemplate these images. And then come the fun questions: "But the vaginal aperture and canal look like the glans and shaft of a penis!?!" "And what are those horn-like structures that seem to be glommed onto the base of the uterus?!?"

As to the second question, the horns are meant to represent the uterine horns, structures that are far more prominent in other mammals, such as pigs, rats, and cows, but are nonetheless present in humans. They are, simply put, where the Fallopian tubes and the uterus meet. Renaissance anatomists believed the uterine horns to be more prominent than they actually are. As to the first question, if you, like my students, found yourself encountering

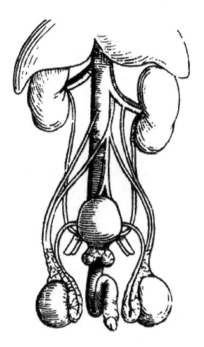 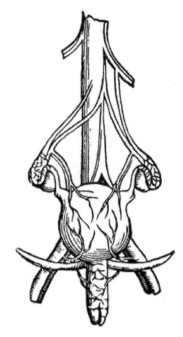

Figure 3.3 Sexual and reproductive organs from Andreas Vesalius, *Tabulae Anatomicae Sex* (1538), ed. Sir William Stirling- Maxwell (London: Privately printed for Sir William Stirling-Maxwell, 1874). Wellcome Collection. Attribution 4.0 International (CC BY 4.0).

difficulty distinguishing between the glans and shaft of a penis in the image on the left and the vaginal aperture and canal in the one on the right, this visual collapsing of difference can be attributed to the cultural and historical milieu out of which these images were produced, a tradition of "natural philosophy" that extended from Ancient Greece and Rome to Early Modern Europe that cultural historian Thomas Laqueur described as the "one-sex model."[45] As opposed to the "two-sex model" of human sexual anatomy that would, per Laqueur's analysis, come to prominence in the mid-eighteenth century and that would, for all intents and purposes, enshrine a principle of gender difference and sexual dimorphism, the one-sex model posited one essential gender: male. In this model of gender, women were merely unrealized men, and morphological structures that have often since been taken as "self-evident marks of opposition—penis and vagina, ovary and testicle, female menstruation and the absence of monthly bleeding in men—were not understood as such."[46] Rather, each of these organs or bodily processes, "was understood as a version of the other in accord with a metaphysically given relationship," namely that women were less perfect than men and were, indeed, underdeveloped men.[47] Here, the vagina was an inside-out penis that had not, for all intents and purposes, dropped.

It is easy to dismiss these sixteenth-century anatomical drawings and the representational system out of which they emerged as primitive, archaic, or hopelessly naive. After all, biological and medical knowledge has advanced considerably since the sixteenth century, we might, in our chauvinism and hubris, indignantly assert! But as Shannon Dea points out in attending to the various ways our bodies have been understood through the centuries, twentieth- and twenty-first-century representations of the sexual body have introduced a whole host of other problems.[48] Human anatomy and physiology textbooks that include representations of the sexual and reproductive systems often leave out the internal clitoris, for example (if they include the clitoris at all), while emphasizing only the vaginal canal of the vulva complex. Moreover, like the Mercator Projection discussed above, in the drive to make images "clear and accessible," many "real-life details have been idealized away" and the "accessible," standardized organization is often visibly that of a thin, white human, noticeably without any pubic hair.[49]

Beyond the realm of visual representation, we might also attend to the ways language is used to privilege certain kinds of erotic experiencing and limit ways of relating with sexual bodies. For example, we often refer to the vulva as the vagina. Doing so, as Laurie Mintz points out in *Becoming Cliterate*, may seem innocent, but beyond being medically inaccurate to refer to the vulva by one of its parts, this languaging in many ways serves a cis heteropatriarchy that would seek to "culturally privilege [cis het] male sexual pleasure."[50] That is, when we have vagina stand in for vulva we linguistically reduce the vulva solely to its functions as a birth canal and as an orifice for engaging in penetrative, namely, PIV (penis-in-vagina) sex.

We will never not in some way embody the social. We are born into it; we are steeped in it; we are formed and informed by it. Moreover, humans are social animals. Research in the theory of attachment has repeatedly shown how important relationships and connection are to our mental health and overall wellbeing.[51] We can, however, shift the social we embody. One of Michel Foucault's chief contributions to critical and cultural theory is the insight that, in the words of Michael White and Daniel Epston, "[there] exists a stock of culturally available discourses that are considered appropriate and relevant to the expression or representations of particular aspects of experience."[52] The grand illusion propagated by these unitary sources of knowledge and experience is that they are the only game in town. But, as Foucault points out, there exist alternative sources of knowledges, what he terms *subjugated knowledges*.[53] These subjugated knowledges have been obscured, written out, pushed to the margins of history, and "denied or deprived of the space in which they could be adequately performed" and embodied.[54]

The conceptual stance of coming into passionate relationship with the embodied sexual self is an invitation to eschew the cultural scripts that would seek to define how to relate to or understand our sexual bodies and to select and craft new analogies, new metaphors, new sexual stories, new ways of being and relating. What we call parts of our bodies, how we embody those parts, and how we seek to have others interact with our sexual bodies is solely up to us to imagine into. The mechanism for doing so, recalling the Proust proverb I quoted above, but also the verb *to revise*, is what I call *embodied re-visioning*.

Embodied Re-Visioning

To engage in embodied re-visioning is to leverage the distancing brought about by the mystifying mode discussed above to revise one's understanding of one's sexual body. Instead of having to enact a particular script originating in dominant discourses or cultural scripts, one is able to place oneself in the ecstatic position of drawing from subjugated knowledges, intergenerational sources of wisdom that have been borne out of community struggle and resistance, passed down so that we might "inhabit our own skin" on our own terms and as part of our own unique generative imaginal process.[55]

Having engaged in a process of mystification, it becomes possible to form a new relationship to our sexual selves, one steeped in curiosity, wonder, and what Harlene Anderson has called "not-knowing," "a tentative posture [that] portrays respect for and openness to the other and to newness."[56] Every body part and every sensation holds the possibility for pleasure and embodied joy. In what follows, I will discuss three potential ways that embodied re-visioning might look like in working with clients.

First, re-naming parts can be a powerful aspect of embodied re-visioning. A re-naming can be a way of reclaiming a part that would otherwise be cloaked in dysphoria. It can also help signal partners how they might interact with said body part. As Tobi-Hill-Meyer and Dean Scarborough wrote in *Trans Bodies, Trans Selves*,

> *One way many of us show our bodies love is by rewriting the language we use to describe them. Many of us have body parts that feel gendered in ways that do not match our sense of self. This can make it difficult for some of us to hear those body parts called by their standard names. [...] Many of us create our own names for our body parts. For example, some of us born with a vagina may prefer to call it a 'front hole' because this term is less gendered. Some of us create new words that are just ours, or that we share with our sexual partners. Others may use terms, such as*

'cock,' 'clitoris,' or 'vagina,' to refer to other parts of our bodies that we use or think about in these ways. For example, some of us who do not have a front hole may call our anus our vagina.[57]

And trans and non-binary folx have come up with an array of wonderfully clever and creative names for various body parts. In the BTToP section that immediately follows this one I've included a table (Table 3.1) with just a few of those names to give you a small sense of the variety out there. Some gender-affirmative providers, such as Washington, DC-based pelvic floor specialist Hannah Schoonover, even go so far as to ask clients to indicate on intake forms how providers should refer to various parts, particularly in the genital region.[58]

Beyond renaming, we might invite the client to consider how many of the ways we interact with our sexual bodies are culturally scripted. In the words of Kimberly Dark in her biomythography *The Daddies*, "gender operates, is created, and reinforced in intimate sexual relationships."[59] Think, for example, of how the ways we engage in oral sex are mapped onto particular types of genitalia. I'm speaking here of what AASECT-certified sex educator Jamie Joy calls *bobbing* and *swirling*. Visualize those two words and take note of the types of genitalia you associate with those actions. When we think of bobbing we often visualize penises and someone performing a blow job; and when we think of swirling we might visualize vulvas and someone performing cunnilingus, right? But who says penises must be bobbed and vulvas must be swirled, that those are the only prescribed ways a mouth might interact with those particular genital structures? After all, as Emily Nagoski reminds us, vulvas and penises are biological homologues.[60] They both contain erectile tissue, for example. In the vulva, the vestibular bulbs (under the labia), the perennial sponge, and the urethral sponge can all become engorged. When genitally aroused, the labia will become fuller and the clitoris will become more pronounced. So, what stops a person from bobbing on a clit, particularly one that has become enlarged as a side effect of testosterone hormone therapy? Likewise, what would it be to swirl the glans of a penis and the frenulum, the biological homologues of the clitoris?

Furthermore, what would stop a partner from stroking or pumping the glans clitoris, as one might the shaft of an erect penis, particularly for folx whose glans clitoris has seen growth following a year or so on T? To this end, several toy designers have produced strokers for the clitorises of AFAB folx. For those who appreciate this sensation and these forms of touch, interacting with clitorises through bobbing, stroking, or pumping can feel like one is being given a blow job or is able to jerk off. A fairly simple shift in how we or partners interact with particular genitals or parts can be tremendously affirming, and can go a long way toward reducing any gender and/or body dysphoria constellated around one's genitals.

For a number of reasons, including choice but also financial barriers, many trans and non-binary folx do not pursue surgeries, and particularly bottom surgeries. But for those who do, we might once again remember Bellwether's dictum, namely, "The form of someone's body doesn't necessarily determine what that body means, how it works, or what it can do."[61] Just because a trans woman or femme has a vulva, for example, doesn't mean she automatically wishes to use her vagina for penetration. Indeed, that's true of anyone with a vulva! And some trans feminine folx have opted for what are called zero-depth vaginoplasties, as the aesthetics of having a vulva may be prioritized over using it for penetrative sex. In other words, the presence of a part should not necessarily lead one to presume that an individual wishes that part interacted with in culturally prescribed ways.

The third way of engaging in re-visioning involves de-centering the genitalia as the sole locus for erotic pleasure and expanding our conception of where/how sexual pleasure can be experienced. A theme I return to throughout this book is the intergenerational sources of wisdom housed in— and transmitted through—queer and trans communities and spaces. Queer and trans folx are ingenious when it comes to sexual and erotic expression. We've had to be, for it's not like the sex education available in the United States and many other countries takes into account queer and trans experiencing![62] We have had to troubleshoot, innovate, and be "sexy mad scientists."[63] Part of embodied re-visioning is about tapping into intergenerational wisdom— these "subjugated knowledges" in Foucauldian parlance—and adapting for personal use the knowledge gleaned. A clear example of trans ingenuity is a sex act primarily practiced by trans feminine folx, *muffing*. Muffing, simply put, is a sex act that involves penetrating ("palpating") the inguinal canals of one who has genital structures some might refer to as the penis and testicles. The entrance to the inguinal canals (namely, the external/superficial inguinal ring) is accessed by pushing the testicles back into these canals (a process known as "invagination") as one might do through tucking, and gently pushing a finger into the orifice that is created through this. Muffing is essentially what a pelvic floor specialist or a urologist would do when they examine for inguinal hernias.

Folx have probably been muffing each other for ages, but the term itself was coined by Bellwether in *Fucking Trans Women* and popularized through her extensive guide to the practice therein.[64] Trans women may have popularized the practice and coined the term, but I also recommend muffing to my cis male clients, particularly those who might be distressed about an inability to achieve or maintain penile erections. The penis, as Bellwether notes, is often viewed as a simple "hunk of meat" rather than the "delicate instrument" that it is.[65] The pelvis, groin, and genital areas of all genders are packed with nerve clusters that are both interconnected with one another and intersect and branch from larger nerve clusters in the body. Muffing stimulates three of these nerve clusters: the ilioinguinal, the genitofemoral, and the plexus nerves. Indeed, the ilioinguinal and genitofemoral nerve clusters run directly through the inguinal canals. So, there is a ton of pleasure to be derived from muffing. Muffing, in short, constitutes a radical, gender-affirming queering of how penises and testicles can be played with and enjoyed. Bellwether refers to her inguinal canals as her cunts, for example, and fingering said cunts allows those who desire the sensation of being fingerbanged to experience it. Simply put, muffing opens up a vast terrain of pleasure for folx with penises and testicles. Who knew that such an erotic oasis was hiding out in our bodies the entire time?!

Relatedly, if techniques such as muffing allow us to expand our notions of how erotic pleasure can be experienced, we can also explore with our clients ways to de-center genital experiencing when it comes to sexual activity, particularly for clients wherein gender and body dysphoria constellate in and around their genitals. Engaging in genital-focused sexual situations and genital contact can make some non-op and pre-op trans and non-binary folx deeply uncomfortable and trigger body dysphoria. In part, as Hill-Meyer and Scarborough note, this is because some folx do not wish to be "reminded that we do not have the kind of genitals that we feel are appropriate for our gender."[66] Moreover, even for those who have pursued "bottom surgery," pleasure arising from genital contact can be elusive, particularly at first. And other ways of interacting with the body may be more pleasurable. In the second of two BTToP sections that follows I've provided an exercise (re-visioning hands) designed to help you work with clients to do just that.

Other erotic expressions that de-center genital experiencing include tantric sex practices and many forms of kink/BDSM play.[67] One of the hallmarks of kink/BDSM is that it can be conceptualized as bodily exploration that neither implies sex nor genital contact/use—indeed, a great deal of play does not even involve sexual touch, such as boot blacking or other forms of service. Thus, many trans and non-binary folx may engage in play as a way to de-center genitalia, explore a wider range of embodied or psychological experiencing, and push against "the soft, permeable edges of the multiple, overlapping boundaries of gender categories and incommensurable gender systems."[68] If, as Jacob C. Hale notes, many trans folx "must re-map the sexualized zones of our bodies," kink/BDSM play and practices allow for a "deteritorialization" and a "reteritorialization" (analogous to the processes of mystification and re-visioning discussed in this chapter) that can dislocate, dislodge, and "disrupt the dominant cultural meanings" attached to our sexual bodies.[69] The very notion of *leathersex* is that eroticism transcends genitalia. Or, as Joseph Bean suggests, "sex is not a matter of which body part you engage, but of which energy you use."[70]

Emma Turley argues that kink/BDSM can be understood a set of practices that can "enhance feelings of corporeality and explore bodily relationships with the world and with other people."[71] Gender, in the space of the physical space of the dungeon or within a D/s dynamic, can be re-visioned as an "elaborate sex toy," as the narrator of Xan West's short story, "Strong," provocatively suggests.[72] Or, as Susan Stryker puts it in a beautiful reflection on her time in San Francisco Bay Area dungeons in the 1990s:

> So much that constitutes me I did not choose, but, now constituted, I feel myself to be in a place of agency. I occupy a critical space, a distance between stimulus and response created by the complex social pathways converging in the dungeon, in which through my presence I gain the capacity to choose which patterns I will repeat, or which new patterns I might envision and enact. I invent new choreographies of space and time as I dance my whip across the creature's ass. It is not that I somehow internalize as my own the structure or content of the scene in which I participate [...]. It is rather a proprioceptive awareness, as I flog, of the body as medium in the circuit of transmissions, and of the material efficacy I possess in my subjective ability to choose one thing rather than another or to poetically imagine the shape of a new pattern.[73]

The erotic embodiment facilitated by kink/BDSM play "enables a blurring of bodily borders and limits, leading to a more holistic sexual experience with the availability of more choices and bodily possibilities."[74] Crucially, for our purposes in this chapter, the choices and possibilities opened up by play can allow "sex to be removed from the traditionally genitally focused acts," and can illustrate "how the body holds a multitude of possibilities for both genital and non-genital oriented pleasure."[75] For more on kink/BDSM and trans erotic embodiment, see Jaxx Alutalica's piece on the subject in Chapter 6.

BTToP: Parts Names

Trans and non-binary folx have come up with a number of names for their body parts, and particularly chest/breast tissue, genitalia, and the anus. I've provided a list of just some of those names in the table below (Table 3.1), both so that you can familiarize yourself with some of the common terms that you might encounter in working with your clients; and as a tool you might use to help your clients generate their own terms. Whatever terms your clients might use or adopt, it is important for you to mirror and use those names in your work with them. Alternatively, you might follow the protocol suggested by my colleague, Heather Edwards, whose vignette on parts names is included in Chapter 6.

Table 3.1 Table of names utilized by trans and non-binary folx to describe genitals and chest/breast tissue.

Vulva	Penis	Breast/Chest Tissue	Anus
Man Cave	Junk	Breasts	Man Hole
Front Hole	Cunts (inguinal canals)	Chest	Back Hole
Bonus Hole	Strapoff	Chesticles	Bussy
Boy Cunt	Strapless		Vagina
Dicklit	Clit		Pussy
	Hen		Cunt

BTToP: Re-Visioning Hands Exercise

This exercise, in many ways the next step following the Sensate Mapping activity introduced and described above, was first suggested by sexological bodyworker Betty Martin in a series of videos designed to explicate her Wheel of Consent model. It is, like Sensate Mapping, an activity you can do with a client. You might choose to witness and facilitate the client's process, or you can even engage in the activity with them. In essence, if Sensate Mapping is an activity designed to embody mystification (one mystifies an object that might otherwise appear familiar), this activity is designed to facilitate an embodied re-visioning process. Here, the part of the body being re-visioned is the hand.

Our lips, our genitals, and our hands contain the most nerve endings on our bodies. As such, they are potentially enormous sites of pleasure. And, yet, when we think of our hands we don't often think of them as erogenous zones. Rather, in a sexual context, we probably more often think of our hands giving pleasure. Here, our focus when facilitating pleasure with our hands is on a partner's pleasure, as in fingering a vagina or an anus, or our own (as in solo sex when we might engage in stimulation of the areolas, clitoris, or the shaft and glans of a penis). Our attention is centered on what motions best promote a partner's enjoyment or, if in a solo sex context, genital stimulation. Apart from giving pleasure directly, hands are instrumental insofar as they are used grasp and hold things (as in a vibrator or a flogger). Here, the hands are operative in handling or handing over. But what would it be to shift how we understand what our hands do in an erotic context from a partner's pleasure from what we are doing with our hands to a perspective that centers the pleasure being taken or received through the nerve endings of the fingers and hands?

DIRECTIONS:

1. If your office is filled with objects, you might begin to asking your client to look around the room and choose an object that calls to them, an object they might feel curious or intrigued about. Alternatively, you might ask your client to bring an object from home. The objects available or brought in can be any type of object, but perhaps the more mundane the object the better. The object should be large enough that both hands might have enough surface area to explore, but small enough that it can fit comfortably on the lap. A throw pillow, particularly one with a lot of interesting textures, is a common object used for this exercise.

2. Kindly invite your client to sit across from you and to assume a relaxed, comfortable seated pose, in their chair or on a couch or on a floor. Then, invite them to move their chosen object into their lap. For this exercise, the client might choose to keep their eyes closed, or they may leave them open. Whatever is most relaxing to the client—the important thing is that they should be in whatever state is most conducive to bringing their awareness to their hands as they eventually move over the object.

3. The client should be invited to bring their curiosity and awareness to their object and slowly interact with it, however they are moved to do so.

4. As with the Sensate Mapping activity, the client may be tempted to name and identify their object, or relate with it in ways that they might be used to, particularly if the object is familiar to them already. Likewise, during the activity the client's mind my wander. Remind them that these are completely normal impulses. All the same, invite them to resist that identification process, or to engage in it, but choose to ignore any identification that takes place. In this way, the hope is that they will begin interacting with the object without relying upon a process of comparison or identification that might encourage them to interact with a given object in a particular, set way. Additionally, should they notice their minds wandering, you might include in your facilitation prompt

that "this is what minds do, wander. Just bring your attention and awareness back to your hands and the sensations that they are taking in as they move over the object."

5. You might invite the client to move their hands over their object slowly, perhaps slowing even more than they might be in the moment. Suggest that the slower and more intentional their movements, the more they are likely to feel and take in. Perhaps a particular texture on the object is particularly pleasing? Perhaps a particular movement of the hands or a particular part of the hands is yummy. Invite the client to notice what details they can and go where the pleasure of interaction takes them.

6. Engage in this activity for 5 minutes and then process the experience together.

Sometimes this exercise will elicit intense feelings or evoke strong memories or images, feelings, memories, and images the client might not have expected. Sometimes this exercise will even elicit feelings of indifference. Any reaction is normal. Invite your client to take notice of the sensations, images, feelings, thoughts and practice self-care and self-regulation as needed.

Conclusion

In this chapter, I introduced the second of four conceptual frameworks for working with trans and non-binary folx around erotic embodiment, that of coming into passionate relationship with the embodied sexual self. This is an invitation to approach the embodied sexual self with a beginner's mind, "as if it is my first time feeling my flesh, feeling myself awaken."[76] It affords our clients the ability to keep what's working, abandon what no longer serves them, and imagine what adrienne maree brown calls "a whole new landscape of pleasure" in the body.[77] This process involves what I call mystifying and re-visioning. The former entails recognizing the "inherent mystery" of our relationships to ourselves, and our embodied selves above all.[78] We have so much left to discover, unpack, explore, and experience. For its part, re-visioning is an act of creation, one that asks us to throw out what we think we know about our bodies to begin with a blank slate and find new pathways for ecstasy on our own terms. Our bodies truly are amazing, and sometimes, just like our partners and lovers, they need to be approached from a stance of not-knowing.

But exploring is risky business; setting off into the unknown can feel scary; and embracing curiosity can be a challenge, particularly so when one has experienced a history of trauma and when one's body has not felt like an especially yummy place to be. Many of our trans and non-binary clients will approach the work of coming into passionate relationship with the embodied sexual self with a sense of trepidation or even outright fear. Their desires to explore their sexualities may be tempered by anxieties about turning toward the sexual body and embodying eroticism. In the next chapter, I will introduce a conceptual framework for working with clients to find a sense of boundedness in their bodies: coming into compassionate relationship with the embodied sexual self.

Notes

1 Sigmund Freud, "Three Essays on the Theory of Sexuality," in *A Case of Hysteria, Three Essays on Sexuality and Other Works*, vol. 7, The Standard Edition of the Complete Psychological Works of Sigmund Freud (London: Vintage, 2001), 123–243.
2 Bessel van der Kolk, *The Body Keeps the Score: Brain, Mind, and Body in the Healing of Trauma* (New York, NY: Penguin, 2014); Resmaa Menakem, *My Grandmother's Hands: Racialized Trauma and the Pathway to Mending Our Hearts and Bodies* (Las Vegas, NV: Central Recovery Press, 2017).
3 Griffin Hansbury, "Mourning the Loss of the Idealized Self: A Transsexual Passage," *Psychoanalytic Social Work* 12, no. 1 (March 17, 2005): 19, https://doi.org/10.1300/J032v12n01_03.
4 Erik Erikson, *Childhood and Society* (New York, NY: W. W. Norton & Company, 1993).
5 adrienne maree brown, *Pleasure Activism: The Politics of Feeling Good*, Emergent Strategy (Chico, CA: AK Press, 2019), 121.
6 Rupert Holmes, *Escape (The Piña Colada Song)*, Apple Music, Partners in Crime (New York, NY: Infinity Records, 1979).
7 Ibid., 0:16–0:27.
8 Ibid., 1:34–1:37.
9 Ibid., 2:57–2:58.
10 Esther Perel, *Mating in Captivity: Unlocking Erotic Intelligence* (New York: Harper Paperbacks, 2006), 9.
11 Ibid., 25.
12 Stephen Mitchell, *Can Love Last?: The Fate of Romance over Time* (New York, NY: Norton, 2002), 45 and 46.
13 Perel, *Mating in Captivity*, 10.
14 Mitchell, *Can Love Last?: The Fate of Romance over Time*, 46.
15 Ibid., 43.
16 Perel, *Mating in Captivity*, 13.
17 Ibid..
18 Ibid. 11.
19 Mira Bellwether, *Fucking Trans Women: A Zine About the Sex Lives of Trans Women* (CreateSpace Independent Publishing Platform, 2010), 8.
20 Ibid., 7.
21 Perry Zurn, "Puzzle Pieces: Shapes of Trans Curiosity," *APA Newsletter* 18, no. 1 (2018): 15 my textual amendments.
22 Michael White and David Epston, *Narrative Means to Therapeutic Ends* (New York, NY: Norton, 1990), 14–15.
23 Bellwether, *Fucking Trans Women: A Zine About the Sex Lives of Trans Women*, 2 and 3.

24 Ilan H. Meyer, "Prejudice, Social Stress, and Mental Health in Lesbian, Gay, and Bisexual Populations: Conceptual Issues and Research Evidence," *Psychological Bulletin* 129, no. 5 (2003): 674–697, https://doi.org/10.1037/0033-2909.129.5.674; Michael L. Hendricks and Rylan J. Testa, "A Conceptual Framework for Clinical Work with Transgender and Gender Nonconforming Clients: An Adaptation of the Minority Stress Model," *Professional Psychology: Research and Practice* 43, no. 5 (2012): 460–467, https://doi.org/10.1037/a0029597.

25 Stephanie L. Budge and Bonnie Moradi, "Attending to Gender in Psychotherapy: Understanding and Incorporating Systems of Power," *Journal of Clinical Psychology* 74, no. 11 (November 2018): 2025, https://doi.org/10.1002/jclp.22686; Joshua N. Hook et al., "Cultural Humility: Measuring Openness to Culturally Diverse Clients," *Journal of Counseling Psychology* 60, no. 3 (July 2013): 353–366, https://doi.org/10.1037/a0032595.

26 Jeana Jorgensen, "Trans People Aren't Sick, The Entire Patriarchy Is," *Foxy Folklorist: Folklore, Culture, Sex* (blog), April 13, 2016, http://www.patheos.com/blogs/foxyfolklorist/trans-people-arent-sick-the-entire-patriarchy-is/.

27 Stephanie L. Budge, Mun Yuk Chin, and Laura P. Minero, "Trans Individuals' Facilitative Coping: An Analysis of Internal and External Processes," *Journal of Counseling Psychology* 64, no. 1 (2017): 13, https://doi.org/10.1037/cou0000178.

28 Ashley Austin and Shelley L. Craig, "Transgender Affirmative Cognitive Behavioral Therapy: Clinical Considerations and Applications.," *Professional Psychology: Research and Practice* 46, no. 1 (2015): 21–29, https://doi.org/10.1037/a0038642.

29 Darren Langdridge, "Are You Angry or Are You Heterosexual? A Queer Critique of Lesbian and Gay Models of Identity Development," in *Feeling Queer or Queer Feelings?: Radical Approaches to Counselling Sex, Sexualities and Genders*, ed. Lyndsey Moon (New York, NY: Routledge, 2008), 30.

30 Ibid., 30.

31 White and Epston, *Narrative Means to Therapeutic Ends*, 16.

32 Xan West, *Show Yourself to Me: Queer Kink Erotica* (Northampton, MA: Go Deeper Press, 2015), 227.

33 Karl Duncker, *On Problem-Solving*, trans. Lynn S. Less (Washington, DC: American Psychological Association, 1945).

34 Susanna Brisk, *How to Get Laid Using Your Intuition* (Los Angeles, CA: Self, 2018), 83.

35 Michel Foucault, *The Archaeology of Knowledge: And the Discourse on Language*, trans. A.M. Sheridan Smith (New York, NY: Vintage, 2010).

36 Marcel Proust, *The Prisoner*, trans. Carol Clark, vol. 5, *In Search of Lost Time* (New York, NY: Penguin Books, 2019), 244.

37 Brisk, *How to Get Laid Using Your Intuition*, 83.

38 Wilfred R. Bion, "Notes on Memory and Desire," *The Psychoanalytic Forum* 2 (1967): 272–280.

39 Bellwether, *Fucking Trans Women: A Zine About the Sex Lives of Trans Women*, 2.

40 Deborah L. Tolman, Christin P. Bowman, and Breanne Fahs, "Sexuality and Embodiment.," in *APA Handbook of Sexuality and Psychology, Vol. 1: Person-Based Approaches.*, ed. Deborah L. Tolman et al. (Washington: American Psychological Association, 2014), 760, https://doi.org/10.1037/14193-025.

41 S.J. Langer, *Theorizing Transgender Identity for Clinical Practice: A New Model for Understanding Gender* (Philadelphia, PA: Jessica Kingsley Publishers, 2019), 19–20.

42 Tolman, Bowman, and Fahs, "Sexuality and Embodiment," 761 and 759.

43 Susan R. Bordo, "The Body and the Reproduction of Femininity: A Feminist Appropriation of Foucault," in *Gender/Body/Knowledge*, ed. Alison M. Jaggar and Susan R. Bordo (Brunswick, NJ: Rutgers University Press, 1989), 13.

44 Emily Nagoski, *Come as You Are: The Surprising New Science That Will Transform Your Sex Life* (New York: Simon & Schuster, 2015), 17.

45 Thomas Laqueur, *Making Sex: Body and Gender from the Greeks to Freud*, Revised ed. (Cambridge, MA: Harvard University Press, 1992).

46 Thomas W. Laqueur, "The Rise of Sex in the Eighteenth Century: Historical Context and Historiographical Implications," *Signs: Journal of Women in Culture and Society* 37, no. 4 (June 2012): 803, https://doi.org/10.1086/664468.

47 Laqueur, *Making* Sex, 803.

48 Shannon Dea, *Beyond the Binary: Thinking about Sex and Gender* (Peterborough, Ontario: Broadview Press, 2016), 132–133.

49 Ibid., 133.

50 Laurie Mintz, *Becoming Cliterate: Why Orgasm Equality Matters—and How to Get It* (New York, NY: HarperOne, 2018), 34.

51 For a review of this literature and a discussion of the importance of social connection to wellbeing, see chapter 6 of Emily Nagoski and Amelia Nagoski, *Burnout: The Secret to Unlocking the Stress Cycle* (New York, NY: Ballantine Books, 2019), 133–153.

52 White and Epston, *Narrative Means to Therapeutic Ends*, 27.

53 Michel Foucault, *Society Must Be Defended: Lectures at the Collège de France, 1975 –1976*, ed. Mauro Bertani and Alessandro Fontana, trans. David Macey, Michel Foucault Lectures at the Collège de France 5 (New York, NY: Picador, 2003).

54 White and Epston, *Narrative Means to Therapeutic Ends*, 26.

55 Jordy Rosenberg, *Confessions of the Fox* (New York, NY: One World, 2018), 315.

56 Harlene Anderson, "Collaborative Language Systems: Toward a Postmodern Therapy," in *Integrating Family Therapy: Family Psychology and Systems Theory*, ed. Richard H. Mikesell, Don-David Lusterman, and Susan H. McDaniel (Washington, DC: American Psychological Association, 1995), 36.

57 Tobi Hill-Meyer and Dean Scarborough, "Sexuality," in *Trans Bodies, Trans Selves: A Resource for the Transgender Community*, ed. Laura Erickson-Schroth (Oxford; New York: Oxford University Press, 2014), 355–56.

58 A copy of this form can be accessed via the following URL: https://docs.wixstatic.com/ugd/3480ef_ff8fa9d3ab6c45c78a082373c28d1221.pdf

59 Kimberly Dark, *The Daddies* (Boston, MA: Brill | Sense, 2018), xv.

60 Nagoski, *Come as You Are*, 20.

61 Bellwether, *Fucking Trans Women: A Zine About the Sex Lives of Trans Women*, 2.

62 Al Vernacchio, *For Goodness Sex: Changing the Way We Talk to Teens About Sexuality, Values, and Health* (New York, NY: Harper Wave, 2014); Maxime Charest, Peggy J. Kleinplatz, and Jessie I. Lund, "Sexual Health Information Disparities between Heterosexual and LGBTQ+ Young Adults: Implications for Sexual Health," *The Canadian Journal of Human Sexuality* 25, no. 2 (August 2016): 74–85, https://doi.org/10.3138/cjhs.252-A9; Sharon E. Hoefer and Richard Hoefer, "Worth the Wait? The Consequences of Abstinence-Only Sex Education for Marginalized Students," *American Journal of Sexuality Education* 12, no. 3 (July 3, 2017): 257–276, https://doi.org/10.1080/15546128.2017.1359802; Nova J. Bradford et al., "Sex Education and Transgender Youth: 'Trust Means Material

By and For Queer and Trans People,'" *Sex Education* 19, no. 1 (January 2, 2019): 84–98, https://doi.org/10.1080/14681811.2018.1478808.

63 Bellwether, *Fucking Trans Women: A Zine About the Sex Lives of Trans Women*, 3.

64 Ibid., 15–25.

65 Ibid., 11.

66 Hill-Meyer and Scarborough, "Sexuality," 357.

67 Barbara Carellas' *Urban Tantra* is notable for its attention to trans and non-binary bodies. See Barbara Carrellas, *Urban Tantra: Sacred Sex for the Twenty-First Century*, 2nd ed. (New York, NY: Ten Speed Press, 2017).

68 C. Jacob Hale, "Leatherdyke Boys and Their Daddies: How to Have Sex without Women or Men," *Social Text*, no. 52/53 (1997): 234, https://doi.org/10.2307/466741.

69 Hale, "Leatherdyke Boys and Their Daddies," 230.

70 Joseph W. Bean, *Leathersex: A Guide for the Curious Outsider and the Serious Player*, 2nd ed. (Los Angeles, CA: Daedalus Publishing Company, 2003), 47.

71 Emma L. Turley, "'Like Nothing I've Ever Felt before': Understanding Consensual BDSM as Embodied Experience," *Psychology & Sexuality*, January 21, 2016, 1, https://doi.org/10.1080/19419899.2015.1135181.

72 West, *Show Yourself to Me: Queer Kink Erotica*, 227.

73 Susan Stryker, "Dungeon Intimacies: The Poetics of Transsexual Sadomasochism," *Parallax* 14, no. 1 (2008): 42.

74 Turley, "'Like Nothing I've Ever Felt before,'" 5.

75 Ibid., 10.

76 maree brown, *Pleasure Activism: The Politics of Feeling Good*, 121.

77 Ibid., 121.

78 Perel, *Mating in Captivity*, 11.

4

COMING INTO COMPASSIONATE RELATIONSHIP

Lucie Fielding

"I believe with great conviction," asserts Mira Bellwether, "that what I have between my legs is not a metaphor or an analogy but something new and wonderful. Best to begin from the beautiful explosive moments of pleasure and discovery, and let the rest come after."[1] I share Bellwether's conviction. When I was a baby trans dyke, the one thing I knew in the midst of all the swirling questions about sex, was that the ways I and lovers had, in the past, related to my body, and particularly, "what I have between my legs," just wouldn't work anymore, and, if I'm honest, had probably never worked for me. Using my clit for penetrative, PIV sex felt good and I nearly always experienced orgasm. But the pleasure I experienced lacked a certain *je ne sais quoi*. Something always felt rote, shallow, and never, *ever* transcendent. As I deepened into my gender identity and as my physiology changed, I had to begin anew, "with sensation, not with names, vocabulary, or the things we think we know about our bodies" and how they are supposed to work.[2] I had, in short, to come into passionate relationship with my embodied sexual self.

The problem with the narrative I shared above is that it cuts out a lot. It obscures the fear and doubt that typified the early days of considering my relationship to gender and to my body. Moreover, it largely glosses over how for the first 37 years of my life my body was not what I felt to be a yummy space to inhabit. And, finally, it leaves out all the setbacks and detours I experienced in my journey back to my body, including recovery from two sexual assaults experienced in the spring of 2018. Beginning anew, mystifying, re-visioning—all that is marvelous, but one must concede that coming into passionate relationship is a risky proposition, or, at least, it might very well *feel* that way.

When I reflect on my own process of coming into passionate relationship, I recall the fear. Most thresholds of initiation are scary at the point of embarkation, after all! They don't feel safe, and, in a sense, they are *not* safe—nothing new worth doing ever, truly, 100% is! But somehow, despite the fear, I made the conscious decision to turn toward the fear, to disregard the proverb that would tell me to always look before I leap. I began to see the scariness in which the unknown was cloaked as something I wanted to turn toward, embrace, and meet with curiosity.

This chapter is about the decision to take the plunge into embodied sexuality, to turn (com)passionately toward self and other. And it is about how we might work with our clients to come to that decision to plunge in and welcome pleasure and erotic embodiment with curiosity and tenderness. The plunging in involves what I call coming into compassionate relationship with the embodied sexual self. Coming into compassionate relationship with the embodied sexual self, I argue, can involve the development of three capacities in our clients: a feeling of boundedness, a leaning into awkwardness, and attuning to the *somatic-imaginal*. Each of these capacities will be explored in turn.

On Trauma and Safety

When I first began speaking about this project, and particularly the concept of coming into passionate relationship (see Chapter 3), a question I often got asked was, "If you don't like your body or if you feel unsafe in your body, how do you get embodied?" Or in other words, how do you come into passionate relationship with a body that somehow feels "wrong" or "unsafe"? This chapter emerged from that question. As I came to understand it, this question is essentially about trauma, safety, and risk-taking.

Many trans and non-binary folx have had experiences of having their bodies viewed as freakish or objects of an unethical curiosity that simultaneously fetishizes and objectifies while also de-humanizes. And many of us have had sexual experiences that have felt, to put it mildly, less than affirming of our genders. Moreover, trans and non-binary folx are also all too aware of the ways that their bodies can be sites of tremendous violence; we know the statistics, and we know the names of those who were struck down in violence. Every time I go on a first date with someone I can feel the signs of hyperarousal in my body, the nagging fear that I could easily become one of those names we read out on the Transgender Day of Remembrance (TDoR), merely because I was assigned male at birth, do not possess a vulva, and my date decided to assault me for those reasons in a fit of transphobic fury. After all, our bodies may fail or betray us, speaking inopportune truths that could visit harm upon us. I think of a first date wherein a spontaneous erection of my clit during a makeout session led to my date flying into a rage that I had somehow "deceived" her about being a woman. Or the terror that gripped my body when a pick-up play partner flogging me at a dungeon non-consensually groped between my legs and, thankfully for me, somehow tricked himself into believing that I was "sooooo wet."

And from an intergenerational trauma perspective, to be trans and non-binary, as I explore in Chapter 1, is to be part of a legacy of struggle. As Jordy Rosenberg reminds us in *Confessions of the Fox*, "There is no trans body, no body at all [...] outside" this legacy.[3] Trans and non-binary folx hold identities that place them in the lineage, both directly and indirectly, of peoples that faced serfdom, slavery, colonial repression, and/or settler displacement and annihilation as well as a concomitant erasure of cultural heritage and practices. "Our truth" as queer and trans folx, concur Matthew Reimer and Leighton Brown, "is not the popular tale of steady progress interrupted by momentary lapses of backlash, but rather a history of constant struggle interrupted by moments of triumph," a history marked by a dominant, white supremacist cis hetero-patriarchal culture that would seek at every turn to deny queer, trans and non-binary folx a history and erase "our unique existence in centuries past."[4] Whether or not we ourselves directly experienced historical oppression (such as the systemic erasure of indigenous sexualities and genders or the ways governments ignored and responded callously to the HIV/AIDS epidemic of the 1980s and 1990s), we carry these awful legacies in our bodies alongside the triumphs, the moments of visibility and liberation.

Trauma, whether event-based, insidious, collective, or intergenerational, generally has the effect of making our bodies and the world around us feel precarious. With respect to erotic embodiment, many trans and non-binary folx may approach the idea of sex or someone interacting with our bodies with fear and trepidation. We may find it terrifying to contemplate the idea of settling into those bodies and to approaching them with curiosity and wonder. Instead of facing the prospect of coming into passionate relationship with excitement, we are perhaps more likely to experience feelings of constriction, of pain, of numbness, of depersonalization and dissociation. "The body is where we live," writes Resmaa Menakem. "It's where we fear, hope, and react. It's where we constrict and relax."[5] And because of trauma, that place where we live might not be experienced as a haven for embodying pleasure and eroticism.

One of the insights of trauma-informed therapies is that when a situation or a body state feels intolerable, it becomes near-impossible to engage with the world in anything less than a reactive way. Curiosity, wonder, moving toward change—these are all stifled. We are unable to activate what Stephen Porges has called our social engagement system.[6] As Dan Siegel suggests, our window of tolerance is "a band of arousal in which we function well."[7] When we are outside our windows of tolerance, we slip either into *hypoarousal* (a feeling of shut down, freezing, and/or dissociation) or *hyperarousal* (a flight/

fight response, anxiety, panic, hypervigilance, or racing thoughts). We are, in essence, in survival mode and in a purely reactive state. As Siegel explains, one of our jobs with our clients "is to feel the movement toward the window's boundaries and work at this 'safe but not too safe' zone of treatment where change becomes possible."[8]

That which follows in this chapter is an exploration of how we might help our clients feel bounded, find "safe but not too safe" in their bodies, sit with discomfort, and move toward curiosity. As a concept, coming into compassionate relationship with the embodied sexual self may be heavily trauma-informed, but I should hasten to specify that it is not itself a trauma modality. For many clients, and particularly for those who already have processed trauma, you may be able to engage directly in the work described in this chapter. But for others, intense trauma processing should precede any foray into coming into (com)passionate relationship with the embodied sexual self.

(Com)passion

At its etymological root in Latin (*pati*), passion involves suffering, carrying a weighty burden. In the history of emotions, passion has often been under-stood as a burden, a disruptive force.[9] Passions agitate; they resist efforts at control; they are unrefined. For this reason, passions can be scary to hold. Passion stands for a great many feeling states we so often seem to crave—the spark of the erotic, the thrill of mystery, the fount of not-yet-knowing. But those same feeling states can be attended by fear, apprehension, and discom-fort. To become passionate is to dive head first into a raging conflagration.

If passion is suffering, compassion is about sharing in someone's burdens, reflective of the fusion of the Latin conjunction, *cum* (with), and the verb, *pati*. When we hold space for our clients we are engaging in an act of com-passion. We are coming into compassionate relationship with them—we do not take on their burdens as our own, but we share in those burdens. Likewise, when we, in our personal relationships, provide comfort to our friends and dear ones; or when we engage in advocacy and acts of solidarity and collective-struggle-in-community (as in activism and some forms of allyship), we are also enacting compassion.

When we bring compassion to others—when we come into compas-sionate relationship with them—we are, as Kristen Neff writes, recognizing in them "our shared human condition."[10] That is, instead of experiencing others as abstractions, we experience them as flesh and blood beings. We imagine them as beings capable of pain and joy, yes, but also, to focus our attention more squarely on the subject of this book, desirability and desire-ability. And this experiencing elicits from us an ethical responsibility to serve, to share in the burdens of another, and to make common cause. Here, coming into compassionate relationship with someone is about offering a space that is non-judgmental, ethically curious, and steeped in uncondi-tional positive regard.[11]

But what of our clients, those perhaps yearning to come into relation-ship with their embodied sexual selves? Just as in my discussion of coming into passionate relationship in Chapter 3 I articulated a move from an inter-personal relational dynamic to an *intra*personal one, so, too, we might shift perspective from the sitting with in our relationships with others, to the burden-sharing we extend to ourselves, or to parts of our selves—bringing compassion to self. As Neff notes, so many of the burdens we carry are occasioned by self-judgment and negative self-talk—a seemingly omni-present internal critic who always has a cutting, confidence-demolishing remark for us about our bodies, our behavior, or ideas, or our desires.[12] To be sure, these critical parts serve plenty of adaptive functions. For one, they serve to keep us humble; they can remind us of our ethical and moral obligations to others, and keep us cognizant of other people's boundaries. But these parts can often go overboard too—they can idealize by attributing to others positive qualities and attributes that might already live in us; and they internalize cultural scripts and dominant discourses that would seek to tell us that we are "not enough."

In Chapter 1, I discussed internalized transphobia, and how it can mani-fest for trans and non-binary folx specifically with respect to dating and engaging in sex or play. Internalized transphobia often shows up as a voice dripping with judgment, stemming from a process of *introjective identifi-cation*, wherein an individual unconsciously takes unto themself a given cultural script—a cultural belief or idea about trans and non-binary folx; or about concepts like gender, sex, sexuality; or normative cultural values of gender expression, beauty, etc.—and then identifies it as a belief that is *ego syntonic*, or of-the-conscious-ego. The idea feels natural and, worse, incontrovertible. These critical, shame-nourishing introjects view the self as "inadequate, flawed or bad" or "having characteristics that make one unattractive and thus rejectable or vulnerable to attacks from others."[13] And as Paul Gilbert and Sue Procter note, internalizing the critical messages and normative values of dominant cultures ultimately can lead to a belief struc-ture in which the self begins to "feel overwhelmed, easily fragmented and simply closes down—there is no safe place either inside or outside the self to help soothe or calm the self."[14] In other words, both the individual's external environment and their inner world become compromised and hostile with few, if any, safe harbors left to the self.

Sexuality and embodiment are particularly susceptible to processes of introjective identification. After all, most of us are brought up in intensely sex-negative and body-shaming cultures, cultures that have very specific ideas about which bodies are afforded access to desirability and desire-ability as well as what sex is and what specific consensual sexual thoughts, urges, and behaviors are deemed acceptable. As Gayle Rubin writes, "Most Western societies appraise sex acts according to a hierarchical system of sexual value," with marital, monogamous, procreative cis heterosexuality "alone at the top of the erotic pyramid."[15] "Individuals whose behavior stands high in this hierarchy are rewarded with certified mental health, respectability, legality, social and physical mobility, institutional support, and material benefits," whereas individuals whose phantasies and sex acts, bodies and embodiments fall outside the "charmed circle" of "good" sexualities and embodiments are deemed unnatural, immoral, ugly, undesirable, and pathological.[16] And it becomes easy to internalize and embody that sexual value system. Our so-called self-judgments (i.e., society's judgments masquerading as if they originate in us) are facilitated by a culture that is constantly communicating to us that our perceptions of the microaggressive acts we experience are simply "in our heads" or "not a big deal" or the result of our "bad choices" or "risky behavior."[17] We trans and non-binary folx are thereby recruited by a transphobic culture of doing the work of our own erasure.

This is where coming into compassionate relationship with the embodied sexual self comes in. If hostile introjects lead us to view our bodies and desires as "less than," "not enough," or "unsafe," compassion directed toward self is about self-acceptance and finding a sense of boundedness-in-self. In the next section I shall begin to explore how we, as providers, might nurture a coming into compassionate relationship, first by modeling it within the therapeutic relationship and then by the client internalizing and taking those capacities unto themself. When in a compassionate mode, the client can enjoy a full range of sensations and emotions—they can comfort themself when they have been rejected; they can take risks, knowing they can care for themself; and they can interact with others, knowing that they can hold their own boundaries.

Bounded Chaos

One of the foundational metaphors of psychodynamic psychotherapy is the "therapeutic container," hinted at by Carl Jung, and elaborated upon by Winnicott's concept of the "holding environment" and Bion's notion of "containing."[18] The therapeutic container is, on the one hand, an ethical "frame," one circumscribed by "structural elements such as the place where therapy occurs, the duration and time of therapy," and agreements between client and provider (e.g., fee and billing agreements, confidentiality, informed consent).[19] As Lynne Gravell writes, this "[level] of containment" works to help "provide the client with a sense of stability, from which a degree of trust may ensue."[20]

In a more robust sense, though, the therapeutic container is concerned with "the function of the therapist" and is an emotional holding device.[21] In this second sense of the container metaphor, the provider facilitates a space that transcends the structural frame, one that is designed to hold the client's material, namely, the sensations, images, feelings, and thoughts they bring into "the room." This act of containment allows the client to feel feelings and think thoughts that might otherwise be intolerable, too overwhelming, or too frightening for them to face alone. A corrective emotional experience is ultimately brought about when the client is able to feel and perceive that the therapist is able to hold without judgment material otherwise cloaked in shame or negative affect. And, then, within the emotional frame of the therapeutic container, as Gravell continues, "negative or fearful feelings may become more acceptable and integrated within the person, ultimately helping them to become their own container."[22] Or, to put the container metaphor within a neurophysiological framework, when the provider is able to imbue the therapeutic relationship with a sense of containment, clients are able to acquire "a greater accessibility" to feelings of "openness, and self exploration."[23] This greater accessibility to feeling open, contained, and present to themself "is not only healing in and of itself" for the client, "but allows for the possibility of deeper therapeutic work."[24]

Building on the container metaphor, I conceive of the therapeutic situation as what I call *bounded chaos*. The concept of bounded chaos first occurred to me in the context of kink/BDSM. One of the foundational philosophies of kink is encapsulated in the acronym RACK, or, Risk-Aware Consensual Kink. The idea is that many of the activities engaged in—and many of the emotional states experienced in—a scene imply, by their very nature, risks. Heavy impact might result in injury, however unintentional, and however well-trained and self-aware a Dominant and their submissive might be. Likewise, many scenes touch on psyche. And sometimes, as Xan West suggests, when play "inadvertently step[s] on the minefields" of the players' histories, traumatic material might be activated. Indeed, in play, West continues, "Part of the thrill is that danger."[25]

And this is the point of RACK play: all parties go into a scene well aware of the potential risks and engage in a process of informed consent and negotiation, one that involves discussions of safe words; non-verbal communication (e.g., tapping a particular part of the body or waving as a signal that play should pause or stop altogether); and safety, emergency, and risk-mitigation plans. The sexuality and lifestyle educator Midori counsels that players ask one another as part of negotiation and informed consent, "What might I see and hear when the play is good for you?" and "What might I see and hear when you are in distress or when things aren't good for you?"[26] Both questions are fabulously trauma-informed, and I actually use variations of them when working with my clients in a therapeutic context, particularly prior to engaging in a processing session. The negotiation, the check-ins, the aftercare plans are the container, the boundaries for the scene. And because of the bounded nature of play, emergence can take place. It is in the emergence that healing can happen. The scene, to use a gaming metaphor, is a sandbox—a bounded environment within whose confines players are able to explore and experiment and create their own experiences.

In many ways, the therapeutic situation functions similarly. Imaginal work, depth work, somatic and movement work, and trauma processing are only possible, I contend, when there is a feeling of boundedness, when a container has been established. The client must be able to feel as if they are held and contained, as if the material they bring to us, their providers, can be held; and not merely held, but held with a kind of reverence. They must know that they can end a session, or work within session, at any time and for any reason, just as any player might "red-out" during a scene. And they must know that the sensations, images, feelings, and thoughts shared in session will be kept confidential, and that this material will be held within the confines of our offices so that they can leave it with us at the end of session and pick it back up when they return for the next session.

This boundedness allows chaos to emerge as it will. I mean chaos in a particular sense, by the way. Chaos is often synonymous with disorder, confusion, pandaemonium. I mean the word in a non-pejorative sense to indicate a kind of unpredictability occasioned by a stance of not-knowing on the part of both client and provider. In the therapeutic situation, a state of chaos is one in which we operate "without memory or desire" (*pace* Bion), and without any particular investment in what emerges in session—where session begins, where it goes, what comes into conscious awareness, and where it ends. Whatever happens happens; wherever you go, there you are. It is the space from which we seek permission for "little experiments," lean into intuition or instinct through a reflection or interpretation offered in the spirit of "skillful tentativeness," or host a part or an image that has suddenly shown up, unbidden. And it is the space in which play takes place.[27]

I understand coming into passionate relationship with the embodied sexual self to be the kind of emergence that only flashes into being in the maelstrom of chaos. And if this emergence takes place, it is facilitated—at least at first, and until the client is able to function as their own container—by the structure of the holding environment set by the provider. In a bounded chaos paradigm, the messy realities of life are placed within the therapeutic sandbox, a structured way of metabolizing the process of coming into relationship.

BTToP: Setting the Container

How might we set the therapeutic container, specifically in our work with trans and non-binary clients? I've included a few suggestions below, although you will almost certainly wish to modify them so as to align with your theoretical orientation and practice setting, not to mention negotiate the contours of these boundaries with the client in the room and their treatment goals. You may already be doing many of these things in your work, and some of these suggestions may strike you as foundational, but hopefully this list will give you tools to understand the importance of these foundational practices as you work with trans and non-binary folx.

1. **Create a warm, inviting space:** Our consulting rooms are the very embodiment of the container metaphor, as they are the literal frame in which we interact with our clients and through which we hold their material. If you have any input in how your space is organized and decorated, I would encourage you to populate it with objects that serve the dual purpose of helping both you and your clients ground. These might be objects that are meaningful to you—talismans from loved ones or former clients—or images on the walls that convey, to the extent you feel comfortable, your personality and, particularly, a gender-affirming and pleasure-positive stance. You might also attend to how your bookshelves are populated and organized. Beyond objects, you might consider the lighting in your office to make sure that it is warm and inviting. I also suggest attending to the smells and scents of office spaces to ensure that there are no strong odors, particularly of cleaning products that might aggravate scent sensitivities or asthma. For many trans and non-binary folx, the world in which we daily move can be inhospitable and not constructed with any thought to our existence. Your offices can be oases of calm in the midst of that world, a space where they can breathe, relax, and feel into expansiveness.

2. **Cultivate presence in the client-provider relationship.** Presence, Geller and Porges explain, "involves [providers] using their whole self to be both fully engaged and receptively attuned in the moment, with and for the client."[28] To cultivate presence is to "show up" in such a way that we leave ourselves open to whatever chooses to emerge or present itself within the provider-client relationship. Cultivating presence, then, also refers to holding gently the Bionian dictum to be in the room with your clients without "memory or desire" and while adopting a stance of "not-knowing."[29] Presence also refers to our comportment and affect in the room, namely, maintaining eye contact; a soft, warm voice; and "vocal prosody."[30]

3. **Practice ethical curiosity.** Ethical curiosity is a clinical stance that emerges from the recognition that the clinical gaze can be experienced as invasive, othering, and de-humanizing to many of our clients. As such, we need to reorient our curiosity to one that respects and empowers them, all for the purpose of setting a container from which the client's own capacities for play can emerge of their own accord. To ground one's clinical curiosity in ethics, I explain, is to keep in mind three fundamental principles: dismantling entitlement, seeking permission, and treating the client in the room. See Chapter 2 for a full discussion of these principles and how they might operate in the room.

4. **Bring awareness to power dynamics inherent to the client–provider relationship explicitly and frequently.** Power dynamics are inherent in the client–provider relationship, however we might seek to destabilize them. For example, when we write letters in support of legal and medical transition activities, we can all too often participate in a system that has long sought to gatekeep access to gender affirmation. In the realm of erotic embodiment, "[our] culture sends many explicit and implicit messages about sex and sexuality that are both controlling and damaging."[31] We, as providers, are in a position to help our clients bring awareness to these explicit and implicit messages and how they inscribe themselves onto our bodies. Here, as Constantinides, Sennott, and Chandler suggest, we are called to abandon pretenses of "neutrality" and "name what [we] think is happening for clients both in the room as well as in their lives in an open, honest, and uncomplicated way."[32] Thus, we should also actively ally with clients in naming microaggressions and injustice when they happen.

Feeling Safe vs. Feeling Bounded

As explored earlier in this chapter, it is practically a truism in trauma-informed care that a sense of safety is a necessary self-state condition for growth, change, and an activation of the body's social engagement system. As Shari Geller and Stephen Porges assert, "effective social communication can only occur during states when we experience safety, because only then are [our] neurobiological defense strategies inhibited."[33] I do not dispute the essential thrust of this claim, namely, that change and an openness to curiosity, to wonder, to the unknown or unfamiliar is facilitated by occupying a "sweet spot" that pushes against and gently expands—but does not blow past!—the boundaries of the window of tolerance.[34]

However, this insistence on safety can be a problem in the context of working with clients to come into (com)passionate relationship with the embodied sexual self, because that which most often feels safe for our clients is the comfortable and familiar, as opposed to what might allow them to grow and explore. In other words, clients might need to *be* safe, but they might not always *feel* safe (even when they are). To recall the bounded chaos metaphor explored above, the feeling I am aiming for in work to nurture a coming into compassionate relationship, then, is a feeling of *boundedness* rather than a feeling of *safety*.

To be safe, according the Merriam-Webster Online Dictionary (safe, adj.), is to be: 1. "free from harm or risk;" 2a. "secure from threat of danger, harm, or loss;" 3. "afford[ed] safety or security from danger, risk, or difficulty;" 5b. "unlikely to produce controversy or contradiction;" and 6a. "not likely to take risk."[35] Based on these definitions, I might stipulate without much controversy that our work with clients should not involve harm, or even the threat of harm and danger! Indeed, the principle of *non-maleficence*, which is derived from the Latin translation of a maxim attributed to the Greek physician Hippocrates, *primum non nocere* [first, do no harm], is the prime directive of medical and therapeutic practice. But I stipulate with equal assurance that our work with our clients can never be 100% free of "risk," "difficulty," or producing "controversy or contradiction." Risks are part of our work and we know this because of how we are ethically and legally obligated to outline both the benefits and the risks of treatment as part of gathering informed consent.

Thus, along with educators Brian Arao and Kristi Clemens, I question "the degree to which safety is an appropriate or reasonable expectation" for our work with clients.[36] Indeed, much of our work operating at the intersection of gender, sex, and sexualities "requires the very qualities of risk, difficulty, and controversy that are defined as incompatible with safety."[37] In order for our clients to participate fully, we and they must take risks as well as leaps into the unknown, all of which may provoke feelings of discomfort.

Feelings of safety are often associated with things that are familiar to us. But those things that are familiar, comfortable, and free of risk don't necessarily serve us. Development, change, growth all require a certain amount of discomfort to take place, "growing pains," as it were. If we merely stay within our zones of comfort, where we feel safe, content, and untroubled, then we cannot explore different ways of being. For an example of this in action, consider what many say needs to happen in order to unlearn and dismantle oppressive systems such as white supremacy, misogyny, transphobia, and ableism. As I am writing this chapter in the summer of 2020, in the midst of Black Lives Matter protests and efforts to confront structural racism head-on, many Black folx are rightly suggesting that if we all wish to create a more just society, white folx are going to have to learn to sit with discomfort, rather than falling back into "white fragility."[38]

Another problem with the discourse of safety is that many members of marginalized groups, including trans and non-binary folx, don't often experience many feelings of safety in their bodies. "Safety," argues social worker, writer, and activist Kai Cheng Thom, can be understood as "an inherently classed, raced, and gendered experience that frequently runs the risk of being used to regressive ends," namely so as to restrict "the freedoms of the vulnerable, those who are never really safe."[39] Safety is a state of being that is enjoyed—and, indeed, expected!—by only a select few in American and Western European societies, namely, white, cis, straight, high SES folx. Everyone else moves through a world that is, at least to some extent, unsafe and precarious.

So, if we are to acknowledge that risk and discomfort are part of the growth and change process, and if we are to further submit that a feeling of safety is not necessary, sufficient, or even (often) possible, then what are we left with? How do we work to occupy the "sweet spot" between comfort and intolerability, the zone of "safe but not too safe?"[40] In favor of a discourse of safety, of needing to "feel safe," my suggestion is to adopt a discourse of *boundedness,* and to focus our work on nurturing and sustaining a feeling of boundedness.

Part of this work involves being able to make that which my colleague Rae McDaniel refers to as an "accurate assessment of safety." Rae, who you will hear more from in Chapter 6, describes making an accurate assessment of safety as a form of *reality testing.* One example of this type of reality testing from my own life would be my experience with aerial dance, an integral part of my self-care practice. Seen a performance of Cirque du Soleil? That's basically what I do, only with a lot less talent. I float, fly, and contort my body, often several feet off the ground. Being in the silks allows me to be fully present in my body, no easy task since I spent the first 37 years or so of my life in my head. And sometimes I perform drops, moments wherein I let go of the silks and fall forward or backward.

Although I know I'm safe, I don't feel safe when I'm up in the air. And when I'm suspended in the air, there will always be a part of me that will internally protest, "But, Lucie, remember! We're afraid of heights!" That voice comes from the most primitive structures of my nervous system, that which some have described as our reptilian brains.[41] It would seek to tell me that climbing and wrapping my body in the silks are unsafe. These parts of my nervous system are doing exactly what they are supposed to do—keeping me alive and keeping me from being harmed by threats in the world, a set of processes Porges describes as *neuroception.*[42] And as a queer, trans femme who has experienced event-based traumas and minority stress, my nervous system is pretty well attuned to my environment, neuroceptively scanning and monitoring my environment for threats, internal and external. Indeed, perhaps it is a tad over-attuned!

My hypervigilance and capacities for neuroception are in so many ways life-saving superpowers; but they can also work on overdrive and over-identify threats. My hyperaroused nervous system does not allow me to discriminate between real and imagined danger. And so I move through the world in a near-constant state of at least low-level anxiety and tension. The outside world is not often viewed by my nervous system and embodied psyche as a particularly safe place to be. And when we perceive a threat we lose our ability to engage with the world around us as well as ourselves.

Over the years, I've learned to trust the silks—I know that they are designed to hold a person's body weight. I've also had to learn to trust myself, to know that I am strong enough to hold myself up, that I have practiced the moves and that they are well-ingrained in my muscle memory, so much so that I can get myself down safely or recover my wits whenever I need to, as when something does go wrong. I might not always *feel* safe in the silks, but I know that I *am* safe. Moreover, and perhaps more crucially for our purposes, I feel *bounded*, held by the silks and by my body. I am able to fly, contort, and drop—all actions that involve a certain amount of risk!—because of that sense of boundedness and containment.

In the silks, my sense of boundedness was only achieved after a great deal of practice and lots of drills within those practices designed to help me break down movements and build strength and endurance to execute those movements. There is also a lot of failure, humility, and awkwardness involved, subjects to which I will return in the next section. But over time, with practice and instruction, a move that I may have thought impossible to do suddenly becomes possible. And lo and behold! One day I'm climbing with my feet while hanging upside down.

I would suggest that developing in our work a client's embodied sense of boundedness happens in a similar fashion. It takes practice over time; gentle, strengths-based holding on our part; and tiny experiments in bringing awareness to the body and to the boundedness one can find there. It is, in short, a matter of titration. In the BTToP box that follows I have included an exercise you might engage in with your clients to begin to explore what boundedness might feel like in the body.

BTToP: Come Here, Go Away Exercise

In this BTToP section I outline an exercise that you might introduce to your clients to help build capacities for feeling bounded. This exercise came to me via a somatic sexual healing workshop run by sex educator and sexological bodyworker Charlie Glickman at the 2017 AASECT Conference. Charlie referred to it as "Come Here, Go Away." The exercise does not involve touch, so it satisfies most professional codes of ethics. However, it still may not be a good fit for all clients, or for your own personal approach to boundaries in practice. Because the exercise involves varying physical distance and closeness, it may push on attachment dynamics. The exercise is meant to provoke a certain amount of discomfort but you might include in describing the exercise to your clients a "safe word" that the client might employ if the exercise is beginning to feel overwhelming to them rather than promoting growth-encouraging discomfort. In any case, you will want to process this activity with your client, and I have included a few questions following the prompt to help you do so. If you or the client are uncomfortable doing the exercise together, you might suggest to the client that they bring a friend or partner to do the activity with them.

The "Come Here, Go Away" activity consists of two rounds, one in which the client directs action, and one in which you (or the client's designated partner for the activity) do. The exercise consists of varying closeness and distance, and movement is directed by three hand gestures: come here (a "come hither" motion with the fingers); go away (a "bye bye" motion with the fingers); and stop (basically a held up fist). You will start out 4–6 feet away from one another. The person directing the action during a given round uses the gestures to bring their activity partner closer or move them further away. The stop gesture is used when the person directing action wishes their activity partner to stay put at a particular distance from them. The overall purpose of the activity is to give both participants of the activity a visceral, energetic sense of physical boundaries and boundedness. Once you've engaged in both rounds of the exercise, you might adapt the following reflection questions to process the experience of the activity together.

REFLECTION QUESTIONS:

1. What sensations, images, feelings, or thoughts did you notice as you engaged in this activity?
2. What happened in your body at different points in the exercise?
3. Did you notice that particular directions were hard to give? To receive? What made them difficult? What in your body might have alerted you to the difficulty?
4. Did you notice that particular directions when given or received led to ease and relaxation? What in your body told you that you were more at ease?

5. When directing was there a particular distance that felt too close? Too far? What about "just right"? What did you notice happening in your body as your partner varied their distance and closeness? Are there any sensations, images, feelings, or thoughts you are curious about?
6. Was there ever a point in the exercise during which you felt unsafe or discomfort? What about points that made you feel good or bounded?
7. What do you want to pay more attention to now that you've done this activity?
8. What have you learned about yourself and your sense of physical and energetic boundaries?

Swan Diving into the Awkward

Have you ever actually had sex on the beach, rolling in the sand as the surf crashes into you? What about sex on the stairs? Or sex while standing up? Or a torrid, sweaty dance of peeling clothes off as you back into the bedroom to collapse heavily onto a waiting, rose petal-strewn bed? No? Well, you're not alone. I grew up in the 1980s and 1990s, steeped in the cinematic sensuality of such notoriously steamy hits as *Body Heat* (1981) and *Basic Instinct* (1992). And for the longest time, sex scenes in films like this formed the backbone of my erotic imagination, the musculoskeletal structure of what I believed constituted great sex. And, really, if I'm being honest, not just great sex, but sex in general. I somehow believed that to be "good in bed" meant being acrobatic, bendy to the extreme, and a virtuoso of movement, position, and technique. I also picked up messages about who, or, more properly, what types of bodies had great sex—thin, athletic, white, able-bodied, cis, straight women and men in their 20s and 30s.

As Peggy Kleinplatz and A. Dana Ménard point out, "much of the public discourse on 'great sex' has been dominated by magazine covers and self-help manuals that sensationalize sex but marginalize all but youthful acrobats. [...] They promote technique, novelty, and incredible orgasms as the route to great sex."[43] The unfortunate impact of this mindset is that many folx—and particularly those that show up in our offices, agencies, and consulting rooms—become swayed into thinking that "their neighbors are engaged effortlessly in hot, endless sex" and, as a result, they are made to "feel abnormal or inadequate by comparison."[44]

But you know the thing about sex on the beach? There's sand. And it gets *everywhere*! And sex on the stairs? Those stairs dig into the spine in ways that are phenomenally uncomfortable! Or upright sex, a partner's legs wrapped around me? I did it once, in my early 20s, back when I had not yet heard of sciatica, and even then it was not something I could sustain for very long! And now, when I watch those films of my youth I groan instead of being turned on. I look at the sex scenes from *Damaged* (1992), for example, and worry for Juliette Binoche's head as Jeremy Irons repeatedly slams it into walls as they (literally!) bang one another. The sex scenes I'm most likely to be turned on by now? How about one of the first scenes of the pilot episode for *Sense8*, in which Nomi, a trans woman, finishes fucking her girlfriend, Amanita, with a Pride flag strap-on, and removes the harness. The camera lingers appreciatively over the dildo, still dripping with lube and Amanita's juices. This scene revels in sex as a polymorphous sensory experience, and an unabashedly messy one.

As I discussed in my exploration of compassion and its etymology earlier in this chapter, an aspect of bringing compassion to self and others is a practice of withdrawing judgment—those harsh introjects that would seek to tell us that we are hopelessly deficient and will never, ever be "enough." And one of those introjects we could stand to withdraw or disabuse ourselves of posthaste is the belief that sex, not to mention, coming into relationship with self and other, is not inherently awkward. The truth, to put the sentiment contained in that last sentence in more positive terms, is that sex is intensely awkward, between all the fluids, the smells, the sounds, the coordination of bodies in space. And instead of bringing shame to it, we should be bringing compassion and—goddexx forbid!—some humor to our erotic lives.

Just as we have a lot of received ideas from culture about what great sex should look or feel like, we also get a lot of messages about what bodies are supposed to look like as well as how gender is to be expressed. As I discussed in Chapter 1 when talking about *erotic privilege*, certain bodies are coded as the aspirational ideal—usually, white or light-skinned, cis or cis-assumed, thin, tall, visibly able-bodied, and in their 20s and 30s—while most others are dismissed and marginalized. Add to that the crushing weight of gendered roles and expectations—e.g., the ideas that non-binary folx are either androgynous in presentation or masc-of-center, or that Dominants can't be bottoms, that men pursue and penetrate, or that possessing a vulva and uterus is constitutive of being a woman—and, as Carl Wethers' character is fond of saying on the tv show *Arrested Development*, "baby, you've got a stew going."

So many of our clients come to us operating under the thrall of these punishing messages. In both the small world that central Virginia can be and in wider media representation, my client Kara (she/her) a Black, butch trans woman, didn't see many other trans women who looked like her. It was bad enough that she'd attend events geared toward queer and trans folx and be one of the few Black women there, but to be a butch trans woman in a culture that expects trans women to embody hyper-femininity or present as femme, marked Kara out as different. For the longest time, she agonized that she wasn't "trans enough," as if the lack of visibility of BIPoC folx and butch trans folx was somehow a "failure" on her part instead of an abject failure on the part of a culture that routinely fails to account for bodies and subjectivities that do not docilely conform to cultural scripts, and particularly those of "patriarchal femininity."

As Rhea Ashley Hoskin and Allison Taylor explain, hegemonic and patriarchal norms of femininity (and, gender writ large), "flatten out" difference and erase variability.[45] Hegemonic cultural norms harm cis folx too, of course, but these norms of expression that are impossible to maintain and that mark those who fail to live up to them as "less than," "failing," or "bad," can hit trans and non-binary folx particularly hard because they can also serve as an invalidation of trans identities and embodiments. That is, they can lead trans and non-binary folx to internalize a belief that the very ways they show up in the world are "not enough," "too much," or "not valid."

As Jack Halberstam argues in *The Queer Art of Failure*, aspirational ideals, whether with respect to sexual performance or gender expression, punish us all, cis and trans, insofar as they "discipline behavior" and circumscribe ways of embodying.[46] They set up worlds in which there are winners and losers, "good women" and "bad women," freaks and normal folk, normative sexualities and "alternative" sexualities. According to Halberstam, *failure* is the way out of this impasse. "Under certain circumstances," he writes, "failing, losing, forgetting, unmaking, undoing, unbecoming, and not knowing may in fact offer more creative, more cooperative, and more surprising ways of being in the world."[47] Thus, failure is an option—indeed the only option!—because we all fail.

In the opening of the film *Star Trek II: The Wrath of Khan* (1982), we are treated to Starfleet cadets engaging in a training exercise in which a simulation of the starship Enterprise is sent to rescue the crew of a freighter, the *Kobyashi Maru*, from attacking Klingons. The cadets fail miserably: they fail to rescue the crew of the *Kobyashi Maru* and they manage to kill all the bridge crew and destroy the simulated Enterprise. But here's the catch: the training exercise, we later learn, is not about honing combat tactics, but is, instead, about character, how cadets respond to a "no-win" scenario. Failure is not only assured but *assumed* in the Kobyashi Maru Test. The questions the test presents are: how do you face failure; how do you respond to failure's certainty?

When confronted by certain failure we have a number of choices. We can keep taking the test, trying different solutions each time. But another response is to effectively change the rules of the game altogether. Indeed, we can embrace failure and glory in it, because knowing that we cannot "win" or "lose" means that we can decide how we want to play the game. Working with trans and non-binary clients at the intersection of gender and sexuality, the no-win scenario—achieving normative ideals of sexual performance and/or gender expression—can be transformed through failure into an "always win" scenario, one in which the goals are pleasure and embodied joy rather than constantly seeking to satisfy and uphold rules, roles, and norms set up and enforced by a white, cis heteropatriarchy; and bringing compassion to the self when not feeling particularly joyful or desire-able.

When I began exploring my gender and sexuality I was terrified of being an awkward "newbie," of doing sex, kink, and gender "wrong" and thus showing my utter lack of experience. My fear of myself as inexperienced— a baby queer, and a newbie kinkster—kept me from exploring, and, thus, deepening into the queer, kink, and trans communities. For about a year my fear of awkwardness, of failure, of not measuring up kept me immobilized. As my therapist at the time said to me on many an occasion when I would express concerns about failure and being perceived as awkward, "I think you have this idea that you should be able to emerge from the chrysalis a butterfly without being a larva!" She rightly pointed out that I thought that transition was an event rather than a process, and that I would somehow emerge from it fully formed. But that's not how transitions work, do they? Instead, we must all pass through a period of inexperience and awkwardness, and, likely, many such periods in our lives! Failure, awkwardness—that's where ecstasy, wonder, surprise, and what Halberstam calls the "wonderful anarchy of children" live![48] Far from being a state worth fleeing, what if awkwardness were a state that was prized for its generative possibility, its potential to nurture radical emergence?

We can help our clients fail productively by helping them figure out how they want to change the rules of the game and by allowing themselves to lean into the awkward. Or even, take a spectacular swan dive into it in their embodied erotic lives!

The Somatic-Imaginal

Resmaa Menakem describes trauma as a "wordless story our body tells itself about what is safe and what is a threat."[49] Our bodies, our embodied psyches, tell all sorts of wordless stories about the world we move through as well as the internal landscapes of our bodies, our viscera. Indeed, as Pat Ogden suggests, the body contains a particular wisdom, and can be experienced as "a living, ever-changing source of intelligence, information, and energy that provides ongoing support for our physical and mental functioning."[50] And the language our embodied psyches use to relate their wisdom is made up sensations, feelings, and movements, expressed in image. I refer to the wordless stories our bodies tell us as the *somatic-imaginal.*

Take a moment and bring your awareness to your body in the present moment, and particularly to the feelings and sensations that you notice. Do you feel hungry? Or maybe you're tired? Anxious? Turned on? If so, how do you have a sense of those feelings? How do they visit you or come into conscious awareness? See if you can express warmth toward these sensations and can soften any judgments you might have of them.

Oftentimes, feelings and sensations are pre-verbal, and images are how we relate to these feelings and sensations. For example, as I write this paragraph, I notice a lot of tightness in my chest. At first, I can't attach a word to the feeling, but the tightness feels as if there is a maelstrom at its core, a churning, sticky, gooey, tar-like mass. It's rather unpleasant, I must say. I notice that I'm also holding my breath a lot and that it takes mental effort to get myself to breathe again, even though breathing is supposed to be an automatic, unconscious process. It's as if my breath is being sucked into the maelstrom, this great slimy maw. It's only after sitting with the image for a few seconds that I can tell myself with confidence, "hm, I'm feeling super anxious. I think I'm nervous about how a reader is going to respond to what I'm writing."

In being asked to bring your awareness to your body you might also find that you are unable to localize a sensation or feeling to a particular part of the body. You might notice, as my client Kara (she/her) did when I first asked her to bring awareness to her embodied self-state, a full-body movement image. Kara expressed a sense of wanting to recoil from the prompt and added an "uggghhh!" for good measure to reinforce the movement-image of recoiling. Or you might notice a tonal softening come over you, a desire expressed in an image of leaning in with curiosity to the prompt, as a trans male client, Cam (he/him), reported. Oftentimes body movements of the types Kara and Cam reported (e.g., shifts in posture, leg position, how weight is shifted in the body) manifest physically in the room, but sometimes there is also an imaginal component, an image of that movement experienced internally. Neither Kara nor Cam actually recoiled or leaned in, but their embodied psyches imagined that movement and it was felt viscerally.

Imaginal or internal experiencing is often misinterpreted as a purely cognitive set of processes. However, I contend that images are not only stored in the mind, but also in the body. The body has an imagination. Or, more to the point, there is no binary split between somatic experiencing and cognitive experiencing, between psyche and soma. The somatic-imaginal, as I understand it, is experienced within the embodied psyche. And the embodied psyche often communicates through internal body sensation-images or internal body movement-images.

Part of the process of working with clients to come into compassionate relationship with the embodied sexual self is helping them develop capacities for attuning to the somatic-imaginal. In doing so, we give our clients tools to check in with themselves, to bring awareness to their embodied psyches as they move in and relate to the world. We also give them tools to communicate differently with prospective partners (e.g., romantic, sexual, D/s) so as to clue them into what is happening real time before, during, or following an experience of play. The client can use the somatic-imaginal to track and deepen into their embodied experience and make adjustments along the way as needed to ensure a continued movement toward curiosity, exploration, and emergence, that which queer theorist José Esteban Muñoz referred to as "the thing-that-is-not-yet-imagined."[51]

To illustrate the work of attuning to the somatic-imaginal, I return us to a vignette initially presented in the BTToP section on mystification in Chapter 3. In that vignette, I highlighted my work with Xochi (they/them), a Mexican-American non-binary individual in their 30s, around what pursuing pleasure and euphoria could feel like for them. As we did so, we ended up working a great deal in helping Xochi tap into their somatic-imaginal.

As you may recall, Xochi referred to two embodied feeling states, dysphoria and euphoria. The diagnostic features of gender dysphoria are catalogued in the DSM-5. If gender dysphoria is the discomfort or distress trans and non-binary folx experience in the incongruence between the gender they have been assigned since birth and their gender identity, gender euphoria is understood to be the positive feelings trans and non-binary folx experience when their gender is affirmed and recognized insofar as their gender expression aligns with their gender identity.[52] But these definitions don't tell us how either dysphoria or euphoria are lived in an individual's embodied experience.

In supporting Xochi in attuning to the somatic imaginal, then, our first step was to conjure and embody both dysphoria and euphoria, not as abstract concepts but as embodied entities, how they lived in and were experienced by Xochi. For euphoria, Xochi began by noting a body movement-image— that of a "come hither" motion with their fingers and a tapping to their side, as if they were sitting on a couch or in a bed and indicating that there was plenty of room for a partner next to them. As we deepened into their embodied experience of euphoria, they also identified a few body sensation-images. They spoke of twin flames dancing in their eyes and how they felt them as slight buzzing on the ocular surface. They also noted the surface of their skin felt incandescent and crackling with energy and enthusiasm. Over the course of multiple sessions, we explored each of these images, but let's sit with the first image, the movement-image of Xochi inviting a partner to join them on a bed. In working this movement-image corresponding to Xochi's experience of gender euphoria, we brought the image to life in the here-and-now and engaged in a process of befriending the image.

James Hillman described "befriending" an image as entering or being invited in to its "mood" from a place of (ethical) curiosity, suffused with the desire "to want to know more about [an image], to understand, play with, live with, carry, and become familiar with" it—"as one would do with a friend."[53]

With Xochi's movement-image we worked to gently approach it as we might a rare bird that has alighted near us on a trail walk. I began by asking Xochi to see if they could again evoke the movement-image of themselves on the bed. Xochi talked about what they were wearing (a leopard-print robe, thrown open triumphantly to reveal a bare chest, top surgery scars and all), how they were positioned on the bed, what the lighting was like, and if there were any scents associated with the scene. I then asked Xochi to stay with the image and ask it what it wanted them to know or if it had any requests to make of them. We then discussed how Xochi might move toward the image, to further embody it as an embodied psychic gift from "gender euphoria." "If you could feel this way," I asked, "what would you be doing? How do you imagine you could get back to this image, to embody it once more?" Helping Xochi attune to the somatic-imaginal as described herein allowed them to deepen into their experience of their sexuality and how their gender could indeed become "an elaborate sex toy."[54] It further enabled them to embody a joyously louche and playful energy.

Following this section, I have included two BTToP exercises to help you work with clients to attune to the somatic-imaginal. In the first, I provide an embodied twist on breath work, one designed to help clients begin to bring awareness to their embodied experience in the here-and-now. In the second exercise, I provide a mindfulness activity that is designed to deepen into attuning to the somatic-imaginal itself.

As Ogden observed, "for many of us our bodies have been objects of criticism, disappointment, frustration, unwanted attention, abuse, or injury."[55] This book and particularly this chapter have highlighted ways in which Ogden's observation applies especially to the embodied psyches of many our trans and non-binary clients. It may be difficult, scary, and downright uncomfortable for many trans and non-binary folx to even contemplate coming into relationship with their bodies, let alone to view their bodies as magical playgrounds of wonder. Attuning to the somatic-imaginal is a capacity meant to help our clients compassionately (re)connect with their embodied sexual selves.

BTToP: Anal, or Pelvic Floor, Breath

Confession time. I can't abide many of forms of breath-oriented meditation. And I also hate it when I'm in a yoga or movement class and the facilitator asks me to pay attention to my breath. I feel horrendously self-conscious and *anywhere but* in my body. Part of this is that until I had a septoplasty when I was 38, I couldn't breathe in and out of my nose effectively and consistently. So, all of those meditations focused on breath? I'm wildly uncomfortable and hating on myself the entire time. That was, until I was introduced by sex educator and sexological bodyworker Charlie Glickman to a technique called "anal breath."

Anal breath is kind of a misnomer. It's not breath that passes through the anus. Rather, it is focused on movements of the pelvic floor. The technique is basically as follows:

1. Bring your awareness to movements of your pelvic floor and see if you can activate it (depress it) and then release it (allow the pelvic floor to relax by rising). Do that a couple of times.
2. Now, see if you can bring your breath in alignment with your movements of the pelvic floor.
3. As you inhale, depress, or activate, the pelvic floor.
4. As you exhale, release, or relax, the pelvic floor.

Anal breathing fulfills two important functions: first and foremost, it allows me a tool I can use to relax. I can do it easily without anyone knowing what I'm doing. Second, it is a way of bringing awareness to the body and, moreover, a part of the body we don't often pay that much attention to. And for those of us routinely flummoxed by breathing exercises, it pulls our focus from the rhythm of the breath to instead bring care and compassion to the body. I've introduced many clients to anal breathing over the years, and many of them have reported that it's helped them begin to come into relationship with their body in a compassionate way. It helps them avoid judgment about "breathing the right way" and it helps them feel a sense of boundedness in their bodies.

BTToP: Somatic-Imaginal Activity

This activity is a modification of a body scan visualization, the kind you might do prior to engaging in silent meditation or at the end of a yoga class when in *shavasana*. Like a body scan, the purpose of this activity is to help you tune in to your body. But, as you'll see with the directions below, there's a little somatic-imaginal twist: the activity is designed to help you attune to the body's imagination, its rhythms, sensations, and feelings as expressed through wordless stories and images. I pepper the prompts below with references to songs, nursery rhymes, and other images, all in an effort to help you begin to notice the particular images your own body might wish to share with you about your embodied experiencing. Whatever bubbles up into consciousness, just notice and gently hold them. I've included some reflection questions at the end of the exercise to help you process the experience and perhaps give language to those sensations and feelings as expressed in image.

DIRECTIONS/PROMPTS:

Find a quiet, cozy spot where you can hang out alone for ten minutes or so without disruption. Find a comfy chair or, if you can, lie down on your back on the ground. Whether you are sitting or lying down, settle comfortably into your spot—as a sleepy puppy might their bed—and breathe normally. That is to say, don't be afraid to shift your body around to find where your body feels most at ease, as if in deepening into relaxing breath you might just absentmindedly allow yourself to lose solid form and revert to a liquid state. For this activity, you may keep your eyes open or closed—whatever feels most relaxing to you.

For a minute or so, simply notice how your breath enters your body, whether it is through your nose or mouth, and follow it gently as it goes in and out of your body. What paths does your breath take? Can you feel the breath winding from your nose or mouth down into your lungs, through to your belly, your pelvic floor, and down even to the tips of your toes? What does the breath's path feel like or look like? Does it feel warming? Cooling? Is its path direct, like a flat stretch of highway with no other cars around? Or is it windy, taking a circuitous path, as if your breath is making its way along a mountain pass, all s-curves? And what do you notice about how the inhalations and exhalations of breath are expressed in body movement? Does your chest expand and contract? Your belly? Do you feel it in your crotch? As your body expands and contracts with each breath, how does your chest or belly move in and out?

Now, bring your attention to your feet. If you are seated you might sense the ground beneath them, supporting you, holding you. Feel their connection to the ground and trace that groundedness, as if your feet could send roots through the soil beneath them, and as if those root systems could somehow send electric signals between you and other root systems (as trees in a forest are able to do). If you are lying on your back, you might wiggle your toes. Maybe you're barefoot and you can feel the air moving around them as they wiggle? Maybe as you do so, you start thinking of that old ditty someone might have sung with you when you were a child, "This little piggy went to market, this little piggy stayed home…"?

Gently bring your awareness to your back now. If you are seated, you might notice what it feels like for your back to rest gently against a wall or the back of a chair. If you are on the ground, you might notice how your back connects with the ground and what happens to that connection as you gently breathe. Can you notice the subtle textures of the ground upon which you rest in different parts of your back? Again, like a sleepy puppy, you might allow yourself to gently shift to find the comfiest nesting place.

And, finally, bring your awareness to your crotch and to your pelvic floor, that which is sometimes called the root chakra. If you felt like it, try waking up this part of yourself—a part that speaks to lineage, to community, to connectedness to something larger than yourself—by engaging in a few anal breaths (see BTToP section above on how to do this). As you bring your awareness to your crotch and your pelvic floor, what feelings and sensations might you notice? Where is there constriction? Ease? Warmth? Coolness? Softness or pressure?

If we might stay here for a few moments, here on the floor or relaxed in your seat, allow yourself to deepen even more fully into the path your breath takes and how your body accepts it and moves it. You might find that an image begins to take shape. As it takes form, try to bring some curiosity toward the image. Let go of the temptation to interpret or to make sense of it. Instead, you might pose questions of the image: "Where is this image located?" "What sensations or feelings accompany the image?" "What is happening here?" "Who or what is visiting me in this moment?" "What is being asked of me in this moment?" Sit with the image, turn it over gently. Be patient and allow the image to make itself known to you on its own time. Stay with the image, with your curiosity about it, for as long as you need, knowing you can return to it anytime during your day. When you feel ready, simply wiggle your fingers and toes and gently bring your awareness back to the room and to the present moment.

REFLECTION QUESTIONS:

Prior to launching into these reflection questions you might introduce consent and privacy into the room and the interaction. You might say something like this: "It's most important for *you* to be able to witness this experience. You can choose to keep parts of this experience private and perhaps simply notice for yourself with curiosity why you might make that choice and merely reflect with yourself on these questions." Following the processing of this experience, you might thank your client and the images that were brought into the space for showing up and for sharing their experience with you.

1. Notice any concerns or requests the image might have for me or for yourself prior to processing this experience.
2. What sensations, feelings, or thoughts did you notice as you engaged in this activity? Where would you locate them in your body?
3. Again, if it feels good to share this with me, what images did you attach to those sensations, feelings, and thoughts?
4. What are you noticing in your body in the here-and-now as we process this experience? Are you noticing any commentary or judgment in your body on the experience?

Conclusion

If coming into passionate relationship with the embodied sexual self is about leaping headlong into a space of not knowing, of "I never knew," coming into *com*passionate relationship is about finding a sense of boundedness in oneself that allows one to take that headlong leap in the first place. Compassion is the experience of sharing in someone's burdens. Coming into compassionate relationship with our clients, then, becomes an act of sitting with. We co-create and hold a container with our clients, a facilitating environment of bounded chaos to nurture radical emergence. And like other facilitating and holding environments, the goal is for the client to eventually experience themselves as a container, to bring bounded chaos unto themself. This bringing of bounded chaos unto the self is coming into compassionate relationship with the embodied sexual self, the intrapersonal experience of being able sit with oneself in the discomfort that is essential for any desire the client has to grow, change, and allow curiosity and wonder to come to the fore of the embodied psyche.

In this chapter I elucidated three capacities we can help our clients develop in order to effect a coming into compassionate relationship with the embodied sexual self: developing an internal sense of boundedness, leaning magnificently into the awkwardness inherent in erotic embodiment, and learning to attune oneself to the somatic-imaginal. Our trans and non-binary clients exist in and move through a world that can be hostile to them and to their bodies. In the face of these challenges, it might be very hard indeed for many of our clients to imagine a place of greater safety in themselves and in their erotic lives. Coming into compassionate relationship with the embodied sexual self opens up a pathway for that imagining into.

In the next chapter, I will explore the book's fourth and final conceptual stance, re-centering pleasure. In many ways, this conceptual stance draws from the concepts explored in this and the previous chapter to counter the narratives of function and loss/trade-off explored in Chapter 1. And it does so within the lens of intimate justice.[56] Building on the concept of the somatic-imaginal in his chapter, I will explore what it is to actually feel and experience pleasure in the body, and what it might be to own desire and deepen into the revolutionary act that is speaking desire.

Notes

1 Mira Bellwether, *Fucking Trans Women: A Zine About the Sex Lives of Trans Women* (CreateSpace Independent Publishing Platform, 2010), 3.
2 Ibid., 4.
3 Jordy Rosenberg, *Confessions of the Fox* (New York, NY: One World, 2018), 315.
4 Matthew Reimer and Leighton Brown, *We Are Everywhere: Protest, Power, and Pride in the History of Queer Liberation* (New York, NY: Ten Speed Press, 2019), 16.
5 Resmaa Menakem, *My Grandmother's Hands: Racialized Trauma and the Pathway to Mending Our Hearts and Bodies* (Las Vegas, NV: Central Recovery Press, 2017), 6.
6 Stephen W. Porges, "Reciprocal Influences Between Body and Brain in the Perception and Expression of Affect: A Polyvagal Perspective," in *The Healing Power of Emotion: Affective Neuroscience, Development, and Clinical Practice*, ed. Diana Fosha, Daniel J. Siegel, and Marion Solomon, Norton Series on Interpersonal Neurobiology (New York, NY: W. W. Norton & Company, 2009), 27–54.
7 Daniel Siegel, *The Mindful Therapist: A Clinician's Guide to Mindsight and Neural Integration*, Norton Series on Interpersonal Neurobiology (New York, NY: W. W. Norton & Company, 2010), 50.
8 Ibid., 51–52.
9 Amélie Oksenberg Rorty, "From Passions to Emotions and Sentiments," *Philosophy* 57, no. 220 (1982): 1982.
10 Kristin Neff, *Self-Compassion: The Proven Power of Being Kind to Yourself* (New York, NY: HarperCollins Publishers, 2011), 10.
11 Carl Rogers, *A Way of Being* (Boston, MA: Houghton Mifflin, 1980).
12 Neff, *Self-Compassion: The Proven Power of Being Kind to Yourself*, 11.
13 Paul Gilbert and Sue Procter, "Compassionate Mind Training for People with High Shame and Self-Criticism: Overview and Pilot Study of a Group Therapy Approach," *Clinical Psychology & Psychotherapy* 13, no. 6 (November 2006): 354, https://doi.org/10.1002/cpp.507.
14 Ibid., 354.
15 Gayle S. Rubin, "Thinking Sex: Notes for a Radical Theory of the Politics of Sexuality," in *Deviations: A Gayle Rubin Reader* (Duke University Press, 2011), 149, https://doi.org/10.1215/9780822394068.
16 Ibid., 149 and 152.
17 Laura Westengard, *Gothic Queer Culture: Marginalized Communities and the Ghosts of Insidious Trauma* (Lincoln, NE: University of Nebraska Press, 2019), 15.
18 C.G. Jung, "The Psychology of the Transference," in *The Practice of Psychotherapy: Essays on the Psychology of the Transference and Other Subjects*, trans. R.F.C. Hull, vol. 16, Collected Works of C.G. Jung (Princeton, NJ: Princeton University Press, 1985), 163–327; D. W. Winnicott, *Playing and Reality* (New York, NY: Routledge, 1971); Wilfred R. Bion, *Learning from Experience* (London: Karnac Books, 1962).

19 Ofer Zur, *Boundaries in Psychotherapy: Ethical and Clinical Explorations* (Washington, DC: American Psychological Association, 2007), 5.

20 Lynne Gravell, "The Counselling Psychologist as Therapeutic 'Container,'" *Counseling Psychology Review* 25, no. 2 (2010): 30.

21 Ibid., 30.

22 Ibid..

23 Shari M. Geller and Stephen W. Porges, "Therapeutic Presence: Neurophysiological Mechanisms Mediating Feeling Safe in Therapeutic Relationships," *Journal of Psychotherapy Integration* 24, no. 3 (2014): 181, https://doi.org/10.1037/a0037511.

24 Ibid., 185.

25 Xan West, *Show Yourself to Me: Queer Kink Erotica* (Northampton, MA: Go Deeper Press, 2015), 227.

26 Midori, "ProTip! Questions You Ought To Ask Before BDSM Play," *Medium* (blog), March 31, 2017, https://medium.com/@PlanetMidori/protip-questions-ought-to-ask-before-bdsm-play-621fd87a2f02.

27 Ron Kurtz, *Body-Centered Psychotherapy: The Hakomi Method: The Integrated Use of Mindfulness, Nonviolence and the Body* (Mendocino, CA: LifeRhythm, 2007); David G. Martin, *Counseling and Therapy Skills*, 3rd ed. (Long Grove, IL: Waveland Press, 2011).

28 Geller and Porges, "Therapeutic Presence," 178.

29 Wilfred R. Bion, "Notes on Memory and Desire," *The Psychoanalytic Forum* 2 (1967): 272.

30 Geller and Porges, "Therapeutic Presence," 188.

31 Damon Constantinides, Shannon L. Sennott, and Davis Chandler, *Sex Therapy with Erotically Marginalized Clients* (New York, NY: Routledge, 2019), 16.

32 Ibid., 22.

33 Geller and Porges, "Therapeutic Presence," 181.

34 Siegel, *The Mindful Therapist: A Clinician's Guide to Mindsight and Neural Integration*, 51–52.

35 "Safe," in *Merriam-Webster.Com Dictionary*, accessed June 23, 2020, https://www. merriam-webster.com/dictionary/safe.

36 Brian Arao and Kristi Clemens, "From Safe Spaces to Brave Spaces: A New Way to Frame Dialogue Around Diversity and Social Justice," in *The Art of Effective Facilitation: Reflections from Social Justice Educators*, ed. Lisa M. Landreman (Sterling, VA: Stylus Publishing, 2013), 139.

37 Ibid., 139.

38 Robin DiAngelo, *White Fragility: Why It's So Hard for White People to Talk About Racism* (Boston, MA: Beacon Press, 2018).

39 Kai Cheng Thom, *I Hope We Choose Love: A Trans Girl's Notes from the End of the World* (Vancouver, BC: Arsenal Pulp Press, 2019), 22.

40 Siegel, *The Mindful Therapist: A Clinician's Guide to Mindsight and Neural Integration*, 51.

41 Menakem, *My Grandmother's Hands: Racialized Trauma and the Pathway to Mending Our Hearts and Bodies*, 5–6.

42 Porges, "Reciprocal Influences Between Body and Brain in the Perception and Expression of Affect: A Polyvagel Perspective."

43 Peggy J. Kleinplatz and A. Dana Ménard, "Building Blocks Toward Optimal Sexuality: Constructing a Conceptual Model," *The Family Journal* 15, no. 1 (January 2007): 72, https://doi.org/10.1177/1066480706294126.

44 Ibid., 72.
45 Rhea Ashley Hoskin and Allison Taylor, "Femme Resistance: The Fem(Me) Inine Art of Failure," *Psychology & Sexuality* 10, no. 4 (October 2, 2019): 283, https://doi.org/10.1080/19419899.2019.1615538.
46 Jack Halberstam, *The Queer Art of Failure* (Durham, NC: Duke University Press, 2011), 3.
47 Ibid., 2–3.
48 Ibid., 3.
49 Menakem, *My Grandmother's Hands: Racialized Trauma and the Pathway to Mending Our Hearts and Bodies*, 8.
50 Pat Ogden and Janina Fisher, *Sensorimotor Psychotherapy: Interventions for Trauma and Attachment*, Norton Series on Interpersonal Neurobiology (New York, NY: W. W. Norton & Company, 2015), 81.
51 José Esteban Muñoz, *Cruising Utopia: The Then and There of Queer Futurity*, 10th Anniversary Edition, Sexual Cultures (New York, NY: NYU Press, 2019), 21.
52 American Psychiatric Association, *Diagnostic and Statistical Manual of Mental Disorders: DSM-5* (Arlington, VA: American Psychiatric Association, 2013), 451–459; E E P Benestad, "From Gender Dysphoria to Gender Euphoria: An Assisted Journey," *Sexologies* 19 (2010): 225–231.
53 James Hillman, *A Blue Fire: Selected Writings by James Hillman*, ed. Thomas Moore (New York, NY: Harper Perennial, 1989), 241.
54 West, *Show Yourself to Me: Queer Kink Erotica*, 227.
55 Ogden and Fisher, *Sensorimotor Psychotherapy: Interventions for Trauma and Attachment*, 81.
56 Sara I. McClelland, "Intimate Justice: A Critical Analysis of Sexual Satisfaction," *Social and Personality Psychology Compass* 4, no. 9 (September 2, 2010): 663–80, https://doi.org/10.1111/j.1751-9004.2010.00293.x; Sara I. McClelland, "Intimate Justice," in *Encyclopedia of Critical Psychology*, ed. Thomas Teo (New York, NY: Springer New York, 2014), 1010–1013, https://doi.org/10.1007/978-1-4614-5583-7.

5

RE-CENTERING PLEASURE

Lucie Fielding

A
s I discussed in Chapters 1 and 3, when our focus in working with our trans and non-binary clients is centered on questions of performance, it cuts out a lot of ways trans folx experience erotic embodiment and engage in sex. What about kink/BDSM, for example? Or tantric practices? And what about certain forms of crip sex? Many trans and non-binary folx find that gender dysphoria or body dysphoria constellates around the genitalia, or that the kinds of sex that are affirming for their bodies don't involve genitals or penetrating genitals. Are we to claim that such forms of erotic experiencing are somehow ipso facto "less than"?

Centering our praxis on performance and function also plays into what adrienne maree brown describes as "fearful imaginations," imaginations that "fear Blackness, brownness, fatness, queerness, disability, difference."[1] Such imaginations, as Rhea Ashley Hoskin and Allison Taylor suggest, mark out certain bodies (e.g., fat, disabled, BIPoC, elder, and/or trans and non-binary bodies) as "hyper-visible" for their "failure" to correspond to embodiments that are sanctioned by the white, thin, ableist, ageist, cis heteropatriarchy; while simultaneously subjecting said bodies to erasure, and marking them out as subjects without access to desirability or desire-ability precisely because of the cultural unintelligibility—or illegibility—of their erotic embodiments.[2] By de-centering pleasure we are playing into a cultural script that functions as "an ideological form of space-policing whereby" fat, elder, disabled, BIPoC, and trans and non-binary erotic "subjectivities are devalued and excluded."[3]

If Chapter 1 began to make the case for re-centering pleasure, the present chapter presents what a pleasure-centered and pleasure-positive praxis might look and feel like. In the sections to follow I will introduce a pleasure-centered clinical framework steeped in social justice paradigms. I will also devote space to discussing how such a framework can be felt, perceived, and embodied by our trans and non-binary clients.

Intimate Justice

"Was it good for you?" It's a post-sex phrase so cliché that it became the title of a *Sex in the City* episode (season 2, episode 16, 1999). Let's flex our somatic-imaginal muscles here. Read the question again and bring your awareness to any body movement-images or body sensation-images that make themselves known to you.

For my part, an image immediately popped into conscious awareness of a cis dude rolling off his partner after 2–5 minutes of humping, pumping, and jack-hammering. He came and is probably minutes away from a post-coital dozing. As for his partner? They spent the last 2–5 minutes of, let's face it, deeply underwhelming sex probably counting cracks in the ceiling or organizing their underwear drawer or meal planning. Imagining into the question, I felt a groan rumbling in my chest and throat, the makings of a substantial eye-roll, and a feeling of disdain that manifests as a turning over of my stomach. Finally, I imagined myself as the guy's partner and I experienced a body movement-image of me rolling over in response to the largely rhetorical question and decking the dude in the kisser. But that may just be me.

A version of this question is a staple of sexological research, and has been for decades.[4] It appears in studies measuring what is called "sexual satisfaction." This is to say, if you're a sexology researcher reading this passage, congratulations, good chance you've been the groan-worthy clueless dude! Usually measured in surveys (as well as many medical and mental health provider intake forms!) as some variation of "how satisfied are you with your sex life?," the construct of sexual satisfaction in sexological research, as Sara McClelland explains, "aims to highlight whether a person has reached a level of fulfillment with their sexual life."[5] And sexual satisfaction is operationalized in a variety of ways in research as well as practice, including as a means of "assessing your genital health, your psychological state, as well as the quality of your intimate relationship(s) and sexual experience(s)" and diagnostically guiding treatment planning for so-called sexual dysfunctions and disorders of sexual desire and arousal.[6]

There are two problems with the construct of sexual satisfaction. First, it tends to equate satisfaction and fulfillment with orgasm and elide a distinction between pleasure and orgasm.[7] In so doing, experiences that might be intensely erotic and pleasurable but not result in orgasm can be undervalued. Secondly, we must consider the fact that not all bodies have been granted the same access to sexual pleasure or erotic privilege. That is, whether expressed in terms of orgasmic fulfillment or in terms of pleasure writ large, when we ask about sexual satisfaction we "largely assume that the construct of satisfaction is equally available to individuals," and do not often consider how an individual's horizons for *expecting* pleasure are all too often heavily imbricated with their social location.[8] In other words, as we re-center pleasure, we cannot just attend to the mere endorsement of pleasure in a given sexual experience but "how social and political inequities impact intimate experiences," and how they affect "how individuals imagine [...] and evaluate" their erotic lives and experiences.[9] Just as only certain bodies are coded or are legible as desirable and desire-able or invested with erotic privilege, so too are only certain folx granted access to sexual pleasure as inalienable rather than as a privilege.

Many trans and non-binary folx move within cultures that have not long recognized them as sexual beings or individuals deserving of a rich erotic life. From the advent of gender-affirming care in the United States, for example, trans and non-binary folx were told in no uncertain terms that they (were to) have "no overt sex life at all," and were not to have an "erotic sense of their own bodies."[10] To love one's body, and particularly one's sexual body, was to deny oneself access to gender-affirmative care.[11] And, sad to say, earlier elaborations of the belief that trans folx were to unquestioningly loathe their sexual bodies have persisted into the relative present, as evidenced by Walter Bockting and Eli Coleman claiming that trans folx's efforts to create a sense of "personal attractiveness and sexual competence" was "complicated by an aversion to their bodies and genitals, precluding any feeling of personal attractiveness or willingness to become sexually intimate."[12]

Or, consider the many ways Hollywood film and television representations of trans folx have, until quite recently, consistently denied trans and non-binary folx desirability and a sense of erotic agency. As even the most cursory viewing of many of the films and shows featured in Sam Feder, Amy Scholder, and Laverne Cox's documentary film *Disclosure* (2020) will bear out, it is hard to imagine trans and non-binary folx as sexual beings and dating prospects when one is consistently treated to images of trans men as T-fueled rage beasts (see the character Max Sweeney on the original *L Word*) or trans women as deceitful or pitiful creatures whose bodies provoke cis rage, revulsion, rejection, and literal vomiting (see *Soapdish*, *The Crying Game*, *Ace Ventura: Pet Detective*).[13]

These messages and representations are, of course, bullshit. And I hope that by this point in the book, dear reader, you have been furnished with numerous ways of affirming the embodied erotic possibility in trans and non-binary bodies. But if I emphasize within these pages history and rhetoric, word and representation it is because that history and those representations are still very much part of the soup I, we, and many of our clients are swimming in. After all, as actress and writer Jen Richards laments in *Disclosure*, "Every trans person carries within themselves a history of trans representation in terms of what they've seen themselves."[14]

This is the problem of measuring sexual satisfaction in the ways that we typically do. If I, we, or any of our clients are going into dates, sex, or play always already thinking our bodies "less than," or not worthy of pleasure, our horizons for what we expect or what we feel we deserve in terms of pleasure and embodied joy narrow considerably. Thus, we must consider pleasure and desire not as uniquely subjective experiences, but as intimately bound up in cultural dynamics of oppression. This requires we consider entitlement to sexual pleasure within a social justice framework.

Such a framework is suggested by McClelland in her research, namely, intimate justice.[15] Intimate justice, she explains, is "a theoretical framework that links experiences of inequity in the sociopolitical domain with how individuals imagine and evaluate the quality of their sexual and relational experiences."[16] Although intimate justice was originally developed as a theory to guide how sexological research might better be conducted, there are a number of implications for clinical practice.

Adopting the lens of intimate justice challenges us, as providers, to consider a client's social location and their intersectional experiences of stigma and oppression, and how these elements "impact what individuals feel they deserve in their intimate lives" and what they feel they can expect going into a sexual or play experience.[17] Thus, an essential part of our work with trans and non-binary clients involves a dual process of: (1) deconstructing and externalizing the dominant narratives that help shape how they envision sex, desire, and pleasure as well as whose bodies are granted access to desire and pleasure; and (2) helping to replace these problem-saturated narratives of embodied sexuality with alternative ways of imagining their erotic horizons and entitlement to pleasure.

What would it be to imagine sexuality as a terrain of play and wonder rather than as a packed dysphoria minefield? I have included in the BTToP box that follows an exercise you can engage in with your clients to begin a process of mystifying and re-visioning how pleasure might live in—and be expressed through—their bodies. While building on the concept of intimate justice explored in this section, in the next section I shall examine the place of wanting and desiring in the erotic landscape, and specifically the ways we might help clients claim a sense of entitlement to pleasure by expressing likes, wants, and desires with confidence.

BTToP: Intimate Justice Exercise

In Chapter 3 I introduced the idea of the "mystifying question." Similar to the deconstructive questions deployed in narrative therapy, mystifying questions are designed to help carve out space in the client's imaginary so that dominant narratives and cultural scripts might relinquish their hold. Deconstruction and mystifying work should not, in fact, be unfamiliar to our trans and non-binary clients. The specific terrain of sexualities, pleasure, and desire may be unfamiliar, but trans and non-binary folx are no stranger to mystification with respect to gender, a fact we may do well to remind them prior to engaging in deconstructive activities. To repurpose an assertion made by Angela Davis while speaking on police and prison abolition movements at the end of June 2020, the trans community has already "taught us how to challenge that which is totally accepted as normal."[18] What other supposed truths and structures of power might be un-settled as trans and non-binary folx have gender?

Consonant with the concept of *intimate justice* and its attention to both how vectors of oppression impact a person's expectations for pleasure and how experiences of inequity narrow the horizons of the erotic imagination, I have included below a set of mystifying questions designed to help you subtly introduce intimate justice in your work with clients as well as mystify pleasure and embodied eroticism. Although this exercise is designed to be used as a mystification exercise for clients, I would invite you to ask yourself these questions as a way of understanding your own relationships to pleasure and the erotic, and where intimate justice might live in your embodied psyche.

1. What messages have you picked up in your life about pleasure?
2. How have the following people or groups influenced your beliefs or assumptions about sexuality and pleasure?
   - Family members;
   - Friend groups;
   - Sexual or romantic partners;
   - Your communities;
   - Media (film, television, social media, magazines, porn, etc.)
3. Who are your erotic role models?
4. Tell me about a time you experienced pleasure in your body. What images or sensations bubbled up into consciousness? What utterly surprised you?
5. What in your life makes you feel liberated?[19]
6. What does your most pleasurable life look like?

Shoulds vs. Wants

My first mentor in sex therapy, Gina Ogden, would often exhort me to pay attention to the "shoulds and oughts" my clients might offer in session. "Shoulds and oughts" are statements that are characterized by rigid, self-limiting judgments about sex and pleasure. I didn't have to pay that close attention, as it turns out. In my own experience, "should" statements crop up in just about every session devoted to exploring sex, sexualities, desire, and gender:

- "I should pass."
- "I shouldn't find _____ sexy."
- "As a woman, I shouldn't be so brash and forward."
- "Non-binary folx should be androgynous."
- "I should get bottom surgery because no one will fuck me when they find out I don't have a vagina."
- "I should have a deeper voice."
- "I ought to like _____."

The thing about "should and oughts" is that they are "pleasure-killing" as well as curiosity killing, for they nip in the bud any impulse to wonder, to explore, to bring curiosity to our embodied sexual selves, to mystify and re-vision.[20] They foreclose conversation.

In the presence of these "shoulds and oughts," Gina suggested that I high-light the statement and inquire, "And who's 'should' is that?," or "Where did you learn that 'ought'?," or "What messages have you picked up in your life about [insert subject of the should statement]?" Most of the time, my clients do not point to specific events that taught them a "should" or "ought." Rather, they tend to point to messages they picked up over time in relationships or in their fam-ilies of origin about pleasure, sexual values, and gender roles and rules. Media messages are perhaps the most frequently cited, from the covers of magazines to representations of gender, sex, and sexualities in film, television, and novels.

Here's a short sample of some of the responses I've heard from clients over the years:

- "My mom caught me Playing Doctor with a friend when I was 10 and totally freaked out!"
- "I guess you do enough *Cosmo* quizzes and that gives you a pretty warped idea of what sex is supposed to be like when you finally 'do it.'"
- "Sex ed in high school was all about how to not get pregnant and how you have sex once and get an STI and your nose falls off."
- "All of my boyfriends in high school or college freaked out every time I tried to ask them to make an adjustment during sex."

- "I dunno, it just seemed like an unspoken rule of flirting that all the talking, the communication, just kills the mood?"
- "I got pretty clear messages from my dad and brothers growing up about what it was to be a man."
- "Oh my goodness, the porn I watched before I found Crash Pad and the AORTA films! It was so straight, cis, and male gaze-y. And even when something I saw turned me on, I felt guilty about it after."
- "The original *L Word*, between the biphobia and the transphobia, pretty much fucked me up for a good ten years there."
- "All the trans folx on television were either ostracized or had, like, no sex or dating life to speak of."

Gina encouraged me to help my clients replace their "shoulds and oughts" with "want statements." If "should statements" come from without (namely, from messages we've internalized from culture about sex, embodiment, desire, desirability, and pleasure from practically the moment we are able to sense the world around us), "want statements" come from within. They are what *we* want rather than what culture *wants for us* or what a given culture thinks we should want. To be sure, as I noted in my discussion of erotic privilege in Chapter 1, wants and desires are still very much informed by the cultures in which we move. For example, some studies have linked a growth in particular sexual behaviors, such as anal play and pubic hair grooming, to the prevalence of such behaviors in porn.[21] But often "want statements" tend to speak from desires that culture would seek to quash, or at the very least regulate and constrain. These are consensual erotic urges, thoughts, and behaviors that fall outside that which Gayle Rubin refers to as the "charmed circle," which is to say any urge, thought, or behavior that occurs outside the realm of cis, straight, monogamous, non-commercial sexual relationships and are engaged in by bodies that are deemed undesirable or undesire-able.[22]

"Revolutions begin," suggests the writer Dorothy Allison in her foreword to Amber Hollibaugh's book *My Dangerous Desires: A Queer Girl Dreaming Her Way Home*, "when people look at each other in the eyes, say 'I want,' and mean it."[23] Expressions of desire and wanting as radical incitements to revolution?! To extend the logic of second-wave feminism (namely, that the "personal is political"), I posit that queer and trans desire can be precisely that, namely, an act of defiance, a refusal to participate in the ways culture works on—and through—us to shape our expectations of what we feel we should deserve from sex and relationships. When trans and non-binary folx claim desire and express that desire they are, as José Esteban Muñoz argues, "doing the work of imagining another life, another time, another place [...] where our Eros is not conscripted in the fashion that civilization demands."[24] And when we work with our trans and non-binary clients to reformulate "shoulds and oughts" and express desire in terms of "want statements," we are supplying them with a pathway to the "always win" scenario I mentioned in the last chapter. In the following BTToP box I provide a short exercise you might engage in with your clients to help them begin to identify and articulate those want statements.

Coming up with want statements may constitute a spark of erotic revolution, but revolutions don't just spring up out of thin air. Many clients, cis and trans, may have a beastly time trying to figure out what precisely they want and how they might go about distinguishing their desire from societal and cultural demands or prescriptions. In the next section of this chapter I thus discuss how desire might be felt in the body and how that feeling of knowing might be cultivated and supported.

BTToP: "Words of Want"

The following activity was inspired by an exchange between Dorothy Allison and Amber Hollibaugh during one of their first encounters. As Allison recounts, as these two working-class femmes sat across from one another at a midtown Manhattan coffee shop, Allison leans in conspiratorially and says, "I'll tell you mine if you'll tell me yours." "What I offered my friend was the dangerous revelation of desire." What followed was an exchange of want statements: "I want to write a great book—I want to make a difference—I want to have adventures and take enormous risks and be everything they say we are and not give a damn what anyone says."[25]

Taking Allison and Hollibaugh's exchange of wants and desire as a jumping off point, this exercise is about inviting the client to take the risk within the bounded chaos of the therapeutic situation to utter, to cite another femme writer Joan Nestle, their own "words of want."[26] Such statements might be quite difficult at first to say aloud. As both Hollibaugh and Allison suggest, speaking our desires aloud can feel dangerous, as if playing with elemental magic. Expect initial tentativeness, note it, and help the client sit with their discomfort. Over time, what might have been uttered in hushed, conspiratorial tones may be proudly proclaimed.

In addition to want statements, I suggest we can also shut down judgment, criticism, and those curiosity-killing, pleasure-foreclosing "shoulds and oughts" by challenging clients to consider statements that begin with "I wonder..." or "I notice..." or "I'm feeling..." These prompts, as my colleague, Utah-based certified sex therapist Kristin Hodson, notes, tend to "invite curiosity instead of judgment or closed certainty" into a client's erotic self-concept.[27]

Here are some examples of want statements as well as some curiosity-nurturing "wonder," "notice," and "feeling" prompts:

- I want to be desired!
- I want to feel powerful!
- I want to experience muffing/Topping/group sex/rope suspension/anal play!
- I wonder what it would be like to stroke my clit and jerk off as if I had a bio dick!
- Whenever I am bootblacking I notice how masculine and powerful I feel!
- I'm feeling anxious about anal play.

Following this exercise, you might process the exercise with your client, perhaps using the following questions to guide the conversation:

1. What sensations, images, feelings, or thoughts might you have noticed coming into awareness as you considered your "words of want?"
2. Where did you feel excitement/anxiety/curiosity/desire in your body? Can you associate an image with it?
3. What would it be to enact this desire, these words of want?

Feeling Want

In the preceding sections of this chapter, I presented a conceptual framework for re-centering pleasure in our work with trans and non-binary clients around erotic embodiment. In this and the next section I want to shift focus from discussing what a pleasure-centered practice might look like to what it might *feel* like in trans and non-binary bodies. In this section I will consider what it is to feel wants and desires in the body, while in the next I consider how pleasure, or liking, might be embodied.

"What can I do to please you?" "What do you want?" "How would you like for me to pleasure you?" These are all lovely questions that speak to a desire for a reciprocal exchange of pleasure. And yet the answers to those questions are not always obvious. It's all well and good to shift from the "shoulds and oughts" to want statements as I counseled in the last section, but sometimes for my trans and non-binary clients, it is a struggle to *feel* wanting and desire in the body, let alone *acknowledge* that wanting and desiring. Faced with a partner asking what we want, some of us might find our minds going blank or our panic rising in our bodies. After I gently challenged them about a "should" they had brought into the room one client asked, "Yeah, but how do I know what I want?" How indeed?!?

We may draw a blank when we are asked what we want for a number of reasons, and I've outlined four of them below:

1) **It can be hard to know what one wants when one doesn't have a sense of what is even possible.** When a client routinely draws a blank around wants and desires, there are a few ways you can help them find their want statements. First, you might provide a client with a list of gender-affirming—and, indeed, trans-authored—novels, memoirs, and erotic literature. You might also consider suggesting ethical porn that explicitly centers a wide variety of bodies and identities, such as CrashPad Series and AORTA Films. Second, you might ask your client to review and create a "Want, Will, Won't" worksheet, otherwise known as a "Yes, No, Maybe" worksheet. Many of these worksheets—generally used as tools to assist in negotiations prior to play—include lists of activities (e.g., breath play, piss play, anal sex), language for parts and self (e.g., cunt, jerk off, slut), and feeling states (e.g., abandoned, cherished, degraded, empowered). Lastly, you might invite your client to explore their body. As Allison Moon suggests in *Girl Sex 101*, "[there] are few sensations a partner can generate for you that you can't generate yourself."[28] Invite the client to find a good, uninterrupted 15–30 minutes and try a host of sensations and moves and different ways of interacting with their bodies. Whether while reviewing the worksheet menus of pleasure or watching porn or playing with themself, encourage the client to bring their awareness to what is coming up in their bodies. Notice the sensations. Note and try to bring curiosity to the feelings and images that might bubble up into consciousness. Or, as I suggest in the BTToP box that follows the next section, the client might check in with themself and ask, "Feels good yes?" or "Feels bad no?" It is in such experimentation that a client can find their "words of want," those sensations, activities, and feelings that excite them and about which they might be curious to try with a partner.

2) **In some cases, we may very well know what we want but "the thing we want feels so shameful or embarrassing that we bury it from even ourselves."**[29] And yet, our kinks, our fantasies, and our fetishes, as June Amelia Rose writes, "have a way of finding us. They seek out the embarrassments we strive to conceal. They illuminate the humiliating pleasures of our hearts."[30] Our desires and fetishes are magical and, as Justin Lehmiller reminds us in his book *Tell Me What You Want*, we are by far not alone in desiring any single one of them, from a love of worshiping beautifully painted soft toes, to consensual non-consent fantasies, to dollification, to puppy play.[31] Working with clients to discharge

sexual shame can be one of the most foundational tasks sexuality professionals engage in, and one of the most meaningful. Through processes of demystification explored briefly in Chapter 3 (e.g., interventions such as psychoeducation) we can help clients normalize their desires and through mystifying and deconstructing questions we can enable clients to disentangle desire from the pathologizing "shoulds and oughts" our cultures produce with merciless efficiency.

3) **Relatedly, trans and non-binary folx might, as Harper Jean Tobin suggests, find our desires unspeakable because "we fear that others will desire us [...] only so long as our own desires don't include sexual activities that they might deem inconsistent with our identities."**[32] Gender rules and roles—already insidious enough to deconstruct and unlearn on their own—become all the more insidious when they intersect with desire. Many of my clients lust and fantasize within rigid gender norms, norms that seek to tell them that gender and sexuality can only be embodied in certain socially prescribed ways. My client Cam (he/him), a white, gay trans man operated so long under the assumption that sexual intimacy with other men required engaging in penetrative anal sex, despite finding penetration of either his front or back holes intensely dysphoria-provoking.[33] Likewise, my client, Kara (she/her), a Black butch trans woman, lamented that even though she was a switch, she often felt as if she could never top for partners because to do so risked marking her out as, in her words, "too threatening," "too assertive," and "too much like a dude." She had also grown up with all sorts of toxic stereotypes of Black women as "sexually aggressive" and hypersexual.[34] In both clients' dating worlds they were running up against cultural scripts that sought to proscribe the kinds of sex and play they could engage in. As with discharging sexual shame, addressing perceived inconsistencies between gender, desire, and erotic embodiment can be a subtle exploration of demystification, mystification, and re-visioning. There may also be some productive skill development work to be done around communicating and negotiating play with partners, building trust with one another's bodies prior to engaging in sex or play, as my colleague Angie Gunn suggests.[35] Communicating misgivings and fears to partners around desire, wants, and needs might very well lead to opportunities to deepen into trust and promote spaces where ecstasy might thrive.

4) **Finally, for some trans and non-binary folx, looking inward to suss out one's desires and then proceeding to express that desire can feel dangerous because we may not feel deserving of that wanting as a result of internalized transphobia and/or internalized transmisogyny.** We might convince ourselves that our desires aren't important—or as important as our partners' desires—or that we should

be grateful for what we have. As a result, we might not readily acknowledge our wants and needs, let alone articulate them and advocate for them with partners. In such cases, to engage in boundary-setting or to acknowledge desire might feel like threats to relational wellbeing. My client Cam lamented, "It's not like the dating pool is huge. Have you seen Grindr or Scruff around here?!? It sucks but I gotta take what I can get." As I discussed in Chapter 1, dating while trans is, unfortunately, a thing. And to deny or downplay its existence could very well be seen as invalidating to many trans clients. We, as providers, are called upon to validate our clients' realities while simultaneously helping them claim their entitlement to desire, to having their wants and needs realized and celebrated in sexual, romantic, and play relationships. With Cam, for example, I used questions similar to those I included in the BTToP Intimate Justice Exercise earlier in this chapter—questions designed to help clients see the ways that dominant discourses on desire, pleasure, and self-worth are not serving them, while building capacity for imagining how a more intimately just life might be embodied. For example, "If you could wave a magic wand and you suddenly woke up in a sexual relationship that felt exciting and affirming and mutually fulfilling, what would that look and feel like?" "What might you be able to do to bring that dream into reality?"

No matter the scenario—or combination of scenarios!—a given client might embody, our work as providers is to help our clients connect to what they want, those desires and fantasies that impassion them. In this and in the next section (on feeling pleasure), working with a client to nurture awareness of the somatic-imaginal can be immensely helpful. Here, the work is in providing a feeling of boundedness that allows the client to tap into the feelings and sensations that clue them into the presence of desire and allow them, ultimately, to articulate their "wants" with confidence.

When Cam first came to work with me, I noticed how he held himself straight away. Despite having had top surgery years before, he still walked with his shoulders hunched forward, his back curved. Some trans masc folx refer to this posture as a "trans slouch." Prior to top surgery, you might see masc-of-center clients engaging in the trans slouch to hide and/or minimize the presence of chest tissue. In Cam's case, he confided in one session, the slouch spoke to a desire to shrink himself, to take up as little space as possible. And, as noted above, this minimization of self played out in his relationships as a minimization of his wants and needs. I asked Cam if he would consent to experimenting a bit with posture. As he shifted his shoulders back and took on his full height of 5'8" I asked him what sensations, images, feelings, and thoughts he might be noticing in that moment. "I feel so much taller, so much more confident. And it's weird, but can that both feel exciting and terrifying at the same time?" After having devoted a session or two to the ambivalence that came up around the feeling of confidence evoked by adjusting posture, I asked Cam if he would be willing to recall a fantasy, something he'd always wanted to do with a partner but had never felt comfortable expressing aloud. Cam opted not to share the fantasy with me, but as he brought the fantasy into conscious awareness, I invited him to notice what the desire felt like in his body. Ultimately, this work allowed Cam to be able to notice when he desired something and how he experienced knowing—and embodying—desire.

Desire is dangerous. And in a trans body, expressing desire can be a way of actively resisting a cultural discursive apparatus that tells us that we are not entitled to expect much of anything from sex and play, that our desires are not important or worthy of finding expression. Having explored in this section how we might help our clients claim their entitlement to desire, I now turn to how pleasure might be felt and embodied.

Feeling Pleasure

"What kinds of reward can failure offer us?" asks Jack Halberstam in *The Queer Art of Failure*. "Perhaps most obviously," he responds, "failure allows us to escape the punishing norms that discipline behavior and manage human development with the goal of" producing docile, orderly, productive subjects under white supremacy, patriarchy, and capitalism.[36] In the particular cases of gender and sexuality, "failure often means being relieved of the pressure to measure up to patriarchal ideals."[37] When the culturally scripted imperatives to perform sexually or function in particular ways are ignored and refused, what possibilities open up, what spaces are created for pleasure and embodied eroticism to flourish? In my discussion of reveling in queer failure and "swan diving into the awkward" in Chapter 4, I discussed how an enthusiastic embrace of awkwardness could allow our trans and non-binary clients to experience an always-win scenario. It is high time I described what that always-win scenario is and, in particular, what it might feel like in trans and non-binary bodies.

The always-win scenario is one in which, to quote Emily Nagoski, "pleasure is the measure" of erotic wellbeing.[38] This means that sex or play is not oriented around the presence or achievement of orgasm. It also means that the ways of achieving that pleasure become polymorphous, and not just centered around sex or play that involves genitals, or genitals performing in particular ways. Cultural scripts, norms, and discourses of performance and function that would seek to narrowly define and regulate erotic embodiment are met here with, as narrative therapist Michael White puts it, "obstreperous resistance," while a deliciously "perverse interest" in forms of sexuality and erotic experiencing that challenge "the narrow legitimated forms of contemporary culture" are ecstatically pursued.[39] The always-win scenario is essentially, then, the dual recognition that (1) all pleasure counts, not just orgasm or genitally focused sensation, and (2) any pleasure is an expression of joyful, transgressive presence. Pleasure bites back!

Here, I recall the concept of polymorphous perversity. While this is a concept that is Freudian in origin, we need neither adopt Freud's deeply flawed theories of human sexuality nor, specifically, his psychosexual stages of childhood development to draw upon it. The word "perverse" in and of itself is freighted with a long history of the legal, medical, and psychiatric establishment working to define and regulate desire and pleasure. I use this term carefully and in the sense Dorothy Allison uses it, namely, that perversity refers to a "deliberate rebellion against shame and fear," and to seeking "one's own definitions and ideals regardless of what others insist are the limits to what you may want or have."[40]

Polymorphous perversity, simply put, refers to an embodied psychic disposition of being able to derive sensual, sexual, and erotic pleasure from just about any part of the body. That is, the entire body is approached as erogenous, rather than erotogenic potential being situated in only specific zones of the body. Polymorphous perversity is a disposition to which all bodies have access across the lifespan. But the cultures in which we move are horribly effective at obscuring that fact, and tend instead to delimit a "permissible range of expressions of physical sexuality," as Sandy Stone put it—namely, sexuality that is genital-focused and goal-oriented, involving, ideally, hard, penetrating cocks and well-lubricated, receptive pussies.[41]

If there is anything I've learned from my experiences in kink it is that sensual/erotic pleasure can be found through numerous means and in numerous parts of the body. I have experienced intense pleasure being trussed and tied in rope, or having various parts of my body struck by floggers and canes, or while a knife's edge warped and weaved across the surface of my skin. I have reached ecstatic heights of orgasmic delight after having gazed into a partner's eyes and brought my breath in sync with theirs. I've delighted in the paroxysms of glee one trans masc partner of mine experienced as I kissed and licked their top surgery scars. And, finally, I've seen partners thrilled by running the pads of their fingers over my skin, the naked equivalent of the re-visioning hands BTToP exercise I provided in Chapter 3.

The point is this: our bodies are infinitely expandable and capable of experiencing pleasure in multiple ways. Indeed, trans and non-binary folx have already modeled some of those ways, from finding affirming ways to interact with genitals (e.g., muffing or, say, bobbing or stroking the glans clitoris) to de-centering genital experiencing and re-mapping the terrain where pleasure can be experienced. Our task as providers is to help our trans and non-binary clients release themselves from the thrall of dominant sexual scripts and realize the multitudinous possibilities already present to them. When pleasure becomes the aim rather than orgasm or performing and functioning under some culturally constructed and circumscribed sense of "normal operating parameters" (*pace* Commander Data), our trans and non-binary clients always win.

Inasmuch as we are all, cis and trans, entitled to sexual pleasure, we are also entitled to sexual and play experiences that affirm the polymorphous perverse potential of our bodies and move us toward euphoria. But what is it to feel that pleasure, to feel gender euphoria in the body, and, indeed, as my client Xochi sought to do, to actively seek pleasure and euphoria out? It is to this question that I now turn.

In introducing the somatic-imaginal in the last chapter, I spoke of the body sensation-images and body movement-images that bubbled up through Xochi's embodied psyche as they deepened into what gender euphoria felt like in their body. You may remember the twin flames Xochi spoke about dancing in their eyes or how they described feeling their skin crackling with kinetic energy. And surely the image of a goofily louche Xochi beckoning their partner to join them was seared on your memory?! In that passage, though, I spoke only of Xochi's embodied sense of gender euphoria—the positive feelings Xochi experienced when their gender was affirmed and ecstatically embodied—and not their experiences of gender dysphoria. But Xochi's experiences of how gender dysphoria is held in their body were explored in much the same way gender euphoria was and, indeed, dysphoria was the jumping off point for the evocation of euphoria. This is because sometimes the evocation of "negative" values and sensations can be how we can begin to notice what wanting, pleasure, and euphoria feel like, how they are held in us. To return to the phenomenon of wanting and desiring, isn't it sometimes easier to elicit from oneself knowledge of those things we *don't* want than what we *do* want? When my wife and I talk about what we want for dinner on a given night, it is often so much easier for me to start with what I don't want to cook. In much the same way, it might be easier for some clients to engage in the work of attuning to how pleasure is experienced in the body by starting with what how discomfort, displeasure, or dislike are experienced. Indeed, dislike and dysphoria aren't merely the opposites of liking and euphoria; they can also give us clues for how we might begin to imagine and embody liking and euphoria. This may seem paradoxical but I suggest that dysphoria can hold within it the possibility for euphoria.

"Hm," Xochi reflected, "dysphoria is easy to feel." Xochi winced as they said this and almost seemed to shiver in that moment as he allowed a wave of dysphoria to wash over them. I had invited them to evoke how they experienced gender dysphoria in their body because euphoria had, at first, felt elusive to them. "Sometimes it feels as if my insides have been melon-balled. It's like an absence of feeling. Like someone just sucked me out of my body. Sitting here, I feel on edge—uneasy, anxious, maybe even just bracing myself for something bad to happen?" One might say that we were at that point in our work far from the chest-baring, leopard-print robe and the "come hither!" motions that Xochi would later associate with their embodied experience of pleasure and euphoria. And yet, the evocation of dysphoria, in fact, took place mere minutes before we turned to evoking euphoria. Imagining into dysphoria allowed Xochi to experience how they could attune to the somatic-imaginal in the first place and use that capacity to imagine into gender euphoria and pleasure. "You know how in those 1940s Hollywood melodramas where there's those old, dusty, musty houses with the furniture covered in sheets? That's dysphoria for me. I'm shut down for the long winter. And we know how much I hate winter," Xochi added, chortling at that last observation but crumpling forward as if bracing themself against the winds of a cold, lonely winter.

"And what would happen," I asked, beginning the pivot to euphoria, "if you dramatically threw open the curtains and tore the sheets from the furniture?" Taking in this image, Xochi almost seemed to squint their eyes and I observed a micro movement in their hands, as if they were about to move them to shield their eyes from sunlight. Xochi's moody, dilapidated gothic manor suddenly seemed to come alive. It felt like a home Xochi could imagine living in. And from there it was not too far a leap to get to Xochi and their retro-Hollywood playboy smoking jacket.

The pivot from dysphoria to euphoria will necessarily look and feel different for other clients. Working with the somatic-imaginal is almost like doing improv theater, where we animate and riff off whatever our clients may bring into the room with them at a given moment. For Xochi it was the sheet-covered furniture, but for other clients an entirely different multiverse of image, feeling, and sensation may bubble up into embodied consciousness. Our task is to be present for whatever comes up, for whatever body sensation-images or body movement-images our clients happen to bring with them; and to know when to dramatically throw open the curtains, as it were.

There are, of course, other ways that we can help our clients find and evoke pleasure in their bodies. In the BTToP section that immediately follows, I've included a less imaginal way to do this. We can also deploy mystifying and revisioning questions help clients attune to the somatic-imaginal. For instance, we can ask clients to think about a time when they felt pleasure, whether it was erotic or not, and what the pleasure felt like. From there, you might inquire where the pleasure was located in the body, what the conditions were that allowed them to feel pleasure, and how those conditions might clue them into how they could come to know the sensations of pleasure in more erotic domains. In the first BTToP section of this chapter, I provided a list of such mystifying and re-visioning questions, and you might start there.

Whatever questions or techniques you deploy to help your clients evoke pleasure and/or euphoria, I would invite you to consider how that pleasure can be polymorphous, and how it can be found and experienced in many different ways. I would also invite you to help them give themselves permission to be joyously perverse, and to find the many ways pleasure can be a tool for liberation.

BTToP: "Feels Good Yes"

Much of how I described the embodied phenomenology of feeling want and feeling pleasure in the previous two sections was undertaken in the spirit of the somatic-imaginal I introduced in Chapter 4. But sometimes attuning to the somatic-imaginal is difficult. This is particularly the case at the beginning of one's practice of coming into (com)passionate relationship with the embodied sexual self. Accordingly, I introduce in this BTToP section a more foundational take on embodied awareness, or at least a first step in the journey to developing embodied awareness.

A few years back, a dear friend of mine, a masc-of-center nonbinary person (they/them), was having a very rough time of it. They were unable to work and they were easily overwhelmed by most social interactions. Traumatic flashbacks, hypervigilance, emotional lability, and panic attacks were features of their daily life. In short, my friend found themself in the throes of depression- and anxiety-nurturing acute traumatic stress. Although they were not able to do much, one thing they could do was check in with themself in the present moment. In a given situation, my friend would query their body, "Feels good yes?" "Feels bad no?" If the response was "feels good yes!" they would continue doing what they were doing at that time; if the response was "feels bad no!" they would stop whatever they were doing and do something else. Between friends, a therapist, and a partner who were doggedly supportive, this dear human was able to move out of that dark period of acute stress. But "feels good yes"/"feels bad no" remained a way that they checked in with themself. And those of us privileged to be in their life started checking in with ourselves that way too.

Although neither this friend nor I are particularly big fans of binary choices, "feels good yes"/"feels bad no" is one binary choice we can really get behind. To my mind, it represents a lovely, simple way we can check in with ourselves that doesn't require a great deal of embodied awareness. Indeed, it can be a visceral, split-second check-in, modeled after how in consent education there is only an enthusiastic "yes" or a full-stop, no-further-explanations-needed "no" (here, "maybe" is best considered a "no" too—there's no such thing as "feels 'meh' maybe"). Another benefit of this particular check-in for our purposes is that it applies equally well to both wanting and liking. As such, it is responsive to the two preceding sections on feeling want and feeling pleasure.

- Do I want to go make out with this cutie? Feels good, yes! "You lead, I'll follow!"
- Does the particular way my partner is torturing my nipples feel yummy? Feels bad no! "Hey, could you loosen the clover clamps a bit?"

Try this out yourself and check in with yourself about feelings of wanting and liking throughout your day. Track what comes up for you as you check in, "feels good yes?"/"feels bad no?"

Some clients may be able to check in with themselves and evoke an embodied psyche replete with image, sensation, and feeling. But for many clients, this shift into a binary choice—"feels good yes"/"feels bad no"—may be their route, at least initially, to determining whether they like or want a given something or situation. And in the midst of sex or play, "feels good yes"/"feels bad no" is far more accessible a check-in response than an open-ended one that might require a great deal more mental energy to be responsive to.

Some clients may not yet quite know what a "yes" or a "no" feels like in their bodies. Because white supremacist cis heteropatriarchy! Thus, in introducing "feels good yes"/"feels bad no" to a client, you might help them practice paying attention to what "yes" or "no" feels like in their body by attending to some low-stakes, non-sexual yes/no queries and having them respond aloud with either "feels good yes" or "feels bad no." Examples of such queries include:

- Do you like the music that is playing?
- Do you want spicy food for lunch today?
- How do you feel about the color red? How about chartreuse?
- Do you want to take a walk right now?
- Would you like a nap?
- Do you like the scent I'm wearing?

As Allison Moon suggests in her treatment of the "embodied yes" in *Girl Sex 101*, with each of these questions (or those you or they might generate), you might suggest giving the client "a little time to explore each [question] before moving on to the next."[42] It is best if the questions provoke a visceral, gut response. You want the client's belly, ears, and nose responding to the questions rather than allowing the psyche to cognitively process them with the mind's penchant for discerning, picking apart, and judging.

And after the exercise you might process the experience with your clients using the following questions:

- What does "no" feel like in your body? What about "yes"?
- Were there particular questions that elicited particularly strong sensations, images, or feelings or where "feels good yes" or "feels bad no" felt harder to suss out or verbalize?

The goal of such an exercise, as Moon asserts, is for your client "to get to a place where it's as easy to answer a question about sex" and play as it is to answer about whether you want spicy food for lunch or like the scent of patchouli.[43]

Conclusion

In this chapter, I introduced the fourth, and final, conceptual framework of the book, re-centering pleasure. To re-center pleasure in our practices is not merely a matter of moving beyond the discourse of (sexual) performance and function and of placing a greater emphasis on pleasure in our work with trans and non-binary clients (although these tasks are vitally important ones!). Building on my discussion of both erotic privilege and the discourse of function in Chapter 1, I contended in this chapter that re-centering pleasure needs to happen within a human rights and social justice framework, namely, through the lens of intimate justice. As Sara McClelland observes with respect to sexological research focused on measuring sexual satisfaction, our work as providers must attend to the ways our clients' social locations and experiences of oppression "impact what [they] feel they deserve in their intimate lives."[44] To find and feel pleasure in the body and in sexual relationships—the "feels good yes," rather than the "feels bad no"—our trans and non-binary clients must first be supported in recognizing that they are entitled to pleasure and desire, that the fullness of sexual liberation is not merely the right and privilege of those of cis experiencing. Trans desire matters; trans pleasure matters!

And, as sex educator Ignacio Rivera writes, a "radical sexuality begins from within," from the sexual body, from a place our clients are empowered to define for themselves. "It is the sexual place that allows you to feel comfort, have agency, ask for what you want, say no, communicate about sex, expose your desires, and much more."[45] This act of coming into erotic embodiment,

Rivera continues, is radical precisely because it means, particularly for BIPoC trans and non-binary folx, "reclaiming" for the self a body "that has been probed by society and the state."[46] As Rivera notes, and as I have argued at numerous points in this book, trans and non-binary bodies have so often been defined by or extrapolated from cis experiencing. Our opportunity in work on trans erotic embodiments, is to flip the script, and to find a radical sexuality that comes *from* us rather than *without* us.

In Chapter 6, this book's final chapter, the focus will shift from conceptual frameworks to clinical practice. The next chapter will also largely constitute a shift in voice from mine to an array of providers who have generously contributed reflections and interventions, vignettes and exercises, meant to bring theory to practice. Despite the shift in focus and voice, however, the four clinical frameworks and stances articulated in this and Chapters 2–4 will remain ever in mind, the critical establishing foundation for all that will be introduced and proposed in Chapter 6. If we are to see manifest in the world glorious revolutions of trans desire, to echo Dorothy Allison, the contributions offered in Chapter 6 might be seen as blueprints for sparking those necessary, and long overdue, insurrections.

Notes

1 adrienne maree brown, *Pleasure Activism: The Politics of Feeling Good*, Emergent Strategy (Chico, CA: AK Press, 2019), 10.
2 Rhea Ashley Hoskin and Allison Taylor, "Femme Resistance: The Fem(me)inine Art of Failure," *Psychology & Sexuality* 10, no. 4 (October 2, 2019): 293, https://doi.org/10.1080/19419899.2019.1615538.
3 Ibid., 293.
4 See, for example, Susan Sprecher, Anita Barbee, and Pepper Schwartz, "'Was It Good for You, Too?': Gender Differences in First Sexual Intercourse Experiences," *The Journal of Sex Research* 32, no. 1 (January 1, 1995): 3–15, https://doi.org/10.1080/00224499509551769; E. Sandra Byers, Stephanie Demmons, and Kohli-An Lawrance, "Sexual Satisfaction within Dating Relationships: A Test of the Interpersonal Exchange Model of Sexual Satisfaction," *Journal of Social and Personal Relationships* 15, no. 2 (1998): 257–267, https://doi.org/10.1177/0265407598152008; Diane Holmberg and Karen L. Blair, "Sexual Desire, Communication, Satisfaction, and Preferences of Men and Women in Same-Sex Versus Mixed-Sex Relationships," *Journal of Sex Research* 46, no. 1 (February 3, 2009): 57–66, https://doi.org/10.1080/00224490802645294; Léa J. Séguin and Robin R. Milhausen, "Not All Fakes Are Created Equal: Examining the Relationships between Men's Motives for Pretending Orgasm and Levels of Sexual Desire, and Relationship and Sexual Satisfaction," *Sexual and Relationship Therapy* 31, no. 2 (April 2, 2016): 159–175, https://doi.org/10.1080/14681994.2016.1158803; Claire M. A. Salisbury and William A. Fisher, "'Did You Come?' A Qualitative Exploration of Gender Differences in Beliefs, Experiences, and Concerns Regarding Female Orgasm Occurrence During Heterosexual Sexual Interactions," *The Journal of Sex Research* 51, no. 6 (August 1, 2014): 616–631, https://doi.org/10.1080/00224499.2013.838934; Val Wongsomboon, Mary H. Burleson, and Gregory D. Webster, "Women's Orgasm

and Sexual Satisfaction in Committed Sex and Casual Sex: Relationship Between Sociosexuality and Sexual Outcomes in Different Sexual Contexts," *The Journal of Sex Research* 57, no. 3 (March 23, 2020): 285–295, https://doi.org/10.1080/00224499.2019.1672036; Patrícia M. Pascoal, Krystelle Shaughnessy, and Maria Joana Almeida, "A Thematic Analysis of a Sample of Partnered Lesbian, Gay, and Bisexual People's Concepts of Sexual Satisfaction," *Psychology & Sexuality* 10, no. 2 (April 3, 2019): 101–118, https://doi.org/10.1080/19419899.2018.1555185.

5 Sara I. McClelland, "Intimate Justice: A Critical Analysis of Sexual Satisfaction," *Social and Personality Psychology Compass* 4, no. 9 (September 2, 2010): 663, https://doi.org/10.1111/j.1751-9004.2010.00293.x.

6 Ibid., 663.

7 Ibid., 668–669.

8 Ibid., 666.

9 Ibid., 672.

10 Harry Benjamin, *The Transsexual Phenomenon*, Electronic Edition (Düsseldorf: Symposium Publishing, 1999), 31, http://www.mut23.de/texte/Harry%20 Benjamin%20-%20The%20Transsexual%20Phenomenon.pdf; Sandy Stone, "The 'Empire' Strikes Back: A Posttranssexual Manifesto," *Camera Obscura* 10, no. 2 (May 1992): 161; J.R. Latham, "Axiomatic: Constituting 'Transexuality' and Trans Sexualities in Medicine," *Sexualities* 22, no. 1–2 (February 2019): 13–30, https://doi.org/10.1177/1363460717740258.

11 Laura Erickson-Schroth and Laura Jacobs, *"You're in the Wrong Bathroom!": And 20 Other Myths and Misconceptions About Transgender and Gender-Nonconforming People* (Boston, MA: Beacon Press, 2017), 57.

12 Walter O. Bockting and Eli Coleman, "Developmental Stages of the Transgender Coming-Out Process: Toward an Integrated Identity," in *Principles of Transgender Medicine and Surgery*, ed. Randi Ettner, Stan Monstrey, and Eli Coleman, 2nd ed. (New York: Routledge, 2016), 145.

13 Sam Feder, *Disclosure*, Documentary (Netflix, 2020). For a fuller treatment of the deceitful and pitiful trans woman tropes in popular culture, see Julia Serano, *Whipping Girl: A Transsexual Woman on Sexism and the Scapegoating of Femininity*, 2nd ed. (Berkeley, CA: Seal Press, 2016).

14 Feder, *Disclosure*, 7:02–7:06.

15 McClelland, "Intimate Justice," September 2, 2010; Sara I. McClelland, "Intimate Justice," in *Encyclopedia of Critical Psychology*, ed. Thomas Teo (New York, NY: Springer New York, 2014), 1010–1013, https://doi.org/10.1007/978-1-4614-5583-7.

16 McClelland, "Intimate Justice," 2014, 1010.

17 Ibid., 1010.

18 Dr. Davis' remarks were part of a panel on the subject of police and prison abolition held in mid-June 2020. They were transcribed from video of the event excerpted in a tweet by @nkat95, which went viral. See Angela Davis, "Dr. Angela Davis on the Role of the Trans and Non-Binary Communities in the Fight for the Feminist Abolition She Advocates For," libcom.org, June 25, 2020, http:// libcom.org/library/dr-angela-davis-role-trans-non-binary-communities-fight-feminist-abolition-she-advocates.

19 I am indebted to Dalychia Saah, sexuality educator and co-founder of Afrosexology, for this question, which posed to attendees of her plenary address at the 2019 AASECT annual conference in Philadelphia, PA.

20 Gina Ogden, *The Heart and Soul of Sex* (Boston, MA: Trumpeter Books, 2006), 69.

21 See, for example, Breanne Fahs and Jax Gonzalez, "The Front Lines of the 'Back Door': Navigating (Dis)Engagement, Coercion, and Pleasure in Women's Anal Sex Experiences," *Feminism & Psychology* 24, no. 4 (November 2014): 500–520, https://doi.org/10.1177/0959353514539648; Margo Mullinax et al., "In Their Own Words: A Qualitative Content Analysis of Women's and Men's Preferences for Women's Genitals," *Sex Education* 15, no. 4 (July 4, 2015): 421–436, https://doi.org/10.1080/14681811.2015.1031884; Martin S. Weinberg et al., "Pornography, Normalization, and Empowerment," *Archives of Sexual Behavior* 39, no. 6 (December 2010): 1389–1401, https://doi.org/10.1007/s10508-009-9592-5.

22 Gayle S. Rubin, "Thinking Sex: Notes for a Radical Theory of the Politics of Sexuality," in *Deviations: A Gayle Rubin Reader* (Durham, NC:Duke University Press, 2011), 152, https://doi.org/10.1215/9780822394068.

23 Amber Hollibaugh, *My Dangerous Desires: A Queer Girl Dreaming Her Way Home* (Durham, NC: Duke University Press, 2000), xiii.

24 José Esteban Muñoz, *Cruising Utopia: The Then and There of Queer Futurity*, 10th Anniversary Edition, Sexual Cultures (New York, NY: NYU Press, 2019), 144.

25 Hollibaugh, *My Dangerous Desires: A Queer Girl Dreaming Her Way Home*, xii.

26 Joan Nestle, "Our Gift of Touch," in *The Persistent Desire: A Femme-Butch Reader*, ed. Joan Nestle (Boston, MA: Allyson Publications, 1992), 486.

27 Kristin B. Hodson, "4 Easy Prompts to Start a Conversation about Sexual Health...," Instagram Post, @kristinbhodson, February 3, 2020, https://www.instagram.com/p/B8HH5QghCFI/.

28 Allison Moon, *Girl Sex 101* (Lunatic Ink, 2014), 49.

29 Ibid., 58.

30 June Amelia Rose, "Foot Fetishism and the Erasure Politics of Dyke Sexualities," *FIST Zine*, January 2019, 11.

31 Justin J. Lehmiller, *Tell Me What You Want: The Science of Sexual Desire and How It Can Help You Improve Your Sex Life* (New York, NY: Hachette Books, 2018).

32 Harper Jean Tobin, "The Perils and Pleasures of Sex for Trans People," in *Sex Matters: The Sexuality and Society Reader*, ed. Mindy Stombler et al., 4th ed. (New York, NY: W. W. Norton & Company, 2014), 24.

33 Cam was cheered, however, by reading in a piece from volume I of the *Trans Sex Zine* that he could still be a fabulous gay man and not engage in sex that didn't feel yummy to him. See, "Destabilising the Narrative of Penetration," *Trans Sex Zine, Volume I*, 2017, 8.

34 See, for a gloss of these toxic stereotypes, Melissa V. Harris-Perry, *Sister Citizen: Shame, Stereotypes, and Black Women in America* (New Haven, CT: Yale University Press, 2011).

35 Angie Gunn, "How To Have Great Sex With Someone New (By Building The Right Kind Of Trust)," *YourTango* (blog), December 20, 2017, https://www.yourtango.com/experts/angie-gunn/how-build-trust-sex-someone-new.

36 Jack Halberstam, *The Queer Art of Failure* (Durham, NC: Duke University Press, 2011), 3.

37 Ibid., 4.

38 Emily Nagoski, "Pleasure Is the Measure," *Medium* (blog), August 19, 2015, https://medium.com/@enagoski/pleasure-is-the-measure-d8c5a2dff33f.

39 Michael White, "Addressing Personal Failure," *The International Journal of Narrative Therapy and Community Work*, no. 3 (2002): 45.

40 Hollibaugh, *My Dangerous Desires: A Queer Girl Dreaming Her Way Home*, xi.

41 Stone, "The 'Empire' Strikes Back: A Posttranssexual Manifesto," 161.

42 Moon, *Girl Sex 101*, 69.

43 Ibid..

44 McClelland, "Intimate Justice," 2014, 1010.

45 Ignacio Rivera, "The Sexual Body," in *Trans Bodies, Trans Selves: A Resource for the Transgender Community*, ed. Laura Erickson-Schroth (Oxford/New York: Oxford University Press, 2014), 357.

46 Ibid., 357.

6

BRINGING THEORY TO PRACTICE

Lucie Fielding

If Chapters 1-5 presented conceptual frameworks and theoretical models for exploring trans sexualities and erotic embodiments, this chapter focuses on operationalizing the concepts explored in this book in order to enliven clinical practice. Most of this chapter consists of contributions from other providers who come from different social locations and professional backgrounds than I do; many of them work in very different ways than I do too. Here, I understand "provider" in its most expansive sense, namely, as a means of describing anyone who might support trans and nonbinary folx in their explorations of sexualities and erotic embodiments—sex educators and sex therapists; pelvic floor physical therapists, professional Dominants, bodyworkers, and other sexual health and somatic professionals. This is an important reminder that we need to expand our definition of who belongs in a multidisciplinary team and that we can all expand our horizons for what is possible, and for how we can be more creative and imaginative practitioners. I very much would like to see doctors and therapists work closely with massage therapists, energy workers, surrogate partners, providers steeped in indigenous healing practices, and professional dominants!

The chapter will begin with a brief discussion of a few of the concerns related to trans sexualities and erotic embodiments with which clients might present for work with us. It will then present vignettes featuring providers demonstrating the work they do, as well as a few activities and exercises drawn from an array of modalities. It is my hope that you will be able to see yourself in at least a few parts of this chapter as you work with the embodied sexual self.

Presenting Concerns

Trans and non-binary folx come to see us for numerous reasons related to sexual health, relational health, sexualities, and erotic embodiment. Here are a few of the many potential concerns that our clients might present, with an accent placed on concerns that may not have gotten a ton of attention in the book.

Sexual Shame and Concerns About Sexual Health:

While some trans and non-binary folx experience gender euphoria as they or others affirm their gender identity, or as they feel greater access to embodiment, others may find shifts in how they experience arousal, desire, and pleasure disconcerting, and, indeed, may experience these shifts as their sexuality run amok, utterly out of their control. Other clients might come to us carrying burdens of sexual shame about their consensual sexual urges, thoughts, and behaviors. In both cases, normalizing client experiences of their sexualities is vitally important—they and their desires are normal; they may feel out of control, but they are not, in fact, out of control! To the extent that client distress persists, you might consider working with your clients to articulate and promote their own, unique vision of sexual health.[1]

Post-Surgical Pleasure:

Once the swelling goes down and the scars look less prominent, trans and non-binary folx who pursue top or bottom surgeries may greet their freshly contoured chests, ample cleavage, or neo vulvas and neo penises with tremendous excitement. Gender-affirming surgeons will do their best to preserve nerve clusters and sensitivity so tissues retain their pre-surgical potential for being sites of pleasure. They will, moreover, provide clients with detailed instructions for post-surgical care. All the same, some clients might initially struggle with how to tap into pleasure at the sites of those surgeries. This can be a place where coming into (com)passionate relationship with the embodied sexual self can be especially helpful. We can help our clients leverage that excitement, that sense of gender euphoria, post-surgery to build capacities for embodied awareness through attuning to the somatic-imaginal or in considering how they want a surgically-facilitated body part to be interacted with and felt. Sensation will almost certainly be different post-surgery and, as Laura Jacobs notes in her contribution within this chapter, excitement may be accompanied by grief. We can help our clients mourn what has changed, celebrate what was so profoundly anticipated, and resist cultural scripts of function and performance to embrace how pleasure shows up for them.

Asexuality:

Asexuality is an orientation that many trans and non-binary clients who come to see us hold. Asexuality exists on a spectrum: some clients merely view sexual attraction as something that does not play an important role in their lives, while others experience sexual attraction occasionally and in certain contexts. This is not to say that asexual folx can't enjoy caresses, kissing, cuddling, and forms of touch or eroticism that are not strictly sexual. After all, many asexual folx are active in the kink/BDSM community. There is a long and deeply unfortunate history of asexuality being pathologized as a form of disordered, hyposexual desire instead of being understood as being part of normal human variation. It is incumbent upon us as sexuality professionals to affirm asexual folx when they present themselves to us. To be sure, we can be gently and ethically curious in exploring, with client permission, a client's avoidance of—or aversion to—sex or play as such aversion arises *specifically* out of gender or body dysphoria. But to the extent that the client identifies as asexual or draws a sense of pride and recognition from being asexual, it is *never* our place to question it.

Relationships and Relational Identity:

Historically, as Arlene Lev has written, trans clients were often "viewed as people without families" and practitioners often ignore their relational realities.[2] In this book I have focused on individuals. Most of the frameworks introduced in this book apply in a relationship context, but it is worth noting a few presenting concerns that you might encounter.

Individuals transition, but any existing partnerships transition too, and said transitions can be moments of shared celebration, but also a context for grief to settle if not given space to be processed. One potent area of grief can be shifts in relational identity. For example, a cis woman in relationship with a trans man may "struggle with their non-heterosexuality being rendered invisible" as their partner transitions.[3] If the cis partner is a lesbian, what does it mean for her suddenly to be read as being in a straight partnership?[4] Relationship work can also be a space to increase communication skills, develop capacities for empathy, and discuss the fears and anxieties held by each partner.[5] Finally, partners may find that a gender transition provides an opportunity to come into passionate relationship with one another.

Dating and Playing:

Many trans and non-binary clients will come to us with well-established relationships, but others may seek support as they navigate dating and/or work to gain access to gender-affirming, sex-positive spaces/communities. As discussed in Chapter 1, "dating while trans" is a thing and clients may have stories of having been rejected for being trans. Others may anticipate rejection or non-affirming interactions. Still other clients might have limited experience dating or hooking up in the first place and may host a great deal of apprehension about how to pursue romantic and sexual relationships.

Communicating with Partners:

Some clients may need support in developing how to communicate with potential partners or in the midst of sex or play. We might introduce clients to want/will/won't list templates that can help them engage in and initiate conversations about the types and intensities of touch desired; the places where touch might, or must not, take place; words that might be used; and the emotional states they might wish to experience. We might teach them strategies for checking in with partners during play. Check-ins can take the form of yes/no or either/or questions that can be answered quickly and without needing to devote a ton of brain power such as: "More pressure or less?" "More lube?" They can also include open-ended questions like "What would make this better?" Checking in like this allows partners to make adjustments to ensure that a given experience is maximally pleasurable to all involved. Some clients might need support feeling able to express wants and needs in the first place. Here, many of the strategies discussed in Chapter 5 might be of use.

Exploring Kink/BDSM:

There are currently no estimates of the prevalence of trans and non-binary folx who are kinky. As Laura Jacobs notes, anecdotal reports would suggest that participation rates in kink communities among trans and non-binary populations are higher than in cis populations.[6] Sometimes trans and non-binary clients will come to you with years of experience as kinksters. These clients may merely wish you to be kink-affirming or kink-knowledgeable so that they do not have to be in a position to educate their provider about BDSM. But sometimes your clients may come to you wishing to explore kink/BDSM for the first time. Work with these clients can run the gamut from concrete resourcing, imaginal work to explore fantasies, and efforts to discharge any sexual shame present. For our part, we, as providers, should work to maintain a non-judgmental, kink-positive stance and banish older, kink-pathologizing frameworks from our practice. To do so, we should actively seek out training, education, and consultation/supervision experiences to build kink cultural competence. For sexuality professionals, for example, a trans- and BIPoC-centered Sexual Attitudes Reassessment (SAR) experience can help providers bring awareness to biases around a range of erotic identities and practices and help them learn to avoid "yucking someone else's yum." For medical providers specifically, you might find ways to signal openness to kink/BDSM. For example, in a pre-surgical consult, a provider might ask: "Do you have any questions about how this surgery may affect your sex life? In the past patients have asked about everything ranging from pleasure sensitivity and nerve function to how they can safely incorporate kink practices following this intervention." This question invites the patient to talk about their kink practices while not going so far as to assume the patient has them.

Sexual Trauma and Boundary Violations:

Trans folx experience sexual violence at rates much higher than the larger US population.[7] It stands to reason that many of your clients will experience sexual boundary crossings or violations, sexual violence, and intimate partner violence; or come to you with a sexual trauma history. As discussed in Chapter 4, experiences of sexual trauma and/or sexual boundary crossings/violations can lodge themselves in our bodies, making it difficult for us to imagine dropping into our bodies and experiencing them as sites of pleasure. Indeed, pleasure and being in the body might seem like the furthest things from a survivor's mind! Numerous modalities exist for processing sexual trauma which can be applied to great effect with cis and trans clients alike. That said, most techniques for trauma processing were not designed with trans and non-binary folx in mind, not to mention members of other marginalized groups. For one, many trauma modalities are steeped in a discourse of safety, a discourse that can be alienating to those who have rarely felt safe (see Chapter 4).

Working with Other Sexuality Professionals:

Enshrined in our professional codes are the legal principle of scope of practice (what a provider is permitted to undertake in keeping with the terms of their license/certification) and the ethical principle of scope of competence (ways of working delimited by training, education, and experience). We run up against these scopes often in our work and they either necessitate referring out or additional certifications, education, or experience. For example, as a resident in counseling, it is outside my scope of practice to provide medical counsel, or to engage in certain forms of touch. I can neither prescribe medication nor suggest what a client should be taking. Likewise, I'm prohibited from engaging in the kinds of touch that my bodyworker colleagues can engage in. In both cases, I refer out.

Vignettes, Activities, and Interventions

In this section, a group of providers generously contributed a set of vignettes, interventions, and exercises that you might deploy in your practice to work with trans and non-binary clients consonant with the conceptual frameworks introduced earlier in the book. A full list of contributors, along with bios and contact information, is provided at the beginning of the book after the table of contents.

Many of these providers are white and most were assigned female at birth. For a chapter that is supposed to in some ways reflect trans heterogeneity, it goes without saying that it doesn't meet that aspiration. I own this failure while also using this as an opportunity to exhort my fellow white colleagues to look around themselves, for we all must do better. Despite a growing number of trans providers, we've still a long way to go in un-settling/decolonizing our practices and professional organizations. My hope is that a future edition of this book will be able to feature even more trans BIPoC providers.

Queering the Trans Narrative of Suffering
Rae McDaniel, LCPC, CST

"I'm afraid that no one will want me."

Kate (she/they), a 28 year-old, Latinx non-binary person, sat in my office and expressed a fear that many transgender/non-binary clients had said to me before while processing a disappointing end to a potential romantic and sexual relationship.

This ubiquitous fear is a symptom of a larger cultural narrative about gender transition and life as a transgender/non-binary person that puts suffering smack dab in the middle of the experience.

The typical narrative of transition goes something like this:

A trans person feels a sense of "being in the wrong body" from a very early age. This young child exhibits gender non-conforming behavior that is severely punished by an attachment figure in the child's life. That child represses the feelings of incongruence about their gender identity and expression.

↓

The child hits puberty and all of those feelings come back full force and cause significant distress. This distress increases anxiety, depression, and other psychological difficulties that make high school a dreadful experience. Did I mention bullying?

↓

The child becomes an adult and starts exploring their gender. This process involves intense psychological suffering as they wrestle with their gender identity and expression.

↓

The adult comes out as a binary transgender person and suffers greatly with consequences like the loss of family, partners, jobs, cultural discrimination, etc. The adult has significant gender and body dysphoria and feels disconnected from physical pleasure.

↓

The adult now needs to navigate life, including sexuality and romantic relationships, as a transgender person. They struggle to feel comfortable in their body and experience pleasure. They struggle to find a sexual and/or romantic partner who sees them for who they are and are forced to settle for, at best, a mediocre sex life or, at worse, a partner that treats them badly but "is the best they could do."

It breaks my heart that the typical narrative of gender transition and trans sexualities includes suffering as an essential part of the story. This narrative is reflective of some people's stories and that is a valid and painful experience. But, as Lucie points out in Chapter 1, suffering is not in itself a defining aspect of trans and non-binary experiencing.

I believe the cause is two-fold:

1. Our culture doesn't celebrate transgender/non-binary folx's identities, transition, and existence. In many cases, trans and non-binary folx are actively discriminated against and told that their identities are invalid. This typical narrative will not fully shift until society begins actively celebrating and supporting trans folx on every systemic level.
2. Trans folx have internalized the narrative that transitioning your gender and living and loving as a trans/non-binary person must include suffering. Situating transgender sexuality as something that must include suffering, rejection, and fear is causing trans folx to start their exploration of pleasure and sexuality in changing identities and bodies at a deficit. By having a culturally internalized narrative that includes suffering as a *de facto* part of transition, we are setting trans folx up to feel invalid, unworthy, have an intense fear of being alone forever, and to settle for "whatever they can get." This leads to trans folx "settling" for partners out of a sense of scarcity and getting into sexual situations that are not pleasurable and potentially unsafe because they don't think they deserve better.

We deserve better

I believe that gender transition and trans sexualities can be sites of ease, discovery, and curiosity. By changing the narrative of transition, we empower trans folx to not accept less than a sexual partner who sees them for who they are, treats them with respect, and lights them up. The stories we tell ourselves are powerful and when that story is one of discovery, curiosity, and ease, it also becomes one of self-respect and self-efficacy.

To begin changing the typical narrative on an individual level, therapists have a lot of tools in their toolbox. For my part, I typically use tools derived from Positive Psychology and Cognitive Behavioral Therapy (CBT). CBT has demonstrated great efficacy in helping trans/non-binary clients begin to shift these internalized negative self-beliefs.[8]

One intervention for taking on Kate's belief of "no one will want me" is to identify, get curious about, and reality test the cognitive distortions present in this thought. This creates cognitive space for Kate to "turn down the volume" on negative self-talk and make a different decision about how they want to respond to this negative thought with more agency.

A sample of cognitive distortions present in this thought and some questions to get curious about with the client include:

- All or nothing thinking
- Do you know of any transgender/non-binary people in loving relationships?
- Have you heard of any trans folx having great and pleasurable sex?
- Have you ever had the experience of being sexually or romantically desired by someone who respects your identity?

Challenging this involves looking for exceptions. If there is just one exception, then this thought doesn't past the reality test.

Kate was able to identify several trans/non-binary folx on social media and that they knew personally who appeared to be in satisfying relationships and to articulate that there are people in the world who respect and celebrate trans folx and are sexually and romantically attracted to folx of trans experience.

Overgeneralization

- *How do you know that you will be alone forever?*
- *What is your "sample size"? Who are you basing this assumption on?*

With this cognitive distortion, we are looking for evidence that the thought has been generalized based on a small sample size or assumptions vs. facts. In this case, Kate was basing the thought on a small sample size of five dates with cisgender, straight men.

Mental Filter

- *Have you looked for examples of other transgender/non-binary people in loving relationships for the same amount of time and intensity as looking for evidence that trans/non-binary folx are doomed to be alone?*

- *Have you thought about/written about/talked to others about your positive experiences in an equal amount to your negative experiences?*

We want to look for evidence that Kate might be unfairly weighing negative experiences over positive ones and only looking for evidence to support the idea that they will be alone forever. Our intervention here is not to ask Kate to stop reading and researching negative experiences of trans folx in romantic and sexual relationships but to require Kate to experiment with spending an equal amount of time researching and thinking about positive stories and experiences.

Mindreading and Personalization

- *How do you know that the people you went on dates with/talked to online are not sexually or romantically interested in you because of your trans/non-binary identity?*
- *Are there other possible reasons, including ones that have nothing to do with you, that they might not be interested in a sexual or romantic relationship at this time?*

Challenging this cognitive distortion involves pointing out where assumptions are being made about other people's motives and thoughts when we cannot confirm the reason for their behavior.

Future Telling

- *You've been rejected in the past and that's understandably very difficult. I'm curious about what that has to do with the future?*
- *Is it possible that your experience in the future might be different?*
- *If you think back to six months/a year/three years ago, would you have thought that where you are now is possible? If not, is it possible that you might be wrong about what is possible in the future now too?*
- *If you were to look back on yourself three years ago and offer encouragement, what would you say?*
- *What do you want to be different in three years/ten years?*
- *What if the next three years felt more like a process of ease, curiosity, and discovery instead of suffering? What would be different about the journey through the next three years if the journey was as pleasurable as the destination?*
- *What might your three-years-in-the-future/ten-years-in-the-future self say to you today to offer encouragement?*
- *What is one step you could take towards that vision that you have for yourself in three years?*

Research shows that marginalized people struggle to imagine positive futures for themselves. Addressing this cognitive distortion moves beyond pointing out where the client has been making assumptions about the future and into imagining a more positive vision of what their life could look like.[9]

The power in this line of questioning is in helping your client to identify when the story their brains are telling them is based on bad data and is no longer helping them, co-creating a vision for a future that feels inspiring and exciting, and exploring what tiny steps they could take to move closer to that vision today.

A Decolonizing Approach to the Erotic and Medicine
Jamee Pineda, LAc, MAcOM, MPA

Decolonizing medicine is vital to working with the erotic. Colonization disrupts ownership of our bodies, identities, and ancestral traditions. This is apparent in our relationships to pleasure, sex, bodily autonomy, and gender. Western paradigms replace traditional ways people care for their bodies and souls. In working with patients who want to explore eroticism or focus on their sexual health, it is helpful to explore the effects of colonization and white supremacy on their relationships to their bodies. As a provider, it is equally important for me to understand my location relative to those forces. Here, I focus on ancestral medicine and clinical application, two aspects of decolonizing medicine.

Ancestral Medicine

I am a *hilot binabaylan*,[10] which comes from my ancestral traditions in the Philippines, as well as a practitioner of acupuncture and Chinese medicine. Traditionally, people who exhibited masculine and feminine characteristics were often chosen to be trained as *babaylan*.[11] It was believed that these characteristics brought one closer to the divine. The ability of babaylan to experience multiple genders meant that they could exist in multiple dimensions: the divine and the mundane. By today's Western concepts of gender, some of the babaylan may have identified as transgender or nonbinary. Babaylan were multidimensional warrior healers who actively resisted Spanish rule. They were hunted and persecuted by Spanish colonizers for defying European ideas of gender, Catholic teachings, and colonial rule.

Each person we encounter is an accumulation of social, physical, emotional, mental, spiritual, financial, and environmental health. They also hold their ancestors' experiences. Difficulty being in our bodies (even with a desire to feel embodied) or accessing the erotic can come from physical or nonphysical causes. It can look like individual, collective, and/or ancestral trauma. For instance, white supremacy and colonization forced many to internalize white European gender roles and standards of beauty.

Growing up, my siblings and I were warned by our *titas*[12] to stay out of the sun to avoid getting "too dark." We were admonished for not wearing enough sunscreen especially when we went swimming. It was not until I moved away for college that I was able to recognize how much this affected who I found desirable and how I felt about my brown body. What I thought was a coincidence of only dating white folks was really internalized racism keeping me in a rigid, European standard of beauty. I also encountered a lot of Asian fetishization, another aspect of white supremacy and colonization. My experiences of this extended through straight and queer, mostly white, communities. It took years of deprogramming and healing from the intergenerational effects of white supremacy to fully step into my erotic self and define what desirability and pleasure look like for me. It is a transforming of toxic, white-centric eroticism into something that is empowering, restorative, and healing. Eroticism and medicine can be intimately connected. Both have their place in disrupting oppressive systems and bringing us back to our fuller selves.

Decolonizing is a constant process. Even though I have experienced harm from white supremacy and colonization, it is important to note my location in power and privilege. I come from an immigrant family whose ancestors were colonized, but my family is not indigenous to the stolen land we immigrated to. I have an obligation to support the ancestral healing practices of indigenous people where I live as just one piece of reparations work. As part of this, I also donate money to indigenous healing work and refer other practitioners and clients to indigenous two-spirit practitioners. Just as I strive to be in right relationship with my ancestors, I should also work to be in right relationship with the people whose land I am occupying.

Clinical Approaches

Decolonizing medicine shapes my work as a clinician. Patient autonomy and experience is of the utmost importance to practice. Decolonizing medicine can look like informed consent: educating patients about all of their choices and partnering with them on their decision. For some patients, decolonizing medicine is working slowly, describing each acupuncture point I would like to use, and checking in with them before I continue with insertion. Decolonizing medicine is respecting and being attuned to boundaries, verbal and nonverbal. If a patient's body tenses or flinches when I touch them, but they say they wish to proceed with treatment, that becomes an opportunity to discuss what full consent looks like with that patient. I can easily avoid sensitive areas and work distally, or even forego physical touch altogether. Non-touch therapies include herbal prescriptions, qi gong, and lifestyle advice.

Respecting the wisdom of the body is integral to a decolonizing approach. Colonization manifests as a violation of autonomy and self-determination on macro and micro levels from using military force to seize a nation to controlling how an individual views their own worth and boundaries. These violations can happen over generations, sometimes in unconscious and nuanced ways. There is overlap here with people who have experienced sexual assault or other types of violation that may or may not be related to colonization. As a practitioner, part of my job is to create an environment that counters that by respecting boundaries and working at a pace that is in line with the whole body. There are many ways I can receive information directly from the body: pulse reading, tongue analysis, and palpation, to name a few. This information is useful because it is not filtered through the intellectual, conscious mind. It is a direct conversation with the body. These methods do not fully replace a verbal interview, but give a more complete picture of the person. It is quite helpful when there is a language barrier or when certain topics are difficult or triggering to talk about. Observing tension or flinching is also diagnostic. There is a story for that response and that needs to be respected and engaged with if and when the patient is ready. Sometimes that story is specific to an individual and sometimes it is a collective, intergenerational story.

Conclusion

Access to healing and access to erotic expression are connected. Colonialism and white supremacy have violently shaped standards of sex, gender, and desire. To facilitate healing so that patients feel safer in their bodies and desires, I keep coming back to ways that are ancient—ways that existed before Magellan set foot on my ancestral land, ways that have survived even while buried under syncretized Catholic practices. There is something so powerful about ancestral medicine that Spanish colonizers tried to destroy it. This is a medicine colonizers relabeled as deviant and evil that recognized many genders and sexualities. Relating more positively to our bodies through pleasure can be an act of deep remembering and a reclaiming of ancestral wisdom.

Working questions for providers:

1. How has the full expression of self, including the erotic, been impacted by white supremacy and/or colonialism?
2. What does erotic expression and healing look like outside of this? If it is not separable, then how can we define them on our own terms?

Anatomy Talk
Heather Edwards, PT, CSC

As a pelvic physical therapist, I work with genitals much more directly than my mental health colleagues do. In nearly all of the Trans 101s, blogs, and articles, there is a sense that talking about genitals with trans and non-binary people should be avoided. While this is very helpful messaging to avoid misplaced medical curiosity or an invasive, dehumanizing gaze, it can put those of us who need to talk about genitals in a precarious situation. While it may not seem relevant for your medical provider to ask about what sexual acts you do with your genitals if you're coming in for an office visit for urinary urgency, it's all, in fact, closely related.

Current practices typically lean toward mirroring the language offered by the patient or allowing them to choose the words that they like to use for their genitals. But the problem is that for a provider that needs to know specific information in a medical history, that language barrier can be stifling and create a need for potentially more extensive physical examination than what would be needed if a more thorough verbal history could be obtained.

An issue with mirrored language is that if people create names for their genitals, those names are much more likely to be names they use with intimate partners, not medical providers. I know I use different names for *my* genitals in those two settings. It's understandable why those terms aren't used when describing a painful rash.

The other option is to use the terms and diagrams that are readily available. For some patients, those may be fine. However, many patients are emotionally activated by anatomy terms that are heavily gendered.

What can we do as professionals who want to be affirming and accurate in our assessment (because the more we can talk, the less we have to poke, in many situations)?

After struggling with this in the clinic, I came up with an alternative for the wording and the images. It's composed of three basic factors:

1. Have non-binary terms that you are comfortable using for anatomy and allow this as an option for your patients.
2. Have images that are unlabeled (preferably more than the male/female binary options)
3. Learn to draw simple "stick figure" versions of crotches.

To break those down further:

Non-binary language for genitals. Some basic swaps that can be made for any anatomy:

- External Genitalia (instead of vulva)
- Erectile tissue (instead of clitoris or penis)
- Glans (instead of clitoris or head of penis)
- Lateral folds (instead of labia)
- Canal, Opening, or Introitus (instead of vagina)

- Gonads (instead of ovaries or testes)
- Skin or pouch covering gonads (instead of scrotum)

Have images that are unlabeled.

- Instead of keeping only a standard anatomy chart in your office, keep some images that have details but are not labeled so you can use your own words for them.
- Take images that you have and create a version with the non-binary labels above
- Having more than two options can show that you are comfortable thinking of genitals as more varied than "binary." Consider having an image of a vulva with enlarged erectile tissue or a micropenis.

Learn to draw crotches (at least stick figure versions). Here are a few helpful diagrams to show you show that can be done (Figures 6.1 and 6.2).

With these diagrams, you can modify your images based on what you know about your patient's anatomy, hormone use, and/or intersex variation as they help to explain it. Allowing your patient to create their own narrative is important for their story and creates a safer space for talking about their genital anatomy. And allowing your understanding of their genitals to come from your client and then tailoring your education to their body can be affirming and help to deconstruct the toxic narrative that "there is a normal and you are not it."

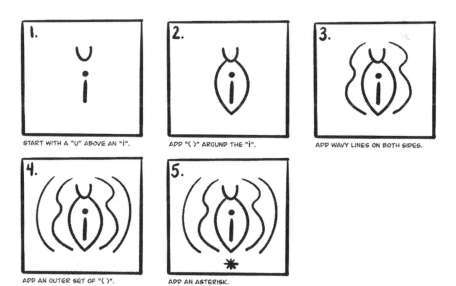

Figure 6.1 Directions for drawing a crotch (vulva)

Courtesy of Heather Edwards, PT, CSC

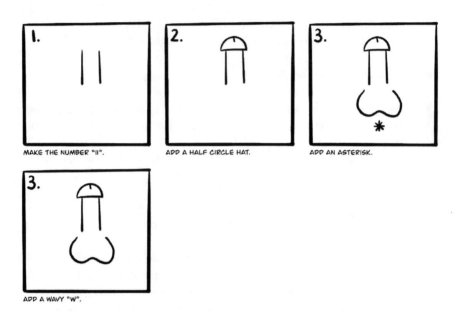

Figure 6.2 Directions for drawing a crotch (penis)

Courtesy of Heather Edwards, PT, CSC

Awakening Body Awareness Through Bodywork

Frances Reed, LMT

My bodywork practice centers queer, trans, and non-binary clients and is rooted in trauma-informed, body-affirming and sex-positive approaches to care. My work focuses on the ways in which the body's sensations are a conversation that the body is trying to have with the brain. Bodywork can act as the third-party conduit to connect communication between a client's brain and their body—I provide the touch and then support the client in developing a listening relationship to the information that comes through that touch. With each noticing, I ask the client to bring awareness to the physical, emotional, mental, and energetic information that comes into conscious awareness.

In some cases, the sensation a client notices is purely physical in nature, such as a painful sensation in the legs. By noticing that sensation they might become aware of a feeling in their body that they were previously unaware of. Noticing the sensation connects them to awareness of their physical body. But the sensation may also serve as a portal to additional communication from the emotional, mental, or energetic body. For one client struggling with intermittent weakness in their legs, both occurred. The initial awareness of physical pain in the lower body helped the client feel a part of their body that they had cut themself off from. Where they had previously been unable to identify sensations for their doctors (e.g., tingling, stabbing, or aching pain), they developed language to describe these sensations anew! The client's experience of discomfort in their legs in response to my touch eventually allowed them to make a connection to a fear of inheriting their mother's MS and losing the ability to walk. Becoming more present in their physical and emotional pain allowed their treatment and empowerment in healing to increase profoundly.

Therapeutic touch can also bring a client into awareness of an unexpected emotion. For one trans masculine client who was recovering from top surgery, moving their arms away from their body brought up anger that they were not expecting. By giving words to that somatic experience and sharing it aloud, they allowed themselves a release of emotion through tears and guttural noises. I encouraged the client to be curious about this emotional connection. As the release subsided, they could connect with the origins of the emotion. The client was able to connect the anger and the touch to a transphobic assault that they had experienced before their surgery. The anger arose from a combination of the assault and the subsequent immobilization of the body while healing from surgery. For this client, the source of the emotional response came like a lightning bolt. Yet for other clients, their bodily responses are not so easy to unpack. Regardless of the degree of understanding, the somatic signals still serve to increase the communication clients have with their body.

I have also worked with clients to heighten their body awareness by guiding them to imagine a state of being, or suggesting that a client imagine light or color entering a part of their body. The sensation that they experience can unlock a relationship to the body that heals and empowers them. In one such case, a client was seeking bodywork to reconnect with a sense of sexual and sensual energy in their body following a battle with cancer. We discovered quickly that meditating on color was effective at generating and describing sensations in their body. Filling their body with a particular color or journeying to a part of their body to observe the colors they "saw" there, opened a way to discuss the connection and disconnection that they felt since undergoing treatment. At one point this client descended into their belly to discover a rich purple with gold glitter. They associated the glitteriness and purple with a feeling of delight. I encouraged them to move the colors throughout their body, noticing the sensory information that it evoked as it moved. In their legs and hips they felt fluid movement like dancing, and in their head it felt playful. However, as they tried to move the colors into their lungs, chest, heart, and arms they found those paths obstructed and cut off. They stayed focused on observing the purple and gold while I provided physical contact to the upper body. The combination of the client's inner exploration and the actual touch to the arms, chest, and ribcage enabled them to direct their awareness to these places of disconnection. Over the course of months and many similar sessions, the client's multifaceted connections to the body's sensory communication enabled them to develop a new relationship to their post-cancer body, reintegrating their sensual and sexual energy.

In all of these examples, my work is to apply physical contact and/or imagined stimuli and invite the client to notice the bodily sensations. I encourage the client to share what they notice so that I can assist them in deepening their conversation with their body by asking questions and tracking for them what arises.

Language about sensation is woefully inadequate at describing the experience in the body, and so I encourage clients to use sounds, color, smells or more elaborate metaphors to encapsulate their inner experience. Giving people permission to defy conventional descriptive language is often the liberating factor that allows them to begin "hearing" the body's communication.

The Pieces of the Puzzle

Fitz

"What is sex?" I asked as my client blinked back at me. "Just tell me the first thing that comes to mind."

The client sighed, "Penis-in-vagina. It's like a blaring neon sign in my head."

"Between two cis het folx?"

"Yeah, though I cringe when I hear myself say it. I know it isn't right, but it's what I feel. It's like I don't like what I should like or what I want isn't what I think my partner expects…"

In my work, I use a variety of tools to help folx engage with the narratives that shape their life. I support explorations of how people, systems, and institutions shape narratives over time; highlight shoulds and oughts to uncover how narratives try to tell us how the world works; and introduce tools to help clients tune into self and desire. Each of these approaches helps problematize things we take for granted and invite the possibility of discovering a more authentic, embodied existence.

"Who defines what sex is? Do you remember where you first learned about the cis het PIV narrative of sex you spoke of earlier?"

"I hadn't thought about that before … definitely at church, that's all they acknowledged in sex ed class. It's what you see on tv or in movies."

"What stands out about these sources? Do they have something to gain from that understanding of sex?"

"It's about power, right? How culture is set up to support patriarchy? I mean, I know it's more complicated than that, but that definition of sex definitely prioritizes cis men."

"Is maintaining power and patriarchy important to you?"

"No, not at all."

"So, what is important to you about sex?"

"Well, I want it to be enjoyable for me, to feel good in my body. I want to feel connected to my partner and for them to enjoy sex as well."

"So, pleasurable? Gender affirming? Mutual trust, connection?"

"Yeah! So, if those are my goals, I have to figure out how to get there?"

After exploring cultural scripts, I often introduce a metaphor that draws on the experience of putting together a puzzle.

"Have you ever put together a jigsaw puzzle before?"

"Yeah. Why?"

"How do you put together a puzzle? Describe it to me, as if I've never done one."

"Okay… I dump the pieces out of the box and sort them into edge and center pieces. I sort the pieces into piles by similar color, lettering, or ones that probably go together. The picture on the box helps me figure out where pieces go or how they might fit together. It's a lot of trial and error. But at the end all the pieces fit. It looks like the picture on the box."

"So, what if I handed you a bag of puzzle pieces and asked you to assemble a puzzle?"

"I'd have no idea what to do. I feel frozen."

"Good observation. What about it makes you freeze?"

"I mean, it changes a lot of things. I thought 'I haven't done this before.' "

"So, fear of the unknown?"

"Yeah."

"Why is the box known and comfortable but the bag is unknown and uncomfortable?"

"There's no box. I have no idea what the pieces are supposed to look like once it's all put together and the bag makes my mind question if all the pieces are from the same puzzle … so, what do I do with that?"

"What do you want to do with the bag of pieces?"

"Throw them out the window!"

"Hahaha, fair! It's new and unknown. That can feel overwhelming pretty quick! Let's back up for a minute. What do puzzles have to do with sex?"

"I think I get it. I never recognized there were expectations about how I should put together a puzzle, until you suggested there could be a different starting point. It's like I never questioned my gut reaction to what sex is until you suggested there could be something else. I think the bag of puzzle pieces is supposed to spark curiosity about a different, 'queerer' context for what sex could be."

"Yup, you got it."

"Okay, but I'm still not sure what's next. Can I get a hint?"

"So, earlier you said the picture on the box determined how you looked at and sorted all the pieces. How does that change without an image to guide you? How do you interact with each piece now? How do you decide how they go together if there is no guarantee they will all snap into place?"

"So you're saying I have to take the bag of pieces and just make something? Based on how I feel about the pieces? The anxiety is back!"

"Anxiety isn't all bad, it can overlap with excitement. How did you feel about the puzzle pieces in the box scenario?"

"I don't think I felt much at all. I just matched them to the image."

"But, if we are aiming for pleasure, that won't do, we have to start feeling something! Are you open to trying an exercise with me?"

"Sure"

"The little box on the table is filled with puzzle pieces. Randomly grab a piece. Now, look at the piece and notice your reaction to it. Use your eyes, your fingers … you can even smell and listen to it if you want."

"Okay, this one is mostly one color, the bumps are relatively even, the finish is really shiny. I hadn't noticed that before. It's kind of boring to be honest."

"Grab another."

"The finish on this one is different. It's more matte. And I like the yellow dots. The shape is interesting too, one really tiny edge opens into a larger one."

"What do you notice in your body?"

"Excitement. A little bit of energy rises up in my spine and chest. I want to keep touching it, looking at it, and put it in my pocket for later."

"So, if you were making your puzzle, what would you want to do with these two pieces?"

"Not sure yet. I know I want to keep this one, and feel indifferent to the first."

"Great insight! You found a fun, exciting experience that fits for you! Just as with sex, you are going to like some things and not others. And you can listen to your body to tell you what those things are."

"So that feeling I had about something being wrong with me because I wasn't enjoying sex … was that my body's way of telling me that version of sex wasn't 'sexy', wasn't right, for me? Ok, but what does that mean for the overall puzzle?"

"You get to decide that too. I like to think of it as a gradual collection of puzzle pieces. Collect the ones that fit, set aside the ones that don't. Over time you'll see ways they fit together that make sense to you. You don't have to know the whole picture in order to recognize pieces you like and enjoy the experience. Does that make sense?"

"Yeah, it does actually. I just have to collect pieces. One pleasurable piece at a time."

Sex on Our Terms

Bianca Palmisano, MSN, RN

The trauma of our transness is all around: side-eye from grocery clerks, aggressive misgendering in the doctor's office, our own fears of being "not trans enough," "not passing enough." This exercise, which I offer in my trans-only sexuality workshop, *Sex On Our Terms*, invites that pain into the room so that we might rewrite it.

To facilitate this exercise, I use two large sheets of poster paper hung on the wall, an abundance of post-it notes, and lots of markers. First, I ask the room, "What has our trauma told us?" Who in our lives has devalued us, made us feel unsure, scared, or hurt? I request that my attendees reflect on the moments where they felt small or powerless, wounded, or troubled. These reflections could be personal experiences, thoughts about ourselves, or examples of the cultural pressures that push us into boxes where we do not fit.

I invite everyone to pick up a marker and fill the poster paper with these moments and feelings, however small or amorphous they may be. The words on the poster could be thoughts about our bodies, our sexuality, our identity, our trauma, our clothes, or our voice. Things I've seen on the poster paper include:

> *"I want to have sex, but the dysphoria makes it too painful"*
> *"I never see myself on TV, in movies, in clothing ads"*
> *"Getting called ma'am when I try to make an appointment at the dentist"*
> *"How can I feel sexy when none of my clothes fit?"*
> *"Bathroom bills in the legislature"*

When the paper is full, I acknowledge the heaviness in those words. I tell the room that these experiences are hard, and we carry them with us in so many ways. Often, they follow us into the bedroom. It's hard to love ourselves in all our complexity when the federal government continues to strip away our rights to housing and healthcare. It's hard to feel strong in our identity when it is erased and ignored by a society that makes us choose "Male or Female" on every intake form. It's hard to embody our sexuality when our lovers have told us that our bodies are not lovable.

Then I remind my participants of the love, support, and affirmation that they have felt in their lives. I invite them to take dozens of post-it notes and to write on each one something beautiful that has happened to them, something that makes them feel whole and rooted in themselves. I ask, "What has love told us?" Slowly, we take the post-it notes of love and cover up all the negative messages on the poster board with positive ones. Memories of hearing their true name spoken for the first time, memories of speaking their truth to people they love, memories of great sex.

When we have exhausted our reservoir of positive thoughts and memories, I invite everyone to look at the wall of love we created. It was difficult, truly, because for every negative experience we wrote down, multiple positive post-it notes were necessary to cover it. In this way, the exercise reflects real life. Negativity bias is a cognitive process wherein we are more likely to remember negative experiences than positive ones, and it takes multiple positive encounters to undo the impact of a single negative encounter. I remind the people in the room that the wall of love was a group effort, that covering up those negative statements isn't a task to undertake alone. It is through interdependence and sharing that we can heal. Through loving and witnessing others, we can begin to support ourselves.

This exercise is meant to be facilitated in a large group workshop setting; however, it can be adapted for one-on-one use. Keep the poster board, but have a client bring in objects that remind them of affirming memories instead of writing on post-it notes. Your client can cover the negative writing with their own talismans—scarves, postcards from friends, and photographs—and create a piece of art that they can keep with them.

Alternatively, you can write the negative experiences directly on your client's body and they can cover those statements with beautiful clothes or fetish-wear. The important component is the ability to cover over the negative thoughts with something beautiful and affirming. We can't erase the negative in this activity; society will always throw transphobic vitriol at us. But we can cover it with love, however that looks for your client and you.

Gender Play: Centering Gender, Reclaiming Pleasure

Ignacio G. Hutía Xeiti Rivera and Aredvi Azad

"I'm gonna fuck you now," said Sir V, as he wiggled his way out from under his boyfriend, and swiftly got on top and slid the cock inside his front hole. Sir's boyfriend's cock was already slippery enough from a combination of lube, saliva, and vaginal fluids. Sir locked eyes with his boyfriend as he slowly moved back and forth on his boyfriend's torso. The duo already knew how this was going to go. In a moment, Sir moved his body back and lifted his boyfriend's legs up in the air, but kept the cock inside him. Reaching his arms around the boyfriend's legs—now resting on his shoulders—Sir pushed himself up and secured his position.

Sir V started thrusting into his boyfriend's body. It was the classic missionary position, but to him, it was so much more than that. The cock was not attached to Sir's body, but they both knew Sir was in charge of the cock, and its energy. They locked eyes again; Sir grabbed the back of his boyfriend's neck, and thrusted even deeper. With every thrust, he felt his cock entering his boyfriend's hole, the tip moving past his opening, and occupying a tight grip inside. His boyfriend started moaning after each and every one of Sir's grunts. "Fuck my ass, please," his boyfriend let out the charming plea. Sir reached in for a kiss, as he closed his eyes and soaked in the joy of filling up his boyfriend's ass with his very own cock.

This is a brief account of a scene from Aredvi's sex life, a genderfluid connoisseur of gender play. For Aredvi (they/them/theirs), who was assigned female at birth, genderfluidity is an observation and acceptance of gender journeying through their body. Most days, Aredvi lives their life gender-free. Other times, they dive deep into an experience of masculinity, allowing masculine energy to take over: maybe grow an astral cock, wear a prosthetic one, or claim the biological cock of a willing partner who will call Aredvi "Sir V" and "he" for the duration of their play.

Gender play has been Aredvi's sexual refuge since they came out as trans. For Aredvi, who has not medically transitioned, gender play is the space where instead of feeling "tolerated," Aredvi centers their gender, and *celebrates* the abundance of pleasure in their gendered body. Gender play, in its reincarnation in Aredvi's practice, amalgamates gender expansiveness with an active imagination to conceive an evolving yet affirming dynamic that suits Aredvi's pleasure needs.

Ignacio (they/them/theirs), dressed in femme attire, walked into the lounge feeling powerful. Headed to a swingers club for anonymous sex, Ignacio was wearing a tight black dress, with bright red lips, thin hoop earrings, and heels, while carrying a fitting purse. It had been months since they had let their femme out to play. That evening, they wanted to feel free and fuck; to blur the gender lines and wave in and out of their constructed femininity.

For Ignacio, whose circle of available partners typically stayed within the queer community, a brief visit to the cis-hetero-binary realm in a femme persona was an adventure in and of itself. This was Ignacio's hold-the-gender-discussion-please moment. They walked into the bar, introduced "herself," and after a few drinks and sharing of cigarettes, went home with an older white woman and a younger Black man.

Ignacio, assigned female at birth, experiences gender outside of trans binary relations. Ignacio, who has had top surgery and has been undergoing hormone therapy for years, prefers to flow through genderfulness and genderlessness, the expression of which isn't consistently affirmed in a gender binary world. A roleplay practitioner, Ignacio intentionally uses masculine, feminine, and androgynous expressions as a *healing* modality to manage the trauma of living under cis-binary supremacy.

In kink and BDSM, gender play typically refers to fetishes related to sissification and feminization. Cis men take on submissive roles and are humiliated by wearing feminine clothing, putting on makeup, and engaging in otherwise typical feminine activities. While we see this type of gender play as a potential release from, and power over, gender roles, for trans/non-binary folx, gender play can also provide an extended container to feel home in our very *right* body and mind, no matter what kind of medical intervention we may have experienced.

Gender non-conformity and its many siblings (i.e. genderfluidity, genderqueerness, non-binary people)—or as we use the term "G/no," stand as isolating identities in a world that barely accepts trans people who conform to binarism, let alone those who denounce it altogether. The rejection of G/no existence negatively impacts G/no folx's relationships, sex, and intimacy practices. From internalized G/no-phobia to the constant often-invisible pressure to "pick one," G/no identity has become an incredibly undesirable and insulated space to hold onto.

In the hegemony of gender binary, techniques like gender play help shift the role of power in short and long-term sexual and romantic interpersonal relationships. As two AFAB G/no's who are also sexuality educators and coaches, we have seen ourselves and our clients find agency, self-esteem, and gender affirmation through sexual and erotic engagement with gender play. Instead of treating G/no gender expressions and explorations as a nuisance, gender becomes a tool for challenging and shifting of the very power that gender creates.

In working with clients and students, we encourage G/no folx to begin by exploring the boundaries of their gender experience, both in identity and in expression. Gender play can be an affirming tool for gender identity, however, one's experience of gender and its performativity has to inform the acceptable limits of gender play. Gender, especially the gap between how one feels inside—at any given time—and how they are perceived, is a source of trauma for many G/no folx. Staying aware of how this trauma may show up, and including these conversations in negotiations for gender play helps set up our clients for success. We also use *Gender Evolution Mapping (GEM)*, a tool for tracking gender experiences over time developed by Ignacio, to assist clients as they explore their relationship with gender, personally and as a whole.

Gender play, as a versatile tool available to anyone including intersex and AMAB G/no folx, reclaims pleasure from the parts of ourselves that we have learned to ignore, dismiss, and shame for far too long. Whether we relinquish or exert power through our gendered bodies, the physical and psychological maneuvers of gender are potently pleasurable and healing.

The Patient, the Pelvis, and the Gender Expanse: The Role of Pelvic Floor Physical Therapy in Gender-Affirming Care

Hannah Schoonover, PT, DPT

Author's note: the following piece was written specifically about a trans masculine person. However, ALL anatomies can benefit from the work and expertise of a gender-inclusive pelvic health practitioner. Supporting people of all genders (or lack thereof) should be the standard in this profession.

When Greg first called me, I gave him my elevator pitch.

"Pelvic floor physical therapists examine and treat the structures that comprise or influence the pelvic floor. This encompasses the treatment of urinary, bowel, reproductive, and sexual dysfunction as well as orthopedic issues."

I added that, essentially, my job is to help people better understand and trust their bodies.

Body parts don't just "break" or "stop working;" be it emotional, structural, neurological, genetic, etc., there is always a reason. Pursuing a symptom without deference to the cause might provide some short-term relief, but it will neither fix the problem nor prevent recurrence. Long-term symptom management lies in the fundamental understanding of why a structure is struggling to perform. Physical therapy is easier when patients understand their individual symptomatic circumstances; it provides a rehabilitative roadmap and takes away the uncertainty, the confusion, and the fear of "having done this" to themselves.

Greg (he/him) and I communicated extensively via phone and email before we ever met in person. Having recently had a gender-affirming hysterectomy, he was concerned about pelvic organ prolapse, a condition that involves organ herniation and causes painful pelvic pressure. He was also understandably nervous about pelvic floor therapy and wasn't convinced that having more medical eyes and hands near his genitals was the right answer.

Given that pelvic PTs often perform internal muscle evaluations via the posterior and/or anterior pelvic opening(s), there is a belief that we hyperfocus on the genitals. While it's true that most pelvic symptoms are the result of a pelvic floor that is too tight, weak, or stretched to optimally function, the pelvic floor is rarely independently dysfunctional.

Due to the location of the pelvic floor within the pelvic bowl, and its synergistic relationship with the other three core muscles, it is usually on the receiving end of increased intra-abdominal pressure. The anatomical core—also composed of the respiratory diaphragm, deep abdominal, and spinal stabilizing muscles—provides a supportive base during dynamic activities and helps control pressure that goes through the abdominal cavity during activity.

Core function relies on muscular coordination, where each core muscle rhythmically functions at a specific time. For example, when the diaphragm lowers during inhalation, the pelvic floor should relax; during exhalation, the floor should contract. This is important to pelvic functioning because contraction of the pelvic muscles keeps us safe during exercise, and their relaxation allows us to void. If the diaphragm cannot move properly (due to binder use, chronic respiratory issues, spinal posture, etc.), this relationship is disrupted and the pelvic floor muscles lose their efficiency.

Directly treating the pelvic floor in a patient with diaphragmatic immobility would NOT be in their best interest, as the pelvic muscles are responding appropriately to an inappropriate stimulus. In this instance, it would be more akin to punishment than rehabilitation. Because the pelvic floor muscles are on the receiving end of excessive pressure, they become overly contracted and sensitive. Treating them would provoke pain without promoting function.

That was the case for Greg, whose diaphragm was rock-hard and not interested in moving. We spoke at length about why that was, with the likely culprit being his upregulated nervous system. Being upregulated heightens responses to non-threatening stimuli, making everything seem unsafe. Due to a prolonged history of medical bias and emotional trauma, Greg was in a constant "fight-flight-freeze" state of upregulation. While upregulated, he was unable to diaphragmatically breathe.

With safety as our highest priority, we focused on improving his abdominal tension, spinal posture, and breathing patterns to downregulate his nervous system. Greg had a pronounced arch in his lower back, which we worked to reduce. Improved posture helped him better use his core muscles. Straightening his spine decreased the pressure exerted upon his pelvis and, as a result, he was able to partially relax his pelvic floor without direct contact.

Greg and I worked together for several months before performing an internal posterior evaluation. And he only consented to an internal anterior evaluation several months after *that*. Upon internal examination we quickly ruled out prolapse but found that his pelvic floor muscles couldn't fully relax. This tension led to a lactic acid build-up which made palpation very uncomfortable. Palpatory discomfort further reinforced the tightness and kept him in a consistently contracted state.

For Greg, internal pelvic floor release was not a good option: his pelvic floor was painfully clenching in response to increased abdominal tension. Pressure was being excessively funneled into his pelvis and his pelvic floor was forced to react. Instead of directly palpating and treating his sore internal muscles, we reduced the pressure. Greg learned Myofascial Release techniques and stretching exercises to achieve this goal. And the best part was that he was able to perform these exercises independently, at home, fully clothed. And he was successful.

My job fully relies on trust. And the work doesn't happen if patients don't feel safe, seen, and heard. My patients report that I am usually their only medical provider that uses ungendered anatomical terms; I make a point to remember personal pronouns; I don't document deadnames. Greg would never have come in if I had used the medically accepted term for his anterior pelvic opening. He also never would have come in on just my elevator pitch.

For gender-expansive patients it is imperative that we continue to treat the whole body versus a single body part. The myopic treatment of the pelvic floor is a disservice to our clients, especially those who may be unable or unwilling to have an internal muscular examination. It is not the role of pelvic PT to convince our patients to have examinations they don't feel comfortable with; it is our job to treat what we can, as best we can, with the tools we have available.

If we expand the definition of pelvic floor physical therapy and look beyond the genitals, it becomes clear that it is essential in not only relieving symptoms, but promoting autonomy and empowering patients to heal themselves.

Gender-Affirmative Sex Work: The Basics

Sadie Lune

When I come into Terri's home she always has a kombucha for me and a glass of wine for herself. We hug, and she is not a tight hugger, but I've learned the way she likes to be touched—firmly but very little pain. I compliment her outfit right away because it pleases her, and because we all need to feel seen, appreciated, and desired. I tell her to take her clothes off, but keep her lingerie on. And that is indicative of the work I do with trans and non-binary clients. I do my best to create a space that feels safe, familiar, relaxing, but also sexually charged; a space with someone with whom they can just *be*, and not merely *be gender non-conforming*.

Scenes begin with eye contact. "Is it ok if I touch you?" I initiate, but also ask consent. This isn't just "yes or no" consent but "please tell me if you have an idea, if you would like me to change something, or would like a break"—style consent. I go over the basics: what do you know you like? Is there someplace you don't like to be touched? Any words that feel bad to you? Any pain or injury I should know about? Something you're excited about or looking forward to today? Anything new I should know? Questions like these allow us to enter into an encounter energetically and reinforce a flexible frame for the wild weaving within: entwined threads of intimacy, intensity, vulnerability, and rapture. I model consent as an ongoing conversation; specific, but not gender-specific. I provide tools and cues that my clients can use to help make visible the color and shape of their desire. There is also a point when the questions stop, when I collect most of my answers from the state of my clients' eyelids and pupils, non-verbal sounds, breathing, and muscle tension. Experience has given me the gift of acting with intention and without hesitation. I am proactive with touch and bring easy confidence to each encounter, but stay open to any opportunity for my client to take the reins and fill up the room with their pleasure.

Even though Terri and I have seen each other often, I check in with where she is emotionally and sexually and what she has in mind at the beginning of each session. Sometimes she surprises me and suggests something that I didn't perceive before in her set of interests, and it's lovely to see her approach sexual pleasure expansively, through experimentation and wonder. I want to provide her with joy, revelation, affection and deep pleasure within a safe container. Sometimes Terri asks for something I'm not comfortable with, such as sharing personal information or me bottoming to her. Navigating but maintaining my limits is also part of creating a professional dynamic that is flexible and strong.

One time I misjudged what would feel good to her by quite a bit. It was our first session after she had recovered from surgery, and during our play I commented twice on how sexy her new breasts were. She asked for a pause in the action and shared with me that she actually had a lot of confusing mixed feelings about her breasts, wasn't quite used to them yet, and while usually she loved being verbally objectified by me, in this case she wasn't ready and it didn't feel good. I really appreciated this moment, because while she came to me to feel desirable and controlled, she was able to speak honestly about what her needs and limits were. I realized afterwards that like with most big changes an open-ended question about how she felt about her breasts would've served us both better than a unilateral decision that I should celebrate and sexualize them. In the moment I listened with compassion, apologized, and asked if she wanted a break in the session, or to continue. This incident didn't end our connection, and I was grateful that she spoke up about her discomfort so we had the chance to adjust our dynamic and repair.

I want my clients to hear through my tone and feel in my touch that I am comfortable with myself and with them, that their appearance, needs, desires and fears neither make me uneasy nor want to shrink away. Trans and non-binary folx often have a lifetime of media narratives and personal experience of others telling them that their excitement is questionable and their bodies are abject. It can take a hell of a lot of self-confidence and hope to overcome those messages every time they seek new connections for care, healing, affirmation, and pleasure. It's my job to do what I can to help my clients not just to trust me but to support and strengthen their trust in themselves, their lusts and desirability. With clients who come to me to express their submission, sometimes I blindfold them in front of a mirror and then stroke them as I open their eyes, instructing them to find parts of their bodies they enjoy, to repeat that they're beautiful as I caress or whip them. It's often a very difficult practice to focus on ourselves, to confront all the resistance. But whether with supportive words, erect nipples or Dominant tricks, I try to untie some of the knotted damage done to my clients' personhoods and sexualities by the cultures in which they move.

Sometimes we do slow games and exercises—practicing breath, consensual touch, giving and receiving caresses with our clothes on. We look at each others' bodies and discuss what feels comfortable or uncomfortable, exciting or not. Because my work touches on safety, touch, consent, risk, and transformation, I also endeavor to create a space where my clients can feel an honest tone of my desire. With cis straight male clients, the gendered script of sex and sex work dictates that generally I am the object of their desire; whether or not I desire them or find them attractive holds lesser weight. It feels different for me to work with people who, like me, share a legacy of stigmatized and outlawed gender and/or sexuality. I can directly reflect the love that I have for our community during each session, whether I'm fucking and dominating Terri, gently engaging Rob in flirting and gradually more erotic sessions, or coaching Lola on finding her emotional archetype in the dungeon.

Trans artist and activist Tourmaline calls the actions that reflect a would-be safer, more grateful, joyous, and free future "freedom dreaming."[13] Sex is so big, bodies are so beautiful, and our imaginations are so infinitely expansive. Expressing personal excitement and desire with and toward my trans clients is a way that I freedom dream with them: both that trans sex is well understood as the beautiful, inflammatory, sweet, enticing and intimately magic experience it can be; and that sex work is recognized as the healing, fun, educational, emotional, valuable, multi-skilled profession it can be.

We are often working within or against well-documented assumptions and stereotypes regarding our bodies, our race, age, ability, and gender—as seen by others or by ourselves. These stories are everywhere. Within sexuality the (hetero/cis) gendered scripts are so deeply ingrained, regardless of our preferences we all know them by heart. How sex *should* work, what bodies *should* do, and especially the fairytales of who does what to whom with what genital and for whose pleasure. But how the individual intersects with these stories, where they fit and especially where they don't, what each body wants here and now is something to be discovered in every session.

Shame gives us one-dimensional, binary stories of right or wrong, in or out, and especially stories of failure. But it also gives us fodder to subvert, to pervert, to find ourselves and our people. Giving caring energy to trans and non-binary clients reminds me to give caring energy to myself and my body. I use my smile, voice, ears and hands to invite and listen to the body and the mind, to identify desire and help it be nurtured where we find it. Because we are each individuals but bodies are all bodies. We all share muscle, skin, hair, fat, scars, erectile tissue. Terri and I each have specific preferences in different contexts at different stages of life but we all work with sensitivities, vulnerabilities, strength, and uncertainties. We all have preferences about the kinds of touch, pressure, sensation, and energy we like. There are infinite combinations of textures and patterns to play with, but each body works with the same elements in the webs of our sensual fibers.

Gender Pleasure

Tuck Malloy

Exploring my experience of gender is one of the most pleasurable activities in my life. The feeling of a packer pressed against my body and under my jeans. The curve of my jaw after my barber shears my hairs away, giving me a smooth, sleek fade. The sparkle of golden glitter that lights up my eyes and reminds me of the dress-up games I played when I was little. Smells of pine, whiskey, a perfume I received when I was a child, my own body smell, the rich smell of my ever-transforming and imagined genitals. The sound of my name, a sharp cluck in the back of my throat. The taste of a cottony pillow as I bite down and get spanked. The taste of another's skin as I worship, tease, and devour every part of them.

The experience of being affirmed, radiant, expansive in gender, especially for someone who has been forced to deny the magnificence of their existence, is healing and transformative for all aspects of one's life. There are many parts of being non-binary and trans that are not pleasurable. These are the parts most often discussed in the broader culture. What I know is that experiencing gender affirmation through my physical body, through my senses, is a visceral, neverending delight. My work is, in essence, an endeavor to draw attention to pleasure in human experience. I'm a sex educator. I've always been curious about bodies, sensations, touching, orgasms, fluids, and human connection.

I deeply appreciate the incomprehensibly vast ways a human body can experience the world. And our collective simplicity. I teach many overlapping topics: dirty talk, non-monogamy, communication skills, anatomy, solo sex/masturbation, gender identity, gender expression, gender inclusivity, kink/BDSM, oral sex, hand sex, strapon sex, anal sex, creativity, self-love, boundaries, unlearning shame, and embodiment. I have seen how the experience of gender for so many of my students, and myself, is informed, transformed, created, and destroyed by many different practices, senses, experiences, fears, hopes, and relationships. Teaching about gender lights up a special part of my soul.

Gender is an aspect of our culture. It has an impact. Those of us who are non-binary or agender are equally required to account for our lack of gender as those who experience gender with a distinct name, shape, color, and feel. As an educator, my job is to give students permission to be whatever they are. I offer students tools to explore what they experience—to understand it, transform it, or to reject it entirely. I do this work with people of all genders.

It is not just trans, non-binary, and non-cis humans who are called to explore their relationship to their body, hormones, sex, orientation, pleasure, and self-expression. I believe that creating inclusive spaces for trans and non-binary people requires the investigation and consideration of gender personally and socially by all the people in their circle. I have included below two activities that you might engage in with your clients to do just that, and to consider how exploring gender is exploring pleasure.

Gendered Senses Activity

This activity is designed to create a map of sensation related to gender in the body. When I present this exercise, I suggest that our bodies may experience gender as something tactile, physical, and sensual. Gender is not only abstract, it's immediate and visceral. This activity is not about inherent truths, it's about exploration.

Take a moment to breathe into your body with your eyes open. Notice some things you see around the room. Take a breath with the things you see. Notice some things you hear. Take a breath with the things you hear. Notice some things you can feel. Take a breath with the things you feel. Notice any things you can smell. Take a breath with the things you smell. Notice anything you can taste. (Or recall the last thing you tasted, what was it like?) Take a breath with the things you taste.

Now, breathing into your senses, consider your experience of gender. For students who are less abstract, invite them to recall a memory in which they felt affirmed in their gender, embodied, good in their skin, or ask them to imagine what that would be like. Ask:

- What does your gender look like? (ex: an orchid, stubble, me exactly as I am, a certain celebrity, nothing)
- What does your gender sound like? (ex: clicking heels, fingers moving inside someone's holes, slapping, bird song, wood splitting, a certain song)
- What does your gender feel like? (ex: heavy, fur, soft, feather, a hug, water, being safe)
- What does your gender smell like? (ex: lavender, whiskey, salt, sweat, perfume, body odor, nothing)
- What does your gender taste like? (ex: cum, strawberries, mac n cheese, cake, salt, skin)

Gender-Pleasure History Activity

The inspiration for this activity comes from the Pleasure History exercise. To do a pleasure history, you set a timer for five minutes and then share with a partner your experiences of pleasure throughout your life. The partner is encouraged to listen and not respond, while the speaker shares. Then you switch and repeat the process.

A gender pleasure history follows this same format, but with questions related to pleasure and gender together, to experiences (or lack thereof) related to being gendered, feeling a gender, feeling absence of gender, noticing gender in the self or others, affirming gender, learning about gender throughout one's lifetime. It can be linear or not. And it unfolds from this deceptively simple question: What is your experience of gender-pleasure in your life?

This is an example of a gender pleasure history I wrote for myself:

- As a child I remember playing with mud. I used to bake mud pies and build mud houses. I liked the feeling of mud in my hands. I felt the urge to create, and to be wet and dirty. I didn't feel any gender.
- When I was six or seven I had a friend who I used to play "dolls" with. That was what we called the game, but we didn't play with dolls when we played it. She pretended to be "the mom" and I pretended to be "the dad." In her closet, we lay on top of each other and rubbed our bodies together. I put my thumbs together over her lips and kissed them so our lips wouldn't touch. Growing up I played basketball. I liked the feel of the ball under my fingertips, it left them dirty and dusty and sometimes a little raw. I loved defending my team against the other players. I felt strong and ruthless. I liked when our moms talked about girl power.
- When I was a teenager I went to the ocean. I submerged my body. I felt like a piece of kelp. I realized the ocean is my mother and that I'm her child. I felt her waves crash over me as the essence of feminine power.
- One day, I put on a binder, and I stuffed socks in my pants. I found a pair of baggy pants. I put on my baseball cap. I looked in the mirror. I looked so hot. That night, I meditated. A cis male version of myself came to my mind. He was gentle, strong, kind. He looked like me. He asked to come home. I invited him in.
- One day after I came out as non-binary I put on makeup. As I stared at my face in the mirror feeling strange, I had a good idea. I drew on a moustache and it looked perfect.

Using BDSM as Trans Embodiment

Jaxx Alutalica MA, LMFT, CST

In my clinical practice, I specialize in working with trans and gender non-conforming (TGNC) people who seek gender affirmation and embodiment through the practice of Bondage, Discipline, Dominance, Submission, Sadism, and Masochism (BDSM). The healing properties of BDSM expand into many diverse therapeutic benefits that might be experienced by its practitioners, and are particularly poignant with TGNC individuals as they explore their corporeal relationship with self and others. It is important to note that BDSM should never be utilized in lieu of proper licensed therapy, but can be beneficial when exercised adjacent to a trained therapist and has reported benefits that are arguably only achievable through the unique avenue that is BDSM. This is not to suggest that BDSM participants are particularly in need of healing. Rather, this is to say that we all have our own need for healing and BDSM can be an aid in that process.

For the TGNC individuals I work with, BDSM provides an avenue for self-expression and a deepening of the somatic relationship they have with themselves to move toward a greater experience of embodiment. Among my clients, role play, non-genital touch and sensory stimuli, and interpersonal relationships are particularly important avenues through which BDSM players best experience gender embodiment. There is a small sampling of research that addresses the relationship between gender and BDSM that supports many of the findings reported by my own clinical practice.[14]

Role Play

For those TGNC individuals involved in the BDSM scene, many report finding deeper self-expression through the integration of role play into their practices. For some, this is an opportunity to embody identities and experiences that they may have been deprived of or denied access to because of the sex they were assigned at birth. For instance, a trans individual might role play a young boy as an opportunity to relive an adolescence they were unable to access being raised assigned female at birth. Similarly, some take on caretaker roles of Daddies, Mommies, or other gender-neutral caretakers to embody expressions of masculinity or femininity that are gender-affirming. Some even report finding their gender through role play, what once was a fun trait to try on becomes an expression of who they are and allows them permission to pursue transition or other gender-related expressions. In a similar realm, many of the clients I work with delight in non-human role play such as pet play to offer an entirely un-gendered opportunity for self-expression and sexuality and to express an embodiment of identity that might otherwise be challenging to access. The ability to integrate the imaginative qualities of role play offers a sense of re-negotiation with one's environment, with others, and the self in a profound way. Role play becomes an avenue for self-construction, something that is critical to transgender people's exploration and actualization of self and the process of embodying their sensuality, sexuality, and self-expression.

Non-genital Touch and Sensory Stimuli

It is a common trope that transgender people dislike their genitalia and avoid sensory stimulation of their genitals and/or chest tissue at all costs. This is most certainly not true for every transgender person. However, for those that do feel disidentified from these body parts, BDSM offers an opportunity to receive and give sensations that are stimulating to the body in ways that are not sexually or genitally oriented. The receipt of non-genital touch, frequently through receiving pain or other pleasure-adjacent stimuli to non-genital parts of the body offers an opportunity to embrace the experience of embodiment through touch that is not considered sexual but might provide sexual or otherwise pleasurable stimuli. This opportunity to experience the body outside of traditional genital-to-genital sex is an act of radical embodiment, a reclamation of touch as euphoric instead of dysphoric, and an opportunity to feel present in one's body without the potentially distressing engagement with parts of their bodies that they feel disidentified from. Non-genital touch can manifest as any kind of BDSM activity that involves bodily contact (frequently, but not always, through painful stimulation), and is reported to be one of the most embodying experiences that my clients experience through BDSM.

Interpersonal Relationships

Whether it be their community roles, Dominant/submissive (D/s) dyads, or other interpersonal interactions, TGNC BDSM players report their relationships with others to be another avenue through which embodiment occurs. Similar to role play, the embodiment of different community roles (i.e., being a Daddy to an entire group of individuals, being a title-holder, or otherwise in a position of power or submission) allows for an expression of self and a validation of their gender identity. Many of my clients find D/s dynamics affirming because of the ways in which D/s is often aligned with gendered behavior. By either subscribing to these stereotypes or subverting them, participants engage with gender on a psychological level wherein they have control of how they are perceived and how their gender is processed by others. Being witnessed in our gender is a substantial part of experiencing gendered embodiment for TGNC individuals, and BDSM offers a witnessing that is simultaneously vulnerable and powerful, and within the control of the player.

For my clients, as well as fellow trans BDSM practitioners, the corporeal relationship built through BDSM facilitates a deeper understanding of the self, an ability to express their gender more fully, and ultimately a greater likelihood of experiencing gender euphoria. BDSM is radical in its ability to integrate conscientious representations of power and pleasure with one's self identification and gendered embodiment.

Crotch Coloring
Heather Edwards, PT, CSC

As Lucie discusses in Chapters 1 and 3, we often run into concepts, structures, and systems that would seek to determine what sex is, who has sex, what constitutes "good" sex vs. "bad" sex, what is "normal" in sex, and what sex should look like. These systems and structures further seek to determine what our genitals are supposed to do and what constitutes proper function. We are taught, for example, that "boys have penises and are praised for behaving in masculine ways" and "girls have vaginas and are praised for behaving in feminine ways."

Although we may be able to intellectually understand that these are ideas created within an ableist, White Supremacist, patriarchal system with the intent of policing bodies, gender, and sexualities as well as oppressing any deviation from the norms, it takes time to unlearn patterns and forge our own paths, our own relationships to/with our sexual bodies. That unlearning can take many forms. Here is an idea for unlearning that might work for some of your clients. It involves coloring some crotches!

There are images of genitals on the next two pages (Figures 6.3 and 6.4). They are fanciful and not inherently gendered. Introduce them to your client or patient. You might start by inviting your patient to use words to express observations about the images or feelings about the way they are portrayed. Invite them to consider what colors could be added to make it feel more comfortable (or less comfortable), and then have them color an image or two. Once they've done so you might process the experience with your patient by asking them what sensations, images, feelings, and thoughts they might have noticed bubbling up into awareness as they engaged with and colored the crotches.

Your client/patient could also draw their own versions of genitals, using the Anatomy Talk vignette I provided earlier in this chapter. There are two versions of crotches available in these lessons, but they can be modified and mix-'n-matched to create whatever image is desired. Invite the client to ask themself:

- What parts do I want to draw?
- Do I want to add themes (these can be super basic and easy... stripes, polka dots, flowers, lightning bolts, stars)?
- What colors do I want to align with it (or what colors do I want to add to it to change the vibe of what I drew)?

You could also suggest creating a series that shows a metamorphosis, whether it's with making copies of tentacle vulva and using color to show changes, or to use your drawing skills and draw the changing versions of genitals.

All of these suggestions are merely tools for observing, unlearning, and re-visioning the connections between genitals and gender, and, indeed, the relationship we have to our genitals more globally (see also Chapter 3). Hopefully, this exercise will give your client/patient space to play, to imagine, and dream – our bodies are our own and only we get to determine how we use them.

Use this exercise in ways that work best for you and your client/patient. If you enjoy these images and you want more, there's a Coloring Books for the Crotch Enthusiast series available on my website: www.heatheredwards creations.com.

Figure 6.3 Crotch Coloring Page

Courtesy of Heather Edwards, PT, CSC

Figure 6.4 Crotch Coloring Page

Courtesy of Heather Edwards, PT, CSC

"I want to dance, but how do I start?": Three Days of Embodied Movement

Harmony Lee

I founded "Your Gay Dance Teacher" because I have struggled to find affirming movement classes for gender non-conforming, non-binary and transgender dancers, particularly ones wherein BIPoC folx are centered. I teach healing movement to help folx heal from trauma and emotional pain because this approach saved my life. Movement has so much healing potential, but so many of us are afraid to dance. Attending a dance class may be intimidating, inaccessible, or overwhelming to navigate, but dancing at home can also feel like there is a lack of guidance. For those who are gender non-conforming, it can be difficult to find a gender expansive dance class/teacher/studio where they can be affirmed and accepted in their authentic expression.

Our bodies hold many stories, including generations of genetic messaging in the form of stress response adaptations, survival responses, and intuition. And movement is a language to speak the stories written in tongues we no longer speak. Our bodies contain past adventures, past joys, past lessons, past mistakes, past fears, and past dreams. I like to define "somatics" as the internal relationship between your thinking-mind and your body-mind. We engage our thinking-mind in our everyday cognitive function. We engage our body-mind, on the other hand, when we listen to a gut feeling, or follow instinctual movement, not knowing exactly why. When we move, we embody our imagination; we build and inhabit imaginal landscapes.

If we are seeking more connection to our bodies, we can use movement to find a healing path that supports harmonious connection between the thinking-mind and our body-mind and navigate towards safety and pleasure in our own bodies. Often, our thinking mind holds judgments and stories that do not serve us. These stories can keep us from pleasure. But our body knows the way.

The first step in this journey is to non-judgmentally survey the connection between the messages in our body and the cognitive messages in our thinking-brain. How do they relate to each other? How do they challenge one another? How might they support one another? And how do how they currently co-exist?

I believe that we can use movement to deepen our connection to the body and create a healing map that meets our unique needs. I believe that movement is medicine, and that a re-patterning of the nervous system can be achieved through non-judgmental, intuitive, authentic movement.

For new dancers, or those returning to movement, getting started can be challenging. We live in a culture which tells us that dance is about learning steps and technique, requiring years of training or innate gracefulness. I'd like to offer a different perspective: that's bullshit. Dance is our birthright. Dance is body language. You are already a dancer. Let me say that louder: YOU ARE A DANCER, JUST AS YOU ARE. While that is true, it may take practice to build confidence in your movement and dance. To help you build a movement practice, here are three days of movement prompts to help you and your clients get started and connect with your/their body, wherever you are and at whatever level of dance and movement experience you might have. For four additional days to support you and your clients' unique dance practices, check out my ebook, *7 Days of Embodied Movement*, available for purchase at: https://www.yourgaydanceteacher.com/.

Each of the three days included in this exercise has an intention, a movement prompt, reflection questions, and affirmations to provide structure and support to your personal dance practice. For those in the healing field, I recommend sharing these prompts with your clients if they are seeking embodiment, body awareness, or connection to movement. There is no wrong way to do these prompts. By practicing these prompts, you can explore movement non-judgmentally, and attune to your body's range of motion, needs, natural alignment, and awareness. You may find it helpful to try these prompts with or without music. I've provided suggested music, but you are welcomed to pick your own music that fits your mood. These prompts were designed to be scaled for whatever dance space you have available, and you are invited to dance as big or small as you feel. I hope that dancing over these three days brings you and your clients joy, healing, and greater confidence around movement. From movement, I hope you can continue your journey towards further pleasure and joy. As we practice movement, we practice embodying pleasure and joy. And from this embodiment, we can extend the healing to our sexuality and erotic self. This is just the start of an amazing journey!

Day 1

- Intention: EXPLORE. Today is about exploration. There is no judgment in exploring. We are gathering information about how we move, and noticing the associated feelings involved when we move.
- Music Suggestion: "Trampoline" by SHAED
- Movement Prompt: Imagine you are an alien, who has just been cloned into a new body/form/machine. In your mind, describe and visualize this alien form. How would you move if you were brand new to this form? What does it feel like?
- Reflection Questions: What was it like to move your body in a new way? What did your alien form teach you?
- Affirmations: My body is full of beautiful stories. There is no wrong way to move. I have permission to explore and connect with my body in an entirely new way.

Day 2

- Intention: SENSE. We have senses (sight, touch, taste, smell, hearing, intuition) and we have the ability to sense our bodies in space. Today is an opportunity to connect your senses to movement and discover their potential to deepen your embodied experience.
- Music Suggestion: "5 bit Blues" by Kid Koala
- Movement Prompt: Use your senses to find gravity, and experiment with shifting your body to play with your relationship to gravity. It may help to isolate one body part, tense it, relax, and imagine it is heavy with the pull of gravity. Relating and attuning to gravity while moving provides a stability compass you can return to when balance is challenging.
- Reflection Questions: What did you learn about your connection to gravity? Where did gravity feel easiest to access? Where did it feel more challenging?
- Affirmations: My body has so much wisdom. My body knows how to move in innovative ways. My body is connected to the earth and I have permission to explore this connection through dance.

Day 3

- Intention: FEEL. Today we are exploring tactile awareness (feeling through touch) as well as emotional feelings. Feel free to connect with either, or both.
- Music Suggestion: "Lavender" by Q
- Movement Prompt: Before moving, I invite you to identify a feeling to explore. If you want to explore feeling through touch, you may consider exploring the feeling of a surface, the floor, or your own skin. Tracing, touching, and creating pressure are helpful ways to engage feeling. If you want to explore an emotional feeling, it may be helpful to connect to a feeling in the music you choose. I invite you to be specific in the feeling, and explore ways to move that emotion in your body. If you'd like to shift your awareness, how could you explore that emotion to communicate it to another being, if they were watching you without sound? You may find yourself moving away from this initial feeling, and that is completely fine. This is a starting point to provide specificity, but it is not a commitment you need to uphold.
- Reflection Questions: What did you learn by feeling into your movement? How did this compare to sensing or exploring your movement?
- Affirmations: I am showing up for myself. I am embodying bravery by choosing to move my body.

Safer Sex Bingo

Bianca Palmisano, MSN, RN

As a sex educator, my job is both to explicate and complicate the "rules" of sexuality. How to be sexual, how to protect yourself, and how to connect with others are all deeply individual decisions, yet they invite teaching and discussion to expand beyond the scripts given to us by the media and our peers.

One exercise I do during my sex ed classes aims to expand my clients' understanding of how barriers are used for safer sex. Many of us learned how to put an external condom on a banana in high school sex ed or saw the trope on television at least. However, far fewer folks are familiar with the uses for internal ("female") condoms, dental dams, and nitrile gloves. For those of us with bodies and identities that transgress normative socio-medical boundaries, safer sex tools may need to be re-imagined and reconstructed. This, in turn, opens the door for our cisgender and heterosexual counterparts to reconsider their own sexual lives, and how they might rethink the use of their bodies and safer sex barriers.

For instance, a glove is good for a hand with long fingernails, but it is also good for sliding over the cock of trans guy who has been on T for a year. A dental dam can be used on a vulva, but can also be placed over a butthole, or used to cover a cold sore on a mouth. When I introduce these materials, I try to facilitate a conversation about how they can be used with people of all genders, with all combinations of body parts.

This exercise serves as both a Safer Sex 101 and a conversation about the unique ways that trans bodies exist in space: the way they get wet, grow hard, take up more or less space than cisgender biomedical narratives say that they should.

I often simultaneously introduce my "Safer Sex Bingo Card" (Figure 6.5), as a tool for expanding our vocabulary of what constitutes sex. The Safer Sex Bingo card explodes open the idea of what it means to be sexual with another person, especially for trans people who can have complicated relationships with their genitals or other body parts (such as chest tissue). Phone sex, massages, and sexy showers all feature on the bingo card, divorced from the hierarchy of judgments that tell us what constitutes "real sex." The bingo card creates the space for exploration of our sexual connections, gives permission for experimentation, and encourages intimacy outside and beyond penetration and orgasm.

The card is meant to sit unobtrusively on tabletops in spaces where sex is not usually discussed openly: medical offices, therapy rooms, barber shops, nail salons, car dealerships. Anywhere a People Magazine might otherwise sit. The bingo card isn't meant to be facilitated and it doesn't have instructions or rules; it invites the holder to explore on their own terms. Maybe it becomes a conversation starter about intimacy and safety when an adolescent comes to their doctor for their first pelvic exam. Maybe someone brings it home to

Safer Sex Bingo Card

Mutual Masturbation	Fingering or Hand Jobs	Phone Sex [or Sexting]	Femoral Sex (between the thighs)	Dirty Talk
Strip Tease	Vibrators and Butt Plugs	Showering Together	Taking Photos	Put [External] Condom on Without Using your Hands
Oral Sex	Bondage	FREE SPACE!	Wrestling	Massage
Spanking	Rimming	Watching Porn	Sex with Lube	Sober Sex
Try Out the Internal Condom	Reading an Erotic Story	Teasing	Role Playing	Golden Showers

© ⚛ Intimate Health Consulting
Happy. Sexy. Healthy.

Figure 6.5 Safer Sex Bingo Card

Courtesy Bianca Palmisano, RN and Intimate Health Consulting their partner and they make a game of trying the activities, five-in-a-row for one week of sexual exploration. Maybe someone just sits quietly with it and considers all the new ways they can feel connection to another person.

Just as there is no "right way" to use our bodies during sex, there is no right way to use the safer sex bingo card. It creates space for consideration, opens possibilities beyond structure, and allows us to simply be ourselves.

"The Body is the Shore on the Ocean of Being"

Laura A. Jacobs, LCSW-R

"The body is the shore on the ocean of being," yet so many transgender and non-binary people have constructed defensive walls around the body, around the shore, that the ocean is often inaccessible.[15]

We have complex relationships with our bodies, and many things keep us separated from the greater experiences of connection and joy the body can afford: trauma, whether physical or emotional, disempowerment resulting from sexual assault, objectification, survival sex, trans-hostile policing, shame, the anguish of existing every day in a body so inauthentic, physical and legislative violence, race, socioeconomics, and all the multiple oppressors we face in a world overtly hostile to our existence. But this is where a deeper wisdom can begin.

◆

Trans people, like all human beings, are inextricably linked to our bodies.[16] For any of us in this community, our form may or may not align with our internal self, and yet it is so much grander than a shell; the body is an aspect of life through which we can investigate the human experience. Trans people are blessed with the opportunity to explore in depth, and a skilled clinician can be an essential guide.

The fortifications we've built in response to our trauma are so meticulously constructed. Gender related trauma is often somaticized in an effort to conceal aspects we find inauthentic or want to change, furthering a mind/body divide. One example is the characteristic transmasculine "hunch." The dysphoria of being transmasculine while having tissue commonly labeled "breasts" and coded "female" can be relentless; often anxious to minimize any reminder of their gender assigned at birth and characteristics which could expose someone's "trans-ness" to others, many wear baggy sweatshirts even in summer, use close-fitting binders that restrict their breathing, and rotate their shoulders inward and down to hide. Similarly, many transfeminine people pray beneath blankets to be magically transformed and for their penis to vanish to nothingness, only to wake disheartened. In response someone may minimize any bulge by "tucking," drawing the penis down and back between their legs and relocating their testicles uncomfortably up into the lower abdomen. Those non-binary do or do not desire to alter their bodies and so may have some of the above strains or others, while also being plagued by still less access to affirming healthcare or social validation than their binary friends.

Even more keeps us on dry land. People ill at ease within their bodies rarely care for those bodies, the daily burden exacerbating depression, anxiety, and low self-esteem again making it difficult to be present to one's experience. Trans people of any gender may hide their faces and look away, afraid to view themselves in a reflection or to be noticed by others. Still others are so dysphoric they shower in the dark, aware of the need for hygiene but unable to acknowledge a body so discordant with their internal self. All these behaviors had been adopted for physical and emotional safety. Also, many in this community simply lack the privilege to alter their bodies toward ones more validating, once more interfering with alignment.

And no one wakes from anesthesia suddenly integrated. Shape and identity may now align, but psychological trauma does not vanish as nerves and neural connections require time to heal and remap. We may still enact defenses no longer necessary. There may be grief even for genitalia one has wanted gone for decades.[17]

Progressive mental health, sex therapy, and other allied providers incorporate sex-positive, somatic techniques to aid clients in healing and facilitate mindfulness. Historically, sessions with transgender and non-binary clients were intellectual discussions of the relationship between identity and the body, explorations of the different gender possibilities, and then supports through the making manifest of the options chosen. But by concentrating on the physical experience, therapist and client move beyond questions about genitalia and toward a more pleasure-centered relationship with the body. Ultimately this helps demolish the barricades.

Even those in our community with no ability or desire for hormones or surgeries can improve their relationship to their bodies, and trans people can still better experience their sexual selves after years or decades divorced from them. The techniques used by many providers, cobbled together through experience and trainings, are discussed in more detail throughout this book and blend breathing exercises, body awareness, sensate focus, written and online resources, and sexually focused homework, all alongside discussion so as to help clients become more attuned to sensation while also aiding them to be present to any emotions that arise.[18] Meditation, mindfulness apps, yoga, and other practices can be useful adjuncts.[19] Often suggested to clients for general wellness and as nonmedical interventions to decrease depression and anxiety, these also promote awareness and an ability to find stillness essential for addressing intrusive thoughts, impatience to orgasm, and guilt over receiving sensation while their partner devotes time to one's body.

Even after chest masculinization, R (pronoun: he), an early 20's Caucasian trans man and aspiring standup comic, was chided by instructors for huddling over the microphone, conveying a defensiveness that alienated his audiences and muted the laughter he hoped to get.[20] R's partner had been enamored of his pretransition body though felt a deep lust for his now masculine chest and was increasingly frustrated at R's "grit his teeth and bear it" dissociation when she casually ran fingers through his chest hair. With guidance from his therapist, R began mindful breathing and internal body scans in sessions; initially he winced in a way he could only describe with a primal, agonized moan. Despite this, R sought to continue, and his therapist gently guided him through body relaxation while soothingly talking about safety and the empowered decisions R had made toward a more affirming body. Eventually R incorporated sensate focus with his partner, later moving toward overt erotic touch; at the end of treatment the couple spontaneously initiated deeply passionate and adventurous sex in the bedroom, car, alleyway: wherever possible. Over time his posture, confidence, bond with his partner, and even his career improved, leaving him better able to access transcendent moments through orgasms no longer restrained by trauma and dysphoria.

Some clinicians encourage clients to engage in BDSM.[21] Through its foundations of negotiations and consent, BDSM provides a pleasure-based environment to establish boundaries and trust, control the areas of the body to be touched, roleplay and a playfulness of semantics through which one can depersonalize as needed while gradually moving toward integration, and a sense of belonging, all of which facilitates autonomy over one's own body.

G (pronouns: they or she), a transfeminine non-binary 45-year-old person of color, had little desire for vaginoplasty but could only under limited circumstances tolerate sexually engaging with their penis, instead retaining it in a deliberate politicization of gender and a response to "Black penises are dangerous" social messages, allowing G to feel empowered by actively transgressing racial stereotypes and heteronormativity. They identified as a top in BDSM to feel more control over sexual interactions, interpreting their dominance as a means to bring their partner to orgasm and to limit how G themselves was touched rather than using their partner for G's own pleasure.

G invited their partner to attend sessions and the clinician facilitated negotiation and boundary setting; after several meetings G began speaking, hesitantly, about their multilayered relationship with their penis and all three strategized to cautiously incorporate it more in play. G and their partner reframed it as the more gender congruent "trannyclit," or sometimes as "lollipop," validating the "fuck you" to society and helping G avoid the distressing "penis/cock/dick" associations of the past. The semantic shift also offered G the prospect of building the relationship to their genitalia anew, this time from a place of connectedness and pleasure. Eventually G no longer felt alone in the dysphoria and was even able to occasionally penetrate their partner by reinterpreting the act as a radical queering of traditional sexual expression, much to their mutual delight.

◆

We have such difficulty deconstructing the walls that isolate us from the water, but being trans offers the opportunity for a wondrous curiosity about the intersections of gender and society, relationships, sexuality history, power, privilege, and even existential meaning. We can cultivate deeper associations with others and with our own bodies, gaining a wisdom we each find for ourselves as we move through our lives in open-ended, nonjudgmental exploration. We can subsume ourselves in each caress of our penises, breasts, vulvas, boobs, pussies, dicks, schlongs, backs, cunts, trannyclits, earlobes, tatas, eyelids, manholes, chesticles, butts, feet, navels, cockpits, and every millimeter of our bodies each so deserving of attention. Sensual and sexual ecstasy are avenues to a oneness of being.

We can find our way to the ocean.

Special thanks to Catherine Chinnock and Zoë Entin.

Notes

1 See Douglas Braun-Harvey and Michael A. Vigorito, *Treating Out of Control Sexual Behavior: Rethinking Sex Addiction* (New York: Springer Publishing Company, 2016).

2 Arlene Istar Lev, *Transgender Emergence: Therapeutic Guidelines for Working with Gender-Variant People and Their Families* (New York: The Haworth Clinical Practice Press, 2004), 271.

3 Ben Vincent and Sonja Erikainen, "Gender, Love, and Sex: Using Duoethnography to Research Gender and Sexuality Minority Experiences of Transgender Relationships," *Sexualities* 23, no. 1–2 (February 2020): 29, https://doi.org/10.1177/1363460718796457.

4 For more on the lived realities of trans masculine folx in partnership with cis women, see Carla A Pfeffer, *Queering Families: The Postmodern Partnerships of Cisgender Women and Transgender Men* (New York, NY: Oxford University Press, 2017).

5 Jos Twist et al., "Transitioning Together: A Narrative Analysis of the Support Accessed by Partners of Trans People," *Sexual and Relationship Therapy* 32, no. 2 (April 3, 2017): 229, https://doi.org/10.1080/14681994.2017.1296568.

6 Laura A. Jacobs, "Hormones and Handcuffs: The Intersection of Transgender Identities, BDSM, and Polyamory," in *Sex, Sexuality, and Trans Identities: Clinical Guidance for Psychotherapists and Counselors*, ed. Jan C. Niemira, Gary J. Jacobson, and Karalyn J. Violeta (London: Jessica Kingsley Publishers, 2020), 92.

7 See, for example, Sandy E. James et al., "The Report of the 2015 U.S. Transgender Survey" (Washington, DC: National Center for Transgender Equality, December 2016); Jacobs, "Hormones and Handcuffs: The Intersection of Transgender Identities, BDSM, and Polyamory," 93.

8 Ashley Austin and Shelley L. Craig, "Transgender Affirmative Cognitive Behavioral Therapy: Clinical Considerations and Applications.," Professional Psychology: Research and Practice 46, no. 1 (2015): 21–29, https://doi.org/10.1037/a0038642; Stephanie L. Budge, Mun Yuk Chin, and Laura P. Minero, "Trans Individuals' Facilitative Coping: An Analysis of Internal and External Processes," *Journal of Counseling Psychology* 64, no. 1 (2017): 12–25, https://doi.org/10.1037/cou0000178.

9 Sara I. McClelland, "Intimate Justice," in *Encyclopedia of Critical Psychology*, ed. Thomas Teo (New York, NY: Springer New York, 2014), 1010–1013, https://doi.org/10.1007/978-1-4614-5583-7; Brian A. Rood et al., "Expecting Rejection: Understanding the Minority Stress Experiences of Transgender and Gender-Nonconforming Individuals," *Transgender Health* 1, no. 1 (January 2016): 151–64, https://doi.org/10.1089/trgh.2016.0012.

10 A term, likely Visayan in origin, used to describe those who followed traditional medicine from the islands known by their colonized name, the Philippines.

11 One of several terms used to describe initiated traditional medicine practitioners and ritualists from the Philippines.

12 A term of endearment that means "auntie."

13 Tourmaline, "Filmmaker and Activist Tourmaline on How to Freedom Dream," *Vogue*, July 2, 2020, https://www.vogue.com/article/filmmaker-and-activist-tourmaline-on-how-to-freedom-dream.

14 See, for example, Robin Bauer, *Queer BDSM Intimacies: Critical Consent and Pushing Boundaries* (New York, NY: Palgrave Macmillan, 2014); Robin Bauer, "Cybercocks and Holodicks: Renegotiating the Boundaries of Material Embodiment in Les-Bi-Trans-Queer BDSM Practices," *Graduate Journal of Social Science* 14, no. 2 (September 2018): 58–82; C. Jacob Hale, "Leatherdyke Boys and Their Daddies: How to Have Sex without Women or Men," *Social Text*, no. 52/53 (1997): 223, https://doi.org/10.2307/466741; Susan Stryker, "Dungeon Intimacies: The Poetics of Transsexual Sadomasochism," *Parallax* 14, no. 1 (2008): 36–47.

15 Anonymous Sufi proverb sometimes attributed to Rumi.

16 'Trans' is used in this chapter as an umbrella term for 'transgender,' 'genderqueer,' 'gender nonconforming,' 'non-binary,' and anyone who feels or expresses a gender identity other than that assigned at birth, or outside the norms of society.

17 Grief, once interpreted as an unambiguous sign an individual was NOT trans because it implied a connection with one's gender assigned at birth, is more accurately a natural (though not universal) part of the trans experience. It is not a signal of "having made a mistake." The individual was still attached to those body parts for years or decades and most changes, even toward something more desirable, involve loss. *Grief is healthy*.

18 Sensate Focus is a sex therapy technique to help an individual improve physical and emotional connection through the more mindful offering and receiving of intimate but nonsexual touch. See William Masters and Virginia E. Johnson, *Human Sexual Response* (Boston, MA: Little, Brown, and Co., 1966).

19 Headspace: www.headspace.com, Calm: www.calm.com, and others have been especially useful with my own clients.

20 Details of both case vignettes have been altered to protect anonymity.

21 An acronym incorporating Bondage and Discipline, Dominance and Submission, and SadoMasochism. A disproportionately large segment of the TGNB community engage in some form of BDSM and/or nonmonogamy. For more on this topic, see my article, Jacobs, "Hormones and Handcuffs: The Intersection of Transgender Identities, BDSM, and Polyamory."

GLOSSARY

Here, I define key terms that may not be familiar to all readers. This list of terms is by no means exhaustive. A number of organizations, including the American Psychological Association and Fenway Health have produced excellent glossaries in their own right. The activist and writer Julia Serano has produced a particularly detailed and helpful glossary, available at http://www.juliaserano.com/terminology.html.

AFAB/AMAB: Respectively, Assigned Female at Birth and Assigned Male at Birth. AFAB and AMAB are preferable to the older acronyms FtM (Female-to-Male) and MtF (Male-to-Female), which many trans folx do not find affirming, as they center the sex assigned at birth and transition, and reinforce the gender binary.

Asexuality: A broad spectrum of sexual orientations that describes individuals who experience varying degrees of sexual attraction and/or interest in engaging in sexual activity or relationships. There are many ways of being asexual, and asexuality in no way implies aromanticism (i.e., varying degrees of romantic attraction and/or interest in engaging in romantic relationships).

Binding: The practice of wrapping the chest, taping, or using a compression garment (binder) to flatten chest tissue.

BIPoC: An acronym that stands for Black Indigenous Person(s) of Color.

Bottom Surgery:	A colloquial term for a number of gender-affirmative surgical interventions centered on surgically modifying genitalia, including vaginoplasty, vulvoplasty, orchiectomy, hysterectomy, metoidioplasty, and phalloplasty.
Cis:	A Latin prefix that means "on this side of," as in its use in the compound terms "cisgender" "cis woman," and "cis folx." Cis, whether as a standalone term, or as a prefix to another term (such as woman, man, or individual), refers to anyone whose gender identity aligns with the sex they were assigned at birth (e.g., male, female, intersex). Cis originated as an activist term and a way of indicating that everyone, whether cis or trans, has a relationship to gender. Cis, like trans, has become an umbrella term in its own right, an abbreviation of the term *cisgender*.
Cisnormativity/ Cisgenderism:	A form of systemic discrimination and oppression steeped in gender essentialism and the belief that gender identity and expression are determined by the sex someone was assigned at birth.
Cross-dressing (CD):	A term that refers to individuals who dress as a member of a gender other than the one they were assigned at birth or their own present gender identity. People who cross-dress do not typically identify as trans (although some prominent trans folx cross-dress or perform drag), but there is a long history of some trans folx identifying as cross-dressers prior to coming into their trans identity. Folx cross-dress for a number of reasons and providers should not make assumptions about why individuals choose to do so. For some, it can be a way of experimenting with gender identity and expression; for others, it can be a way of playing with and subverting gender norms; and for others cross-dressing can be a kink. Cross-dresser replaces the archaic term *transvestite*.
Deadname:	Often, the name that a trans or non-binary person used before transitioning. Upon adopting or legally changing one's name, the use of a trans person's deadname is a microagressive act.

Facial Feminization Surgery (FFS):	A set of gender-affirming surgical interventions typically pursued by trans feminine persons that include modifying various bony and soft tissue procedures of the face.
Gender Binary:	A social construct that characterizes gender in terms of two categories: man/male and woman/female.
Gender Dysphoria:	A psychiatric term that refers to the discomfort or distress trans and non-binary folx experience in the incongruence between the gender they have been assigned since birth and their gender identity.
Gender Euphoria:	A recent term that is the converse of gender dysphoria. This refers to the positive feelings trans and non-binary folx experience when their gender is affirmed and recognized insofar as their gender expression aligns with their gender identity.
Gender Expansive:	A term that describes individuals who broaden their cultures' commonly held conceptions of gender identity, expression, and/or norms. This may include trans and non-binary folx as well as anyone else who might be stretching a culture's conceptions of gender. The term gender expansive replaces older descriptive terms such as *gender non-conforming* and *gender variant*. Many people avoid these two terms as they center abnormality or non-conformity rather than variation, difference, and diversity.
Gender Expression:	How one presents oneself, including physical appearance, clothing, and comportment in ways that communicate aspects of gender. With respect to appearance, one may express one's gender in ways that are culturally coded as masculine, feminine, androgynous, or any combination outside of and in-between these socially constructed categories. Gender expression may or may not conform to a person's gender identity.
Gender Identity:	An individual's internal felt sense of their gender, or lack thereof (i.e., agender folx). Gender identity may be fixed or may be fluid,

depending on the individual. A given person's gender identity does not imply particular expressions or presentations of gender.

Intersex: An umbrella term for individuals who possess a wide range of naturally occurring variations in sexual characteristics, variations which might include chromosomal composition, hormone concentrations, and external and internal physical characteristics (gonads, genital form/ structure, etc.). Many of the bottom surgeries presently pursued by trans and non-binary folx were originally developed to address "ambiguous" genitalia perceived at birth and performed by doctors without regard for an intersex person's consent or wishes. In recent years, intersex activism has sought to advocate for an end to so-called "corrective" surgeries.

Hormone Therapy (HT): A medical intervention that involves the introduction of hormones with the explicit desire to feminize or masculinize one's body or appearance to better align one's appearance with one's gender identity. Sometimes referred to as Hormone Replacement Therapy (HRT), although HRT has fallen out of favor with some trans and non-binary folx. Hormones may be administered as pills, topical creams/gels, or patches. They may also be injected subcutaneously (SubQ) or intramuscularly (IM). HT acts to increase levels of estrogen or testosterone in the body (feminizing and masculinizing HT, respectively) and decrease testosterone levels via the introduction of anti-androgens (feminizing HT). Some non-binary folx may opt for a course of HT referred to as low-dose T. Because testosterone is "microdosed," the effects tend to be far more subtle.

Latinx: Pronounced "La-teen-ex," Latinx is a gender expansive term used to refer to people of Latin American descent without reference to a specific binary gender, as in the terms Latino and Latina.

LGBTQIA2S+:	An acronym that stands for Lesbian, Gay, Bisexual, Transgender, Queer, Intersex, Asexual, Two-Spirit. The plus sign at the end indicates the inclusion of other identities apart from those represented by the letters used in the abbreviation.
Metoidioplasty:	A bottom surgery usually pursued by trans masculine folx following growth of clitoral tissue following HT. The procedural involves creating a neophallus from enlarged clitoral tissue.
Misgendering:	The act of attributing a gender to someone or a group of people that does not align with their gender identity. It occurs when using incorrect pronouns, gendered language (e.g., "dude," "hey guys" or "ladies and gentlemen"), or assuming someone's gender without knowing that person's gender identity. Like deadnaming, misgendering is a microaggressive act. It can be avoided by using non-gendered language (e.g., folx, y'all, everybody, persons) and by asking a person for their pronouns.
Muffing:	A term coined by Mira Bellwether to describe a sex act that involves invaginating a person's testicles to thereby penetrate the inguinal canal(s).
Non-binary/Nonbinary:	An individual who does not identify with binary gender and who actively seeks to move beyond, move between, or step outside of the gender binary. Numerous expressions and identities fall under non-binary, including folx who are bigender, gender fluid, genderqueer, neutrois, androgyne, agender, femme, and butch.
Orchiectomy:	A type of bottom surgery that involves the surgical removal of one or both testicles. Orchiectomies can be pursued prior to, concurrent with, or independently of other bottom surgeries. Orchiectomies significantly reduce the production of endogenous testosterone, and are thus often pursued to obviate the need to take anti-androgens.
Packing:	The practice, most commonly engaged in by folx with vulvas, of wearing a penis prosthesis (a packer) or creating the silhouette, look, and feel of having a penis under clothing.

Passing/Blending:	A colloquial term also referred to as "blending" that originated in discourses of race (i.e., BIPoC folx who "passed" as white and were thus extended white privilege), but has since been applied to a trans person who is assumed to be cis or is not perceived as trans based on their appearance. Within the trans community, the issue of passing or blending is complicated. For some, passing is the goal, whether because it is a matter of ensuring their physical safety or they see it as an affirming process that allows them to align their presentation with their gender identity. All the same, passing can be a form of privilege, as individuals who are assumed to be cis are extended the privileges inherent in being cis. And for some people, passing or blending is simply not important. Many activists characterize the concept of passing as problematic. The discourse of "passing" or "blending" implies that all trans and non-binary folx want to appear as cis, which is not every trans person's goal. This also sets up an assumption that trans folx are trying to deceive cis folx. Activists have suggested instead the concept of being *assumed* cis. This places the emphasis on a culture that would seek to impose gender norms and identities onto trans and non-binary folx.
Phalloplasty:	A type of bottom surgery that results in the construction of a penis.
Polyamory:	A type of consensually non-monogamous relationship structure that refers to being in or being open to multiple, simultaneous, sexual and/or romantic relationships. As a descriptor of relationship orientation, polyamory is sometimes abbreviated as "polyam."
Pronouns:	Some trans people use pronouns which place them on the binary (he/him/his or she/her/hers). Others may use they/their/them or neo pronouns, such as ze/hir/hirs and some individuals may use multiple sets of pronouns (e.g., I use both she/her and they/them). Inquiring after someone's pronouns and then using them correctly is one of the most basic ways to affirm

someone's gender. When asking after a person's pronouns, avoid the construction "preferred pronouns." For trans people, this can suggest that their gender identity is just a matter of personal preference, as opposed to a vital part of who they are.

Queer: a term that originated as a slur, but has been reclaimed by many in the wider LGBTQIA2S+ community as an umbrella term. As a verb, to "queer" something is to deconstruct it, to turn it on its head, to destabilize and mystify it. "Queering" is associated with queer theory, a movement of critical theory that emerged in the 1990s. Queerness may also stand in for a radical political positioning that opposes binary and normative categories as well as value systems such as heteronormativity, homonormativity, and cisnormativity.

Sex Assigned at Birth: The sex marker—male, female, or intersex—assigned/given to a person at birth pursuant to an examination of their external genitalia.

Sexual Orientation: An enduring emotional, romantic, and/or sexual attraction to other people. Some have further broken out sexual orientation to sexual identity (the people to whom one is sexually attracted) and romantic identity (the people to whom one is romantically attracted).

T: A common abbreviation for testosterone.

Top Surgery: A colloquial term that refers to a gender-affirmative surgical interventions centered on modifying chest or breast size, shape, or contour.

Trans: A Latin prefix that translates to "across" or "on the other side of." Trans, whether as a standalone adjective, or as a prefix to another term (such as woman, man, or individual), refers to anyone whose gender identity differs to any degree from the sex they were assigned at birth Trans, like cis, has become an umbrella term in its own right, an abbreviation of the term *transgender*.

Transgender: An adjective that refers to anyone whose internal sense or knowledge of gender (gender identity) differs to any degree from the cultural expectations of the sex they were assigned at birth (e.g., male, female, intersex). As an umbrella term, transgender can describe someone who identifies as a trans woman or man as well as someone who identifies as nonbinary, genderfluid, agender, multiple genders, or some other gender identity. In the past, transgender was used as both a noun and a verb: both of these uses are archaic and should be avoided.

Transition: A term that refers to a process through which a trans person takes steps to affirm their gender identity and align their gender expression with their gender identity. Transitions may include social, legal, and medical components. Transition pathways are highly individualized and many trans folx opt not to pursue some aspects of transition. Transitions might best be considered a process rather than a series of events. There is no one true way to be trans or transition!

Transsexual: An umbrella term that typically refers to trans people who have engaged in medical interventions, and particularly both top and bottom surgeries. This term is no longer widely used and may be considered offensive to some trans folx. However, some trans folx still use this term to refer to themselves and it has, in certain circles, become a reclaimed term. Use of the term should, thus, be reserved to those who use it to describe themselves.

Tucking: A practice engaged in by some trans folx with penises to conceal the contours of the penis and testicles by placing the penis between the legs and the testicles up into the inguinal canals. This gives the person the appearance of a smooth front. Much like binding, tucking can be accomplished through compression garments as well as adhesives.

Two-Spirit: A gender identity term used in some Indigenous North American cultures to describe persons who identify as non-binary, agender, a third gender, and/or bigender. In certain Native American cultures, two-spirited individuals fulfill profound social and ceremonial roles. Like other culturally specific terms, the use of the term two-spirit should be reserved to those Natives who use the term to describe themselves.

Vaginoplasty: A type of bottom surgery that results in the creation of a vaginal aperture between the rectum and the urethra which generally also includes the construction of a vaginal canal. Some trans folx opt for what are called zero-depth vaginoplasty. Zero-depth vaginoplasties allow for the cosmetic look of a vulva but the neo vulva includes only a vaginal aperture rather than a vaginal canal.

BIBLIOGRAPHY

Activist Janet Mock Flips the Script on Reporter: Asks Her to Prove Her Womanhood. YouTube Video. YouTube: Fusion, 2014. https://www.youtube.com/watch?reload=9& v=ISsdSvJhniQ.

Adichie, Chimamanda Ngozi. *The Danger of a Single Story.* TED Talk. Oxford, UK, 2009. https://www.ted.com/talks/chimamanda_ngozi_adichie_the_danger_ of_a_single_story?utm_campaign=tedspread&utm_medium=referral&utm_ source=tedcomshare.

American Counseling Association. "ACA Code of Ethics." American Counseling Association, 2014. https://www.counseling.org/docs/default-source/default-document-library/2014-code-of-ethics-finaladdress.pdf?sfvrsn=96b532c_2.

American Psychiatric Association. *Diagnostic and Statistical Manual of Mental Disorders: DSM-5.* Arlington, VA: American Psychiatric Association, 2013.

American Sexual Health Association. "Sexual Functioning." American Sexual Health Association. Accessed August 8, 2020. http://old.ashasexualhealth.org/sexual-health/ sexual-functioning/.

Anderson, Harlene. "Collaborative Language Systems: Toward a Postmodern Therapy." In *Integrating Family Therapy: Family Psychology and Systems Theory*, edited by Richard H. Mikesell, Don-David Lusterman, and Susan H. McDaniel, 27–44. Washington, DC: American Psychological Association, 1995.

———. "Myths about 'Not-Knowing.'" *Family Process* 44, no. 4 (2005): 497–504.

Arao, Brian, and Kristi Clemens. "From Safe Spaces to Brave Spaces: A New Way to Frame Dialogue Around Diversity and Social Justice." In *The Art of Effective Facilitation: Reflections from Social Justice Educators*, edited by Lisa M. Landreman, 135–150. Sterling, VA: Stylus Publishing, 2013.

Austin, Ashley, and Shelley L. Craig. "Transgender Affirmative Cognitive Behavioral Therapy: Clinical Considerations and Applications." *Professional Psychology: Research and Practice* 46, no. 1 (2015): 21–29. https://doi.org/10.1037/a0038642.

Barker, Joanne, ed. *Critically Sovereign: Indigenous Gender, Sexuality, and Feminist Studies.* Durham, NC: Duke University Press, 2017.

Bartlett, Jennifer. "Longing for the Male Gaze." *The New York Times*. September 21, 2016. https://www.nytimes.com/2016/09/21/opinion/longing-for-the-male-gaze.html.

Bauer, Greta R., and Rebecca Hammond. "Toward a Broader Conceptualization of Trans Women's Sexual Health." *The Canadian Journal of Human Sexuality* 24, no. 1 (April 2015): 1–11. https://doi.org/10.3138/cjhs.24.1-CO1.

Bauer, Robin. "Cybercocks and Holodicks: Renegotiating the Boundaries of Material Embodiment in Les-Bi-Trans-Queer BDSM Practices." *Graduate Journal of Social Science* 14, no. 2 (September 2018): 58–82.

———. *Queer BDSM Intimacies: Critical Consent and Pushing Boundaries*. New York, NY: Palgrave Macmillan, 2014.

Beach, Frank. "Characteristics of Masculine 'Sex Drive.'" In *Nebraska Symposium on Motivation*, 4:1–32. Lincoln, NE: University of Nebraska Press, 1956.

Bean, Joseph W. *Leathersex: A Guide for the Curious Outsider and the Serious Player*. 2nd ed. Los Angeles, CA: Daedalus Publishing Company, 2003.

Beemyn, Genny. "US History." In *Trans Bodies, Trans Selves: A Resource for the Transgender Community*, edited by Laura Erickson-Schroth, 501–536. Oxford/New York: Oxford University Press, 2014.

Bellwether, Mira. *Fucking Trans Women: A Zine About the Sex Lives of Trans Women*. CreateSpace Independent Publishing Platform, 2010.

Benestad, E. E. P. "From Gender Dysphoria to Gender Euphoria: An Assisted Journey." *Sexologies* 19 (2010): 225–231.

Benjamin, Harry. *The Transsexual Phenomenon*. Electronic Edition. Düsseldorf: Symposium Publishing, 1999. http://www.mut23.de/texte/Harry%20Benjamin%20-%20The%20Transsexual%20Phenomenon.pdf.

binaohan, b. *Decolonizing Trans/Gender 101*. biyuti publishing, 2014.

Bion, Wilfred R. *Learning from Experience*. London: Karnac Books, 1962.

———. "Notes on Memory and Desire." *The Psychoanalytic Forum* 2 (1967): 272–280.

Blair, Karen L., and Rhea Ashley Hoskin. "Transgender Exclusion from the World of Dating: Patterns of Acceptance and Rejection of Hypothetical Trans Dating Partners as a Function of Sexual and Gender Identity." *Journal of Social and Personal Relationships*, May 31, 2018, 026540751877913. https://doi.org/10.1177/0265407518779139.

Bockting, Walter O., and Eli Coleman. "Developmental Stages of the Transgender Coming-Out Process: Toward an Integrated Identity." In *Principles of Transgender Medicine and Surgery*, edited by Randi Ettner, Stan Monstrey, and Eli Coleman, 2nd ed., 137–158. New York: Routledge, 2016.

Bockting, Walter O., Michael H. Miner, Rebecca E. Swinburne Romine, Autumn Hamilton, and Eli Coleman. "Stigma, Mental Health, and Resilience in an Online Sample of the US Transgender Population." *American Journal of Public Health* 103, no. 5 (May 2013): 943–951. https://doi.org/10.2105/AJPH.2013.301241.

Bordo, Susan R. "The Body and the Reproduction of Femininity: A Feminist Appropriation of Foucault." In *Gender/Body/Knowledge*, edited by Alison M. Jaggar and Susan R. Bordo, 13–33. Brunswick, NJ: Rutgers University Press, 1989.

Bradford, Nova J., James DeWitt, Jilyan Decker, Dianne R. Berg, Katherine G. Spencer, and Michael W. Ross. "Sex Education and Transgender Youth: 'Trust Means Material By and For Queer and Trans People.'" *Sex Education* 19, no. 1 (January 2, 2019): 84–98. https://doi.org/10.1080/14681811.2018.1478808.

Braun-Harvey, Douglas, and Michael A. Vigorito. *Treating Out of Control Sexual Behavior: Rethinking Sex Addiction*. New York: Springer Publishing Company, 2016.

Breuer, Josef, and Sigmund Freud. *Studies on Hysteria*. Vol. 2. The Standard Edition of the Complete Psychological Works of Sigmund Freud. London: Vintage, 2001.

Brisk, Susanna. *How to Get Laid Using Your Intuition*. Los Angeles, CA: Self, 2018.

Brody. "Desirability." *Trans Sex Zine, Volume II*, 2018.

Bronstein, Carolyn. "Pornography, Trans Visibility, and the Demise of Tumblr." *TSQ: Transgender Studies Quarterly* 7, no. 2 (May 1, 2020): 240–254. https://doi.org/10.1215/23289252-8143407.

brown, adrienne maree. *Pleasure Activism: The Politics of Feeling Good*. Emergent Strategy. Chico, CA: AK Press, 2019.

Budge, Stephanie L., Jill L. Adelson, and Kimberly A.S. Howard. "Anxiety and Depression in Transgender Individuals: The Roles of Transition Status, Loss, Social Support, and Coping." *Journal of Consulting and Clinical Psychology* 81, no. 3 (2013): 545–557. https://doi.org/10.1037/a0031774.

Budge, Stephanie L., Mun Yuk Chin, and Laura P. Minero. "Trans Individuals' Facilitative Coping: An Analysis of Internal and External Processes." *Journal of Counseling Psychology* 64, no. 1 (2017): 12–25. https://doi.org/10.1037/cou0000178.

Budge, Stephanie L., and Bonnie Moradi. "Attending to Gender in Psychotherapy: Understanding and Incorporating Systems of Power." *Journal of Clinical Psychology* 74, no. 11 (November 2018): 2014–2027. https://doi.org/10.1002/jclp.22686.

Burnes, Theodore R., Anneliese A. Singh, and Ryan G. Witherspoon. "Graduate Counseling Psychology Training in Sex and Sexuality: An Exploratory Analysis." *The Counseling Psychologist* 45, no. 4 (May 2017): 504–527. https://doi.org/10.1177/0011000017714765.

Byers, E. Sandra, Stephanie Demmons, and Kohli-An Lawrance. "Sexual Satisfaction within Dating Relationships: A Test of the Interpersonal Exchange Model of Sexual Satisfaction." *Journal of Social and Personal Relationships* 15, no. 2 (1998): 257–267. https://doi.org/10.1177/0265407598152008.

Caldwell, Christine, ed. *Getting in Touch: The Guide to New Body-Centered Therapies*. Wheaton, IL: Quest Books, 1997.

Callander, Denton, Christy E. Newman, and Martin Holt. "Is Sexual Racism Really Racism? Distinguishing Attitudes Toward Sexual Racism and Generic Racism Among Gay and Bisexual Men." *Archives of Sexual Behavior* 44, no. 7 (October 2015): 1991–2000. https://doi.org/10.1007/s10508-015-0487-3.

Carrellas, Barbara. *Urban Tantra: Sacred Sex for the Twenty-First Century*. 2nd ed. New York, NY: Ten Speed Press, 2017.

Chang, Sand C., and Anneliese A. Singh. "Affirming Psychological Practice with Transgender and Gender Nonconforming People of Color." *Psychology of Sexual Orientation and Gender Diversity* 3, no. 2 (June 2016): 140–147. https://doi.org/10.1037/sgd0000153.

Chang, Sand, Anneliese A. Singh, and lore m. dickey. *A Clinician's Guide to Gender-Affirming Care: Working with Transgender and Gender Nonconforming Clients*. Oakland, CA: New Harbinger Publications, 2018.

Charest, Maxime, Peggy J. Kleinplatz, and Jessie I. Lund. "Sexual Health Information Disparities between Heterosexual and LGBTQ+ Young Adults: Implications for Sexual Health." *The Canadian Journal of Human Sexuality* 25, no. 2 (August 2016): 74–85. https://doi.org/10.3138/cjhs.252-A9.

Coleman, Eli, Walter Bockting, Marsha Botzer, Peggy Cohen-Kettenis, Griet De Cuypere, Jamie Feldman, L. Fraser, et al. "Standards of Care for the Health of Transsexual,

Transgender, and Gender-Nonconforming People, Version 7." *The International Journal of Transgenderism* 13, no. 4 (2012): 165–232. https://doi.org/10.1080/15532739.2011.700873.

Coleman, Eli, Joycelyn Elders, David Satcher, Alan Shindel, Sharon Parish, Gretchen Kenagy, Carey Roth Bayer, et al. "Summit on Medical School Education in Sexual Health: Report of an Expert Consultation." *The Journal of Sexual Medicine* 10, no. 4 (April 2013): 924–938. https://doi.org/10.1111/jsm.12142.

Combs, Gene, and Jill Freedman. *Narrative Therapy: The Social Construction of Preferred Realities.* 1st ed. New York: W. W. Norton & Company, 1996.

Constantinides, Damon, Shannon L. Sennott, and Davis Chandler. *Sex Therapy with Erotically Marginalized Clients.* New York, NY: Routledge, 2019.

Crenshaw, Kimberlé. "Mapping the Margins: Intersectionality, Identity Politics, and Violence against Women of Color." *Stanford Law Review* 43, no. 6 (July 1991): 1241–1299.

Dark, Kimberly. *The Daddies.* Boston, MA: Brill | Sense, 2018.

Daston, Lorraine, and Katharine Park. *Wonders and the Order of Nature, 1150-1750.* New York, NY: Zone Books, 1998.

Davis, Angela. "Dr. Angela Davis on the Role of the Trans and Non-Binary Communities in the Fight for the Feminist Abolition She Advocates For." libcom.org, June 25, 2020. http://libcom.org/library/dr-angela-davis-role-trans-non-binary-communities-fight-feminist-abolition-she-advocates.

Davy, Zowie, and Eliza Steinbock. "'Sexing Up' Bodily Aesthetics: Notes towards Theorizing Trans Sexuality." In *Sexualities: Past Reflections, Future Directions*, 266–285. New York, NY: Palgrave Macmillan, 2012.

Dea, Shannon. *Beyond the Binary: Thinking about Sex and Gender.* Peterborough, Ontario: Broadview Press, 2016.

DeGruy, Joy. *Post Traumatic Slave Syndrome: America's Legacy of Enduring Injury and Healing.* Revised Edition. Portland, OR: Joy Degruy Publications Inc, 2017.

"Destabilising the Narrative of Penetration." *Trans Sex Zine, Volume I*, 2017.

DiAngelo, Robin. *White Fragility: Why It's So Hard for White People to Talk About Racism.* Boston, MA: Beacon Press, 2018.

Diderot, Denis. "The Indiscreet Jewels." In *The Libertine Reader: Eroticism and Enlightenment in Eighteenth-Century France*, edited by Michel Feher, translated by Sophie Hawkes, 344–541. New York, NY: Zone Books, 1997.

Duncker, Karl. *On Problem-Solving.* Translated by Lynn S. Less. Washington, DC: American Psychological Association, 1945.

Duran, Eduardo. *Healing the Soul Wound: Counseling with American Indians and Other Native Peoples.* New York, NY: Teacher's College Press, 2006.

Erickson-Schroth, Laura, and Laura Jacobs. "You're in the Wrong Bathroom!": And 20 Other Myths and Misconceptions About Transgender and Gender-Nonconforming People.* Boston, MA: Beacon Press, 2017.

Erikson, Erik. *Childhood and Society.* New York, NY: W. W. Norton & Company, 1993.

Eum Kim, Yea Sun. "Understanding Asian American Clients." *Journal of Ethnic & Cultural Diversity in Social Work* 12, no. 3 (February 3, 2004): 91–114. https://doi.org/10.1300/J051v12n03_05.

Evans-Campbell, Teresa. "Historical Trauma in American Indian/Native Alaska Communities: A Multilevel Framework for Exploring Impacts on Individuals, Families, and Communities." *Journal of Interpersonal Violence* 23, no. 3 (March 2008): 316–338. https://doi.org/10.1177/0886260507312290.

Fahs, Breanne, and Jax Gonzalez. "The Front Lines of the 'Back Door': Navigating (Dis) Engagement, Coercion, and Pleasure in Women's Anal Sex Experiences." *Feminism & Psychology* 24, no. 4 (November 2014): 500–520. https://doi.org/10.1177/0959353514539648.

Fahs, Breanne, and Sara I. McClelland. "When Sex and Power Collide: An Argument for Critical Sexuality Studies." *The Journal of Sex Research* 53, no. 4–5 (May 3, 2016): 392–416. https://doi.org/10.1080/00224499.2016.1152454.

Feder, Sam. *Disclosure*. Documentary. Netflix, 2020.

Feinberg, Leslie. *Transgender Warriors: Making History from Joan of Arc to Dennis Rodman*. Boston, MA: Beacon Press, 2005.

Foucault, Michel. *Society Must Be Defended: Lectures at the Collège de France, 1975–1976*. Edited by Mauro Bertani and Alessandro Fontana. Translated by David Macey. Michel Foucault Lectures at the Collège de France 5. New York, NY: Picador, 2003.

———. *The Archaeology of Knowledge: And the Discourse on Language*. Translated by A.M. Sheridan Smith. New York, NY: Vintage, 2010.

———. *The History of Sexuality, Vol. 1: An Introduction*. Translated by Robert Hurley. New York: Vintage, 1990.

Freud, Sigmund. "Freud's Psycho-Analytic Procedure." In *A Case of Hysteria, Three Essays on Sexuality and Other Works*, 7:247–254. The Standard Edition of the Complete Psychological Works of Sigmund Freud. London: Vintage, 2001.

———. "Recommendations to Physicians Practising Psycho-Analysis." In *Case History Schreber, Papers on Technique, and Other Works*, 12:109–120. The Standard Edition of the Complete Psychological Works of Sigmund Freud. London: Vintage, 2001.

———. "Three Essays on the Theory of Sexuality." In *A Case of Hysteria, Three Essays on Sexuality and Other Works*, 7: 123–243. The Standard Edition of the Complete Psychological Works of Sigmund Freud. London: Vintage, 2001.

Geller, Shari M., and Stephen W. Porges. "Therapeutic Presence: Neurophysiological Mechanisms Mediating Feeling Safe in Therapeutic Relationships." *Journal of Psychotherapy Integration* 24, no. 3 (2014): 178–192. https://doi.org/10.1037/a0037511.

Gilbert, Paul, and Sue Procter. "Compassionate Mind Training for People with High Shame and Self-Criticism: Overview and Pilot Study of a Group Therapy Approach." *Clinical Psychology & Psychotherapy* 13, no. 6 (November 2006): 353–379. https://doi.org/10.1002/cpp.507.

Gilman, Sander. *Difference and Pathology: Stereotypes of Sexuality, Race, and Madness*. Ithaca, NY: Cornell University Press, 1985.

Glasser, Carol L., Belinda Robnett, and Cynthia Feliciano. "Internet Daters' Body Type Preferences: Race–Ethnic and Gender Differences." *Sex Roles* 61, no. 1–2 (July 2009): 14–33. https://doi.org/10.1007/s11199-009-9604-x.

Gonzalez, Cesar A., Joseph D. Gallego, and Walter O. Bockting. "Demographic Characteristics, Components of Sexuality and Gender, and Minority Stress and Their Associations to Excessive Alcohol, Cannabis, and Illicit (Noncannabis) Drug Use Among a Large Sample of Transgender People in the United States." *The Journal of Primary Prevention* 38, no. 4 (August 2017): 419–445. https://doi.org/10.1007/s10935-017-0469-4.

Goodman, Rachael D., and Paul C. Gorski, eds. *Decolonizing "Multicultural" Counseling through Social Justice*. International and Cultural Psychology. New York, NY: Springer New York, 2015. https://doi.org/10.1007/978-1-4939-1283-4.

Gossett, Reina, Eric A. Stanley, and Johanna Burton, eds. *Trap Door: Trans Cultural Production and the Politics of Visibility*. Critical Anthologies in Art and Culture. Cambridge, MA: MIT Press, 2017.

Gravell, Lynne. "The Counselling Psychologist as Therapeutic 'Container.'" *Counseling Psychology Review* 25, no. 2 (2010): 28–33.

Gunn, Angie. "How To Have Great Sex With Someone New (By Building The Right Kind Of Trust)." *YourTango* (blog), December 20, 2017. https://www.yourtango.com/experts/angie-gunn/how-build-trust-sex-someone-new.

Halberstam, Jack. *The Queer Art of Failure*. Durham, NC: Duke University Press, 2011.

Hale, C. Jacob. "Leatherdyke Boys and Their Daddies: How to Have Sex without Women or Men." *Social Text*, no. 52/53 (1997): 223. https://doi.org/10.2307/466741.

Han, Chong-suk. "No Fats, Femmes, or Asians: The Utility of Critical Race Theory in Examining the Role of Gay Stock Stories in the Marginalization of Gay Asian Men." *Contemporary Justice Review* 11, no. 1 (March 2008): 11–22. https://doi.org/10.1080/10282580701850355.

Hansbury, Griffin. "Mourning the Loss of the Idealized Self: A Transsexual Passage." *Psychoanalytic Social Work* 12, no. 1 (March 17, 2005): 19–35. https://doi.org/10.1300/J032v12n01_03.

Harris-Perry, Melissa V. *Sister Citizen: Shame, Stereotypes, and Black Women in America*. New Haven, CT: Yale University Press, 2011.

Hays, Pamela, and Gayle Y. Iwamasa, eds. *Culturally Responsive Cognitive-Behavioral Therapy: Assessment, Practice, And Supervision*. Washington, DC: American Psychological Association, 2006.

Heinrichs, Marika. "Queers Know about Loving in the Midst of Virus..." Instagram Post. @wildbodysomatics, March 11, 2020. https://www.instagram.com/p/B9nozx-AS5e/.

Hendricks, Michael L., and Rylan J. Testa. "A Conceptual Framework for Clinical Work with Transgender and Gender Nonconforming Clients: An Adaptation of the Minority Stress Model." *Professional Psychology: Research and Practice* 43, no. 5 (2012): 460–467. https://doi.org/10.1037/a0029597.

Hillman, James. *A Blue Fire: Selected Writings by James Hillman*. Edited by Thomas Moore. New York, NY: Harper Perennial, 1989.

Hill-Meyer, Tobi, and Dean Scarborough. "Sexuality." In *Trans Bodies, Trans Selves: A Resource for the Transgender Community*, edited by Laura Erickson-Schroth, 355–388. Oxford/New York: Oxford University Press, 2014.

Hinchy, Jessica. *Governing Gender and Sexuality in Colonial India: The Hijra, c.1850-1900*. New York, NY: Cambridge University Press, 2019.

Hodson, Kristin B. "4 Easy Prompts to Start a Conversation about Sexual Health..." Instagram Post. @kristinbhodson, February 3, 2020. https://www.instagram.com/p/B8HH5QghCFI/.

Hoefer, Sharon E., and Richard Hoefer. "Worth the Wait? The Consequences of Abstinence-Only Sex Education for Marginalized Students." *American Journal of Sexuality Education* 12, no. 3 (July 3, 2017): 257–276. https://doi.org/10.1080/15546128.2017.1359802.

Hollibaugh, Amber. *My Dangerous Desires: A Queer Girl Dreaming Her Way Home*. Durham, NC: Duke University Press, 2000.

Holmberg, Diane, and Karen L. Blair. "Sexual Desire, Communication, Satisfaction, and Preferences of Men and Women in Same-Sex Versus Mixed-Sex Relationships."

Journal of Sex Research 46, no. 1 (February 3, 2009): 57–66. https://doi.org/10.1080/00224490802645294.

Holmes, Rupert. *Escape (The Piña Colada Song)*. Apple Music. Partners in Crime. New York, NY: Infinity Records, 1979.

Hook, Joshua N., Don E. Davis, Jesse Owen, Everett L. Worthington, and Shawn O. Utsey. "Cultural Humility: Measuring Openness to Culturally Diverse Clients." *Journal of Counseling Psychology* 60, no. 3 (July 2013): 353–366. https://doi.org/10.1037/a0032595.

Hoskin, Rhea Ashley, and Allison Taylor. "Femme Resistance: The Fem(Me)Inine Art of Failure." *Psychology & Sexuality* 10, no. 4 (October 2, 2019): 281–300. https://doi.org/10.1080/19419899.2019.1615538.

Hunter, Margaret L. "'If You're Light You're Alright': Light Skin Color as Social Capital for Women of Color." *Gender & Society* 16, no. 2 (April 1, 2002): 175–193. https://doi.org/10.1177/0891243202016002003.

Iantaffi, Alex. *Gender Trauma: Healing Cultural, Social, and Historical Gendered Trauma*. London: Jessica Kingsley Publishers, 2020.

Jacobs, Laura A. "Hormones and Handcuffs: The Intersection of Transgender Identities, BDSM, and Polyamory." In *Sex, Sexuality, and Trans Identities: Clinical Guidance for Psychotherapists and Counselors*, edited by Jan C. Niemira, Gary J. Jacobson, and Karalyn J. Violeta, 91–108. London: Jessica Kingsley Publishers, 2020.

James, Sandy E., Jody L. Herman, Susan Rankin, Mara Keisling, Lisa Mottet, and Ma'ayan Anafi. "The Report of the 2015 U.S. Transgender Survey." Washington, DC: National Center for Transgender Equality, December 2016.

Jorgensen, Jeana. "Trans People Aren't Sick, The Entire Patriarchy Is." *Foxy Folklorist: Folklore, Culture, Sex* (blog), April 13, 2016. http://www.patheos.com/blogs/foxyfolklorist/trans-people-arent-sick-the-entire-patriarchy-is/.

Jung, C. G. "The Psychology of the Transference." In *The Practice of Psychotherapy: Essays on the Psychology of the Transference and Other Subjects*, translated by R. F. C. Hull, 16: 163–327. Collected Works of C.G. Jung. Princeton, NJ: Princeton University Press, 1985.

Kashdan, Todd B., Melissa C. Stiksma, David J. Disabato, Patrick E. McKnight, John Bekier, Joel Kaji, and Rachel Lazarus. "The Five-Dimensional Curiosity Scale: Capturing the Bandwidth of Curiosity and Identifying Four Unique Subgroups of Curious People." *Journal of Research in Personality* 73 (April 2018): 130–149. https://doi.org/10.1016/j.jrp.2017.11.011.

Kay, Robert. *The Cabinet of Caligari*. DVD, Horror. 20th Century Fox, 1962.

Kerckhof, Mauro E., Baudewijntje P.C. Kreukels, Timo O. Nieder, Inga Becker-Hébly, Tim C. van de Grift, Annemieke S. Staphorsius, Andreas Köhler, Gunter Heylens, and Els Elaut. "Prevalence of Sexual Dysfunctions in Transgender Persons: Results from the ENIGI Follow-Up Study." *The Journal of Sexual Medicine* 16, no. 12 (December 2019): 2018–2029. https://doi.org/10.1016/j.jsxm.2019.09.003.

Kessler, Laura E., and Charles A. Waehler. "Addressing Multiple Relationships Between Clients and Therapists in Lesbian, Gay, Bisexual, and Transgender Communities." *Professional Psychology: Research and Practice* 36, no. 1 (2005): 66–72. https://doi.org/10.1037/0735-7028.36.1.66.

Klein, Carolin, and Boris B. Gorzalka. "Sexual Functioning in Transsexuals Following Hormone Therapy and Genital Surgery: A Review." *The Journal of Sexual Medicine* 6, no. 11 (2009): 2922–2939.

Kleinplatz, Peggy J. "Advancing Sex Therapy or Is That the Best You Can Do?" In *New Directions in Sex Therapy: Innovations and Alternatives*, edited by Peggy J. Kleinplatz, 2nd ed., xix–xxxvi. New York, NY: Routledge, 2012.

———. "Is That All There Is? A New Critique of the Goals of Sex Therapy." In *New Directions in Sex Therapy: Innovations and Alternatives*, edited by Peggy J. Kleinplatz, 2nd ed., 101–139. New York, NY: Routledge, 2012.

Kleinplatz, Peggy J., and A. Dana Ménard. "Building Blocks Toward Optimal Sexuality: Constructing a Conceptual Model." *The Family Journal* 15, no. 1 (January 2007): 72–78. https://doi.org/10.1177/1066480706294126.

———. *Magnificent Sex: Lessons from Extraordinary Lovers*. New York, NY: Routledge, 2020.

Kolk, Bessel van der. *The Body Keeps the Score: Brain, Mind, and Body in the Healing of Trauma*. New York, NY: Penguin, 2014.

Kort, Joe. *LGBTQ Clients in Therapy: Clinical Issues and Treatment Strategies*. New York, NY: W. W. Norton & Company, 2018.

Krafft-Ebing, Richard von. *Psychopathia Sexualis: With Especial Reference to the Antipathic Sexual Instinct; a Medico-Forensic Study*. Translated by F. S. Klaf. New York: Arcade Publ., 1998.

Kurtz, Ron. *Body-Centered Psychotherapy: The Hakomi Method: The Integrated Use of Mindfulness, Nonviolence and the Body*. Mendocino, CA: LifeRhythm, 2007.

Lang, Nico. "Looking for Love and Acceptance: Dating While Trans in America." *The Daily Beast*, October 15, 2016. http://www.thedailybeast.com/articles/2016/10/15/looking-for-love-and-acceptance-dating-while-trans-in-america.html.

Langdridge, Darren. "Are You Angry or Are You Heterosexual? A Queer Critique of Lesbian and Gay Models of Identity Development." In *Feeling Queer or Queer Feelings?: Radical Approaches to Counselling Sex, Sexualities and Genders*, edited by Lyndsey Moon, 23–35. New York, NY: Routledge, 2008.

Langer, S.J. *Theorizing Transgender Identity for Clinical Practice: A New Model for Understanding Gender*. Philadelphia, PA: Jessica Kingsley Publishers, 2019.

Laqueur, Thomas. *Making Sex: Body and Gender from the Greeks to Freud*. Revised ed. Cambridge, MA: Harvard University Press, 1992.

———. *Solitary Sex: A Cultural History of Masturbation*. New York: Zone Books, 2004.

———. "The Rise of Sex in the Eighteenth Century: Historical Context and Historiographical Implications." *Signs: Journal of Women in Culture and Society* 37, no. 4 (June 2012): 802–812. https://doi.org/10.1086/664468.

Latham, J.R. "Axiomatic: Constituting 'Transexuality' and Trans Sexualities in Medicine." *Sexualities* 22, no. 1–2 (February 2019): 13–30. https://doi.org/10.1177/1363460717740258.

———. "Trans Men's Sexual Narrative-Practices: Introducing STS to Trans and Sexuality Studies." *Sexualities* 19, no. 3 (March 1, 2016): 347–368. https://doi.org/10.1177/1363460715583609.

Lehmiller, Justin J. *Tell Me What You Want: The Science of Sexual Desire and How It Can Help You Improve Your Sex Life*. New York, NY: Hachette Books, 2018.

Lev, Arlene Istar. *Transgender Emergence: Therapeutic Guidelines for Working with Gender-Variant People and Their Families*. New York, NY: The Haworth Clinical Practice Press, 2004.

Lev, Arlene Istar, and Shannon Sennott. "Transsexual Desire in Differently Gendered Bodies." In *Handbook of LGBT-Affirmative Couple and Family Therapy*, edited by Jerry J. Bigner and Joseph L. Wetchler, 113–128. New York, NY: Routledge, 2012.

Loeser, Cassandra, Barbara Pini, and Vicki Crowley. "Disability and Sexuality: Desires and Pleasures." *Sexualities* 21, no. 3 (March 2018): 255–270. https://doi.org/10.1177/1363460716688682.

Lord, Catherine, and Richard Meyer. *Art and Queer Culture*. 2nd ed. London: Phaidon, 2019.

Lorde, Audre. *A Burst of Light and Other Essays*. Mineola, NY: Ixia Press, 2017.

Loseke, Donileen R. "The Study of Identity As Cultural, Institutional, Organizational, and Personal Narratives: Theoretical and Empirical Integrations." *The Sociological Quarterly* 48, no. 4 (September 2007): 661–688. https://doi.org/10.1111/j.1533-8525.2007.00096.x.

Luna, Caleb. "On Being Fat, Brown, Femme, Ugly, and Unloveable." *BGD* (blog), July 21, 2014. https://www.bgdblog.org/2014/07/fat-brown-femme-ugly-unloveable/.

Lynch, Paul. "The Naked Now." CBS All Access. *Star Trek: The Next Generation*, October 5, 1987.

Malpas, Jean. "Can Couples Change Gender? Couple Therapy with Transgender People and Their Partners." In *Handbook of LGBT-Affirmative Couple and Family Therapy*, edited by Jerry J. Bigner and Joseph L. Wetchler, 69–85. New York, NY: Routledge, 2012.

Mao, Jessica M., M.L. Haupert, and Eliot R. Smith. "How Gender Identity and Transgender Status Affect Perceptions of Attractiveness." *Social Psychological and Personality Science*, June 27, 2018, 194855061878371. https://doi.org/10.1177/1948550618783716.

Mark, Kristen P., and Julie A. Lasslo. "Maintaining Sexual Desire in Long-Term Relationships: A Systematic Review and Conceptual Model." *The Journal of Sex Research* 55, nos. 4–5 (June 13, 2018): 563–581. https://doi.org/10.1080/00224499.2018.1437592.

Martin, David G. *Counseling and Therapy Skills*. 3rd ed. Long Grove, IL: Waveland Press, 2011.

Marvin, Amy. "Transsexuality, the Curio, and the Transgender Tipping Point." In *Curiosity Studies: Toward a New Ecology of Knowledge*, edited by Perry Zurn and Arjun Shankar, 188–206. Minneapolis, MN: University of Minnesota Press, 2020.

Masters, William, and Virginia E. Johnson. *Human Sexual Response*. Boston, MA: Little, Brown, and Co., 1966.

McClelland, Sara I. "Intimate Justice." In *Encyclopedia of Critical Psychology*, edited by Thomas Teo, 1010–1013. New York, NY: Springer New York, 2014. https://doi.org/10.1007/978-1-4614-5583-7.

———. "Intimate Justice: A Critical Analysis of Sexual Satisfaction: Intimate Justice." *Social and Personality Psychology Compass* 4, no. 9 (September 2, 2010): 663–680. https://doi.org/10.1111/j.1751-9004.2010.00293.x.

McGoldrick, Monica, Joe Giordano, and Nydia Garcia-Preto, eds. *Ethnicity and Family Therapy*. 3rd ed. New York, NY: The Guilford Press, 2005.

Menakem, Resmaa. *My Grandmother's Hands: Racialized Trauma and the Pathway to Mending Our Hearts and Bodies*. Las Vegas, NV: Central Recovery Press, 2017.

Meyer, Ilan H. "Prejudice, Social Stress, and Mental Health in Lesbian, Gay, and Bisexual Populations: Conceptual Issues and Research Evidence." *Psychological Bulletin* 129, no. 5 (2003): 674–697. https://doi.org/10.1037/0033-2909.129.5.674.

Midori. "ProTip! Questions You Ought To Ask Before BDSM Play." *Medium* (blog), March 31, 2017. https://medium.com/@PlanetMidori/protip-questions-ought-to-ask-before-bdsm-play-621fd87a2f02.

Miller, S. Andrea, and E. Sandra Byers. "Practicing Psychologists' Sexual Intervention Self-Efficacy and Willingness to Treat Sexual Issues." *Archives of Sexual Behavior* 41, no. 4 (August 2012): 1041–1050. https://doi.org/10.1007/s10508-011-9877-3.

———. "Psychologists' Continuing Education and Training in Sexuality." *Journal of Sex & Marital Therapy* 35, no. 3 (May 2009): 206–219. https://doi.org/10.1080/00926230802716336.

The Mindful Occupation Collective. "What Is Radical Mental Health?" In *We've Been Too Patient: Voices from Radical Mental Health*, edited by L.D. Green and Kelechi Ubozoh, 139–146. Berkeley, CA: North Atlantic Books, 2019.

Mintz, Laurie. *Becoming Cliterate: Why Orgasm Equality Matters—and How to Get It.* New York, NY: HarperOne, 2018.

Mitchell, Stephen. *Can Love Last?: The Fate of Romance over Time.* New York, NY: Norton, 2002.

Moali, Nazanin. "Coming Out as Transgender from the Sexology Podcast with Dr. Moali." The Sexology Podcast with Dr. Moali. Accessed July 31, 2020. http://www.sexologypodcast.com/2018/07/31/coming-out-as-trangender/.

Moon, Allison. *Girl Sex 101.* Lunatic Ink, 2014.

Moradi, Bonnie, Elliot A Tebbe, Melanie E Brewster, Stephanie L Budge, Alex Lenzen, Engin Ege, Elena Schuch, et al. "A Content Analysis of Literature on Trans People and Issues." *The Counseling Psychologist* 44, no. 7 (2016): 960–95.

Mullinax, Margo, Debby Herbenick, Vanessa Schick, Stephanie A. Sanders, and Michael Reece. "In Their Own Words: A Qualitative Content Analysis of Women's and Men's Preferences for Women's Genitals." *Sex Education* 15, no. 4 (July 4, 2015): 421–436. https://doi.org/10.1080/14681811.2015.1031884.

Muñoz, José Esteban. *Cruising Utopia: The Then and There of Queer Futurity.* 10th Anniversary Edition. Sexual Cultures. New York, NY: NYU Press, 2019.

Murphy, Marie. "Everywhere and Nowhere Simultaneously: The 'Absent Presence' of Sexuality in Medical Education." *Sexualities* 22, no. 1–2 (February 2019): 203–223. https://doi.org/10.1177/1363460717708147.

Nagoski, Emily. *Come as You Are: The Surprising New Science That Will Transform Your Sex Life.* New York: Simon & Schuster, 2015.

———. "Re: Follow up from DC Master Class," November 5, 2018.

———. "Pleasure Is the Measure." *Medium* (blog), August 19, 2015. https://medium.com/@enagoski/pleasure-is-the-measure-d8c5a2dff33f.

Nagoski, Emily, and Amelia Nagoski. *Burnout: The Secret to Unlocking the Stress Cycle.* New York, NY: Ballantine Books, 2019.

Neff, Kristin. *Self-Compassion: The Proven Power of Being Kind to Yourself.* New York, NY: HarperCollins Publishers, 2011.

Nestle, Joan. "Our Gift of Touch." In *The Persistent Desire: A Femme-Butch Reader*, edited by Joan Nestle, 486–487. Boston, MA: Allyson Publications, 1992.

Ogden, Gina. *The Heart and Soul of Sex.* Boston, MA: Trumpeter Books, 2006.

Ogden, Pat, and Janina Fisher. *Sensorimotor Psychotherapy: Interventions for Trauma and Attachment.* Norton Series on Interpersonal Neurobiology. New York, NY: W. W. Norton & Company, 2015.

Orchard, Sam. "But How Do You Go Pee?" *DUDE Magazine*, July 2011.

Parr, Nicholas J., and Bethany Grace Howe. "Heterogeneity of Transgender Identity Nonaffirmation Microaggressions and Their Association with Depression Symptoms and Suicidality among Transgender Persons." *Psychology of Sexual Orientation and Gender Diversity* 6, no. 4 (December 2019): 461–474. https://doi.org/10.1037/sgd0000347.

Pascoal, Patrícia M., Krystelle Shaughnessy, and Maria Joana Almeida. "A Thematic Analysis of a Sample of Partnered Lesbian, Gay, and Bisexual People's Concepts of

Sexual Satisfaction." *Psychology & Sexuality* 10, no. 2 (April 3, 2019): 101–118. https://doi.org/10.1080/19419899.2018.1555185.

Perel, Esther. *Mating in Captivity: Unlocking Erotic Intelligence*. New York: Harper Paperbacks, 2006.

Pfeffer, Carla A. *Queering Families: The Postmodern Partnerships of Cisgender Women and Transgender Men*. New York, NY: Oxford University Press, 2017.

Porges, Stephen W. "Reciprocal Influences Between Body and Brain in the Perception and Expression of Affect: A Polyvagal Perspective." In *The Healing Power of Emotion: Affective Neuroscience, Development, and Clinical Practice*, edited by Diana Fosha, Daniel J. Siegel, and Marion Solomon, 27–54. Norton Series on Interpersonal Neurobiology. New York, NY: W. W. Norton & Company, 2009.

Price, Joan. *Naked At Our Age: Talking Out Loud About Senior Sex*. Berkeley, CA: Seal Press, 2011.

Proust, Marcel. *The Prisoner*. Translated by Carol Clark. Vol. 5. In Search of Lost Time. New York, NY: Penguin Books, 2019.

Rakoff, Vivian. "A Long Term Effect of the Concentration Camp Experience." *Viewpoints*, no. 1 (1966): 17–22.

Reimer, Matthew, and Leighton Brown. *We Are Everywhere: Protest, Power, and Pride in the History of Queer Liberation*. New York, NY: Ten Speed Press, 2019.

Rivera, Ignacio. "The Sexual Body." In *Trans Bodies, Trans Selves: A Resource for the Transgender Community*, edited by Laura Erickson-Schroth, 357–358. Oxford/New York: Oxford University Press, 2014.

Rogers, Carl. *A Way of Being*. Boston, MA: Houghton Mifflin, 1980.

Rood, Brian A., Sari L. Reisner, Francisco I. Surace, Jae A. Puckett, Meredith R. Maroney, and David W. Pantalone. "Expecting Rejection: Understanding the Minority Stress Experiences of Transgender and Gender-Nonconforming Individuals." *Transgender Health* 1, no. 1 (January 2016): 151–164. https://doi.org/10.1089/trgh.2016.0012.

Rorty, Amélie Oksenberg. "From Passions to Emotions and Sentiments." *Philosophy* 57, no. 220 (1982): 159–172.

Rosario, Vernon. "Pointy Penises, Fashion Crimes, and Hysterical Mollies: The Pederasts' Inversions." In *Homosexuality in Modern France*, edited by Jeffrey Merrick and Bryant T. Ragan, 146–176. New York, NY: Oxford University Press, 1996.

———. *The Erotic Imagination: French Histories of Perversity*. Ideologies of Desire. New York, NY: Oxford University Press, 1997.

Rose, June Amelia. "Foot Fetishism and the Erasure Politics of Dyke Sexualities." *FIST Zine*, January 2019.

Rosenberg, Jordy. *Confessions of the Fox*. New York, NY: One World, 2018.

Roth, Maria, Frank Neuner, and Thomas Elbert. "Transgenerational Consequences of PTSD: Risk Factors for the Mental Health of Children Whose Mothers Have Been Exposed to the Rwandan Genocide," *International Journal of Mental Health Systems* 8 (2014), 1–12.

Rubin, Gayle S. "Thinking Sex: Notes for a Radical Theory of the Politics of Sexuality." In *Deviations: A Gayle Rubin Reader*, 143–178. Durham, NC: Duke University Press, 2011. https://doi.org/10.1215/9780822394068.

"Safe." In *Merriam-Webster.Com Dictionary*. Accessed June 23, 2020. https://www.merriam-webster.com/dictionary/safe.

Salisbury, Claire M.A., and William A. Fisher. "'Did You Come?' A Qualitative Exploration of Gender Differences in Beliefs, Experiences, and Concerns Regarding

Female Orgasm Occurrence During Heterosexual Sexual Interactions." *The Journal of Sex Research* 51, no. 6 (August 1, 2014): 616–631. https://doi.org/10.1080/00224499.2013.838934.

Santos, Ana Cristina, and Ana Lúcia Santos. "Yes, We Fuck! Challenging the Misfit Sexual Body through Disabled Women's Narratives." *Sexualities* 21, no. 3 (March 2018): 303–318. https://doi.org/10.1177/1363460716688680.

Schulz, Sarah L. "The Informed Consent Model of Transgender Care: An Alternative to the Diagnosis of Gender Dysphoria." *Journal of Humanistic Psychology* 58, no. 1 (January 2018): 72–92. https://doi.org/10.1177/0022167817745217.

Schwartz, Richard C., and Martha Sweezy. *Internal Family Systems Therapy*. 2nd ed. New York, NY: The Guilford Press, 2020.

Séguin, Léa J., and Robin R. Milhausen. "Not All Fakes Are Created Equal: Examining the Relationships between Men's Motives for Pretending Orgasm and Levels of Sexual Desire, and Relationship and Sexual Satisfaction." *Sexual and Relationship Therapy* 31, no. 2 (April 2, 2016): 159–175. https://doi.org/10.1080/14681994.2016.1158803.

Serano, Julia. *Outspoken: A Decade of Transgender Activism and Trans Feminism*. Oakland, CA: Switch Hitter Press, 2016.

———. *Whipping Girl: A Transsexual Woman on Sexism and the Scapegoating of Femininity*. 2nd ed. Berkeley, CA: Seal Press, 2016.

Shackelford, Hunter. "Bittersweet Like Me: Lemonade and Fat Black Femme Erasure." *Wear Your Voice* (blog), April 27, 2016. https://wearyourvoicemag.com/bittersweet-like-me-lemonade-aint-made-fat-black-women-femmes/.

Shindel, Alan W., and Sharon J. Parish. "CME Information: Sexuality Education in North American Medical Schools: Current Status and Future Directions (CME)." *The Journal of Sexual Medicine* 10, no. 1 (January 2013): 3–18. https://doi.org/10.1111/j.1743-6109.2012.02987.x.

Shipman, Daran, and Tristan Martin. "Clinical and Supervisory Considerations for Transgender Therapists: Implications for Working with Clients." *Journal of Marital and Family Therapy* 45, no. 1 (January 2019): 92–105. https://doi.org/10.1111/jmft.12300.

Siegel, Daniel. *The Mindful Therapist: A Clinician's Guide to Mindsight and Neural Integration*. Norton Series on Interpersonal Neurobiology. New York, NY: W. W. Norton & Company, 2010.

Singh, Anneliese A., Danica G. Hays, and Laurel S. Watson. "Strength in the Face of Adversity: Resilience Strategies of Transgender Individuals." *Journal of Counseling & Development* 89, no. 1 (January 2011): 20–27. https://doi.org/10.1002/j.1556-6678.2011.tb00057.x.

Snorton, C. Riley. *Black on Both Sides: A Racial History of Trans Identity*. Minneapolis, MN: University of Minnesota Press, 2017.

Sprecher, Susan, Anita Barbee, and Pepper Schwartz. " 'Was It Good for You, Too?': Gender Differences in First Sexual Intercourse Experiences." *The Journal of Sex Research* 32, no. 1 (January 1, 1995): 3–15. https://doi.org/10.1080/00224499509551769.

Stone, Sandy. "The 'Empire' Strikes Back: A Posttranssexual Manifesto." *Camera Obscura* 10, no. 2 (May 1992): 150–176.

Stryker, Susan. "Dungeon Intimacies: The Poetics of Transsexual Sadomasochism." *Parallax* 14, no. 1 (2008): 36–47.

———. *Transgender History: The Roots of Today's Revolution*. 2nd ed. Berkeley, CA: Seal Press, 2017.

Syme, Maggie L., Tracy J. Cohn, Sydney Stoffregen, Hanna Kaempfe, and Desiree Schippers. "'At My Age... ': Defining Sexual Wellness in Mid- and Later Life." *Journal of Sex Research* 56, no. 7 (September 2019): 832–842.

Taylor, Allison. "'But Where Are the Dates?' Dating as a Central Site of Fat Femme Marginalisation in Queer Communities." *Psychology & Sexuality*, September 17, 2020, 1–12. https://doi.org/10.1080/19419899.2020.1822429.

Tepper, Mitchell S. "Sexuality and Disability: The Missing Discourse of Pleasure." *Sex and Disability* 18, no. 4 (December 2000): 283–290.

Testa, Rylan J., Janice Habarth, Jayme Peta, Kimberly Balsam, and Walter Bockting. "Development of the Gender Minority Stress and Resilience Measure." *Psychology of Sexual Orientation and Gender Diversity* 2, no. 1 (March 2015): 65–77. https://doi.org/10.1037/sgd0000081.

Thom, Kai Cheng. *I Hope We Choose Love: A Trans Girl's Notes from the End of the World.* Vancouver, BC: Arsenal Pulp Press, 2019.

Tobin, Harper Jean. "The Perils and Pleasures of Sex for Trans People." In *Sex Matters: The Sexuality and Society Reader,* edited by Mindy Stombler, Dawn M. Baunach, Wendy Simonds, Elroi J. Windsor, and Elisabeth O. Burgess, 4th ed., 22–28. New York, NY: W. W. Norton & Company, 2014.

Tolman, Deborah L., Christin P. Bowman, and Breanne Fahs. "Sexuality and Embodiment." In *APA Handbook of Sexuality and Psychology, Vol. 1: Person-Based Approaches.,* edited by Deborah L. Tolman, Lisa M. Diamond, José A. Bauermeister, William H. George, James G. Pfaus, and L. Monique Ward, 759–804. Washington: American Psychological Association, 2014. https://doi.org/10.1037/14193-025.

Tourmaline. "Filmmaker and Activist Tourmaline on How to Freedom Dream." *Vogue,* July 2, 2020. https://www.vogue.com/article/filmmaker-and-activist-tourmaline-on-how-to-freedom-dream.

Tuana, Nancy. "Coming to Understand: Orgasm and the Epistemology of Ignorance." *Hypatia* 19, no. 1 (2004): 194–232.

Turley, Emma L. "'Like Nothing I've Ever Felt before': Understanding Consensual BDSM as Embodied Experience." *Psychology & Sexuality*, January 21, 2016, 1–14. https://doi.org/10.1080/19419899.2015.1135181.

Twist, Jos, Meg-John Barker, Pieter W. Nel, and Nic Horley. "Transitioning Together: A Narrative Analysis of the Support Accessed by Partners of Trans People." *Sexual and Relationship Therapy* 32, no. 2 (April 3, 2017): 227–243. https://doi.org/10.1080/14681994.2017.1296568.

Valenti, Jessica. *Sex Object.* New York, NY: HarperCollins Publishers, 2016.

Vaughn, Mya, Barbara Schoen, Barbara McEntee, and Michele McGrady. "Addressing Disability Stigma within the Lesbian Community." *Journal of Rehabilitation* 81, no. 4 (2015): 49–56.

Vernacchio, Al. *For Goodness Sex: Changing the Way We Talk to Teens About Sexuality, Values, and Health.* New York, NY: Harper Wave, 2014.

Vincent, Ben, and Sonja Erikainen. "Gender, Love, and Sex: Using Duoethnography to Research Gender and Sexuality Minority Experiences of Transgender Relationships." *Sexualities* 23, no. 1-2 (February 2020): 28–43. https://doi.org/10.1177/1363460718796457.

Warner, Christina, Samantha Carlson, Renee Crichlow, and Michael W. Ross. "Sexual Health Knowledge of U.S. Medical Students: A National Survey." *The Journal of Sexual Medicine* 15, no. 8 (August 2018): 1093–1102. https://doi.org/10.1016/j.jsxm.2018.05.019.

Watts-Jones, thandiwe Dee. "Location of Self: Opening the Door to Dialogue on Intersectionality in the Therapy Process." *Family Process* 49, no. 3 (2010): 405–420.

Weinberg, Martin S., Colin J. Williams, Sibyl Kleiner, and Yasmiyn Irizarry. "Pornography, Normalization, and Empowerment." *Archives of Sexual Behavior* 39, no. 6 (December 2010): 1389–1401. https://doi.org/10.1007/s10508-009-9592-5.

West, Xan. *Show Yourself to Me: Queer Kink Erotica.* Northampton, MA: Go Deeper Press, 2015.

Westengard, Laura. *Gothic Queer Culture: Marginalized Communities and the Ghosts of Insidious Trauma.* Lincoln, NE: University of Nebraska Press, 2019.

White, Michael. "Addressing Personal Failure." *The International Journal of Narrative Therapy and Community Work,* no. 3 (2002): 33–76.

White, Michael, and David Epston. *Narrative Means to Therapeutic Ends.* New York, NY: Norton, 1990.

Winnicott, D.W. *Playing and Reality.* New York, NY: Routledge, 1971.

Wongsomboon, Val, Mary H. Burleson, and Gregory D. Webster. "Women's Orgasm and Sexual Satisfaction in Committed Sex and Casual Sex: Relationship Between Sociosexuality and Sexual Outcomes in Different Sexual Contexts." *The Journal of Sex Research* 57, no. 3 (March 23, 2020): 285–295. https://doi.org/10.1080/00224499.2019.1672036.

Wylie, Kevan, Edward Wootton, and Sophie Carlson. "Sexual Function in the Transgender Population." In *Principles of Transgender Medicine and Surgery,* edited by Randi Ettner, Stan Monstrey, and Eli Coleman, 2nd ed., 159–66. New York: Routledge, 2016.

Yehuda, Rachel, and Amy Lehrner. "Intergenerational Transmission of Trauma Effects: Putative Role of Epigenetic Mechanisms," *World Psychiatry* 17, no. 3 (October 2018): 243–257. https://doi.org/10.1002/wps.20568.

Zur, Ofer. *Boundaries in Psychotherapy: Ethical and Clinical Explorations.* Washington, DC: American Psychological Association, 2007.

Zurn, Perry. "Busybody, Hunter, Dancer: Three Historical Models of Curiosity." In *Toward New Philosophical Explorations of the Epistemic Desire to Know: Just Curious about Curiosity,* 26–49. Cambridge: Cambridge Scholars Press, 2019.

———. "Puzzle Pieces: Shapes of Trans Curiosity." *APA Newsletter* 18, no. 1 (2018): 10–16.

INDEX